Compendium of Lettuce Diseases and Pests

SECOND EDITION

Edited by

Krishna V. Subbarao
University of California, Davis
Davis, California, U.S.A.

R. Michael Davis
University of California, Davis
Davis, California, U.S.A.

Robert L. Gilbertson
University of California, Davis
Davis, California, U.S.A.

Richard N. Raid
University of Florida
Belle Glade, Florida, U.S.A.

APS
PRESS

The American Phytopathological Society
St. Paul, Minnesota, U.S.A.

Front cover images:
Top, butterhead lettuce; bottom left, red leaf lettuce; bottom right, green leaf lettuce (Iryna Denysova/Shutterstock.com—Reproduced by permission)
Back cover images:
Top left, bagged lettuce product (stanga/Shutterstock.com—Reproduced by permission)
Top right, green leaf cultivar Australian (Courtesy R. J. Hayes)
Middle left, romaine lettuce in commercial production (Courtesy K. V. Subbarao—© APS)
Middle right, mixed types of lettuce in commercial production (Courtesy K. V. Subbarao—© APS)
Bottom left, Latin-type cultivar Little Gem (Courtesy R. J. Hayes)
Bottom center, Asian stem lettuce cultivar Da Ye Wo Sun (Courtesy R. J. Hayes)
Bottom right, modern crisphead cultivar Pacific (Courtesy R. J. Hayes)

Library of Congress Control Number: 2016963488
International Standard Book Numbers:
Print: 978-0-89054-577-5
Online: 978-0-89054-578-2
Mobi: 978-0-89054-579-9
ePub: 978-0-89054-580-5

Printed in the United States of America on acid-free paper.

The American Phytopathological Society
3340 Pilot Knob Road
St. Paul, Minnesota 55121, U.S.A.

Preface

Since the first edition of *Compendium of Lettuce Diseases* was published in 1997, consumer demand for more nutritious salad products has brought momentous changes in the types of lettuce produced and in the methods of cultivating them. For example, crisphead lettuce was the predominant type grown until the 1990s, when production shifted to the cultivation of romaine, leaf, and baby leaf types of lettuce because of the popularity of value-added salad mixes with longer shelf lives. This shift necessitated a change in lettuce production from narrow beds with two seed lines to wider beds with five or six seed lines and an associated 20–50% increase in plant density. Changes in the types of lettuce grown and the methods of producing them have also brought new challenges to disease and pest management in lettuce production. Since publication of the first edition, many new diseases have been reported that threaten lettuce production.

Compendium of Lettuce Diseases and Pests, Second Edition, provides a comprehensive account of the diseases, pests, and abiotic disorders of all types of lettuce along with practical guidelines for their management. This compendium will be useful to plant pathologists, entomologists, breeders, seed company personnel, crop production specialists, growers, diagnosticians, students, regulatory personnel, crop consultants, educators, researchers, Extension personnel, and others involved in the diagnosis and management of lettuce diseases, pests, and disorders throughout the world.

The content of this new edition is significantly expanded and organized as follows:

- The "Introduction" addresses lettuce production, lettuce breeding, applications of biotechnology and genomics to improve disease resistance, lettuce seed germination under stress, lettuce diseases and disorders, and lettuce-associated microbiota. It also identifies the food safety issues that have emerged as a major concern for the lettuce production industry since the mid-2000s.
- Part I, "Infectious Diseases," outlines types of pathogens and includes sections on diseases caused by fungi and oomycetes, bacteria, phytoplasmas, viruses, nematodes, and a parasitic plant.
- Part II, "Arthropod Pests," is new to this edition and identifies 28 pests of lettuce in the classes Insecta, Symphyla, Arachnida, and Malacostraca. (The role of insects as vectors of viruses and phytoplasmas is discussed in Part I.)
- Part III, "Injuries and Abiotic and Noninfectious Diseases and Disorders," includes sections on mineral deficiencies and toxicities, noninfectious physiological disorders, weather-related injury, ammonium toxicity, soil pH and salinity, and bird damage. A comprehensive table with related images reviews foliar symptoms of herbicide injury by herbicide family, mode of action, and chemical name and includes notes about related factors and prevention. In this edition, information related to herbicide injuries is provided in one place.
- Part IV, "Postharvest Diseases and Disorders," addresses bacterial soft rot, russet spotting, gray mold, brown stain, pink rib, and other diseases and disorders that affect harvested lettuce.

The description of each disease includes a general overview of its importance and world distribution, the most diagnostic symptom or symptoms, the causal organism or agent, the disease cycle and epidemiology, strategies for management, and references that direct readers to additional information. The management strategies presented include all relevant and practical tactics; they apply to most lettuce production areas and can be used to develop integrated pest management (IPM) approaches. This allows for the development of IPM packages for different locations and types of production with maximum flexibility. (Local Extension agents and crop-protection specialists should be consulted for specific recommendations on fungicides or pesticides.) The text is illustrated with 209 images—most of them new to this edition.

Also new to this edition is an appendix that identifies the common names of diseases of lettuce and their pathogens. The same content is available on the website of The American Phytopathological Society in the section "Common Names of Plant Diseases." Any updates that are subsequently made to the taxonomy and nomenclature will be reflected on the website. Throughout the text, the common names of diseases and pests are generally provided, along with the currently accepted scientific names. Authorities for the scientific names of pathogens are included in the appendix. Within the text, plants are mostly referred to by their common names; scientific names are also provided for those plants whose common names may be unfamiliar to readers.

The California Leafy Greens Research Board served as a valuable resource for many of the topics in this compendium and deserves special thanks. The financial sponsors listed inside the front cover are also gratefully acknowledged for their support of this book. In addition, the University of California and the University of Florida provided us with the facilities and time to complete this project.

We thank the international group of authors who wrote or updated sections of this second edition; they are listed in the "Contributing Authors" section that follows. We also thank the following individuals, who supplied or assisted in obtaining photographs for this edition of the compendium:

J. Fletcher, New Zealand Institute of Plant and Food Research Ltd., Lincoln, New Zealand
D. Gibson, New Zealand Institute of Plant and Food Research Ltd., Lincoln, New Zealand
S. Glucksman, Glades Crop Care, Jupiter, Florida, U.S.A.
G. J. Holmes, California Polytechnic State University, San Luis Obispo, U.S.A.
A. Lebeda, Palacky University, Olomouc, Olomouc, Czech Republic
K. D. Puri, University of California, Davis, U.S.A.
G. E. Vallad, University of Florida, Gainesville, U.S.A.

Krishna V. Subbarao
R. Michael Davis
Robert L. Gilbertson
Richard N. Raid

Contributing Authors

J. D. Barak
Department of Plant Pathology
University of Wisconsin–Madison
Madison, Wisconsin, U.S.A.

C. Blomquist
Plant Pest Diagnostics Branch
California Department of Food and Agriculture
Sacramento, California, U.S.A.

C. T. Bull
Department of Plant Pathology and Environmental
  Microbiology
Pennsylvania State University
University Park, Pennsylvania, U.S.A.

P. Castillo
Institute for Sustainable Agriculture
Spanish National Research Council
Córdoba, Spain

S. Castro Bustamante
Department of Plant Sciences
University of California, Davis
Davis, California, U.S.A.

S. Chaudhari
Department of Horticultural Science
North Carolina State University
Raleigh, North Carolina, U.S.A.

R. M. Davis
Department of Plant Pathology
University of California, Davis
Davis, California, U.S.A.

J. P. Dundore-Arias
Department of Plant Pathology
University of Wisconsin–Madison
Madison, Wisconsin, U.S.A.

S. Fondevilla
Institute for Sustainable Agriculture
Spanish National Research Council
Córdoba, Spain

R. L. Gilbertson
Department of Plant Pathology
University of California, Davis
Davis, California, U.S.A.

T. R. Gordon
Department of Plant Pathology
University of California, Davis
Davis, California, U.S.A.

T. K. Hartz
Department of Plant Sciences
University of California, Davis
Davis, California, U.S.A.

R. J. Hayes
Agricultural Research Service
U.S. Department of Agriculture
Salinas, California, U.S.A.

P. Inderbitzin
Department of Plant Pathology
University of California, Davis
Davis, California, U.S.A.

K. M. Jennings
Department of Horticultural Science
North Carolina State University
Raleigh, North Carolina, U.S.A.

R. M. Jiménez-Díaz
Institute for Sustainable Agriculture
Spanish National Research Council
Córdoba, Spain

P. Kahn-Rivadeneira
Yuma Agricultural Center
University of Arizona
Yuma, Arizona, U.S.A.

H. J. Kendrick
Department of Plant Pathology
University of California, Davis
Davis, California, U.S.A.

S. J. Klosterman
Agricultural Research Service
U.S. Department of Agriculture
Salinas, California, U.S.A.

S. T. Koike
Cooperative Extension Monterey County
University of California
Salinas, California, U.S.A.

B. B. Landa
Institute for Sustainable Agriculture
Spanish National Research Council
Córdoba, Spain

J. H. J. Leveau
Department of Plant Pathology
University of California, Davis
Davis, California, U.S.A.

E. L. Little
Department of Plant Pathology
University of Georgia
Athens, Georgia, U.S.A.

Y.-B. Liu
Agricultural Research Service
U.S. Department of Agriculture
Salinas, California, U.S.A.

F. N. Martin
Agricultural Research Service
U.S. Department of Agriculture
Salinas, California, U.S.A.

M. E. Matheron
Yuma Agricultural Center
University of Arizona
Yuma, Arizona, U.S.A.

R. W. Michelmore
Department of Plant Pathology
University of California, Davis
Davis, California, U.S.A.

M. Montes-Borrego
Institute for Sustainable Agriculture
Spanish National Research Council
Córdoba, Spain

E. T. Natwick
Cooperative Extension Imperial County
University of California
Holtville, California, U.S.A.

J. A. Navas-Cortés
Institute for Sustainable Agriculture
Spanish National Research Council
Córdoba, Spain

J. Nunez
Cooperative Extension Kern County
University of California
Bakersfield, California, U.S.A.

T. M. O'Neill
ADAS Boxworth
Boxworth, Cambridge, U.K.

A. J. Pujadas-Salvá
College of Agriculture and Forestry
University of Córdoba
Córdoba, Spain

R. N. Raid
Everglades Research and Education Center
University of Florida
Belle Glade, Florida, U.S.A.

P. A. Roberts
Department of Nematology
University of California, Riverside
Riverside, California, U.S.A.

R. F. Smith
Cooperative Extension Monterey County
University of California
Salinas, California, U.S.A.

D. W. Still
Department of Plant Sciences
California State Polytechnic University, Pomona
Pomona, California, U.S.A.

K. V. Subbarao
Department of Plant Pathology
University of California, Davis
Davis, California, U.S.A.

A. H. C. van Bruggen
Department of Plant Pathology
University of Florida
Gainesville, Florida, U.S.A.

N. Vovlas
Institute for Sustainable Agriculture
Spanish National Research Council
Córdoba, Spain

W. M. Wintermantel
Agricultural Research Service
U.S. Department of Agriculture
Salinas, California, U.S.A.

B. M. Wu
Department of Plant Pathology
China Agricultural University
Beijing, China

F. M. Zerbini
Department of Phytopathology
Federal University of Viçosa
Viçosa, Brazil

Contents

Introduction

Lettuce Production

Lettuce is a widely available salad vegetable regularly consumed by people across diverse cultures and traditions. On this basis, lettuce can be considered a staple crop. Consequently, the successful culture of lettuce is of interest to both home gardeners and professionals involved in its commercial production. In the United States, lettuce is almost exclusively consumed raw as the main ingredient of a salad or as a sandwich filling. Internationally, lettuce stems are sometimes eaten cooked or raw, and oil is extracted from the seeds of specific types of lettuce. Lettuce plants contain sesquiterpene lactones (i.e., lactucin and lactucopicrin) that reportedly have sedative or narcotic effects, and extracts from the wild relative *Lactuca virosa* are used as sleep inducers and cough suppressants in Europe.

Cultivars

Lettuce cultivars are characterized by extensive variation in leaf color, shape, and texture, which undoubtedly contributes to the popularity of lettuce as a salad vegetable (Fig. 1). Lettuce cultivars can be categorized into several market or horticulture types based primarily on leaf shape, rosette architecture, and head formation:

- Crisphead cultivars are known for their thick, crisp leaves, which are typically as wide as they are long. Crispheads are often divided into two subtypes: Batavia and iceberg. The Batavia subtype forms an open-topped head or closed, loosely filled head. The iceberg subtype produces leaves that cup and overlap as the plant grows; new leaves fill the inside of the head as the plant grows, forming a dense, firm, round head that is closed on top.
- Butterhead cultivars also form round heads filled with leaves, but the leaves are generally thin and have a pliable, oily texture. Two subtypes of butterhead lettuce are grown in the United States: Boston and Bibb. The Boston type is larger and lighter green than the Bibb type. In Europe, butterhead cultivars are categorized as summer outdoor types and winter types based on the season in which they are typically grown; the summer types are larger.
- Romaine or cos lettuce cultivars are characterized by leaves that are considerably longer than they are wide. Other characters of these cultivars can vary considerably, although most modern cultivars grown in the United States have green to dark-green leaves with an upright orientation. The top of the head is either open or closed to form a heart.
- Latin lettuce cultivars produce small heads with upright leaves that are longer than they are wide; Latin leaves are similar to romaine leaves but much shorter. The texture of Latin lettuce is similar to that of butterhead.
- Leaf or cutting lettuce cultivars form open-topped rosettes; the remaining characters are highly variable.

Types of lettuce cultivars differ considerably in the time needed to reach peak maturity. Crisphead (or iceberg) lettuce matures from 60 to 130 days after planting. Romaine lettuce matures as quickly as or more quickly than crisphead, and leaf, butterhead, and Latin lettuce all mature more quickly than romaine.

The remaining lettuce types are apparently ancient:

- Stem lettuce (also called "stalk" or "asparagus lettuce") is grown in Egypt, southwest Asia, and China for consumption of the stems. In Egypt and southwest Asia, the stems are eaten raw. The stem types grown in China often have narrow, lanceolate-shaped leaves and the stems are cooked.
- Oil-seed lettuce is grown for harvest of the seeds, which are larger than the seeds of other lettuces and pressed to produce oil. The plants bolt and flower quickly, and their overall appearance is roughly similar to that of some wild relatives of lettuce. Growing lettuce as an oil-seed crop may predate growing it as a food crop for the consumption of leaves.

Botany, Taxonomy, and Origin

Lettuce (*Lactuca sativa*) is a member of the Asteraceae (or Compositae) family and has an annual life cycle. It is the only cultivated species of the approximately 100 species in the genus *Lactuca,* most of which are indigenous to Asia and Africa. The genus is diverse, encompassing annual, biennial, perennial, and occasionally shrubby plants. Most are diploid, but there are a few polyploids. The closest wild relatives of lettuce—*L. serriola,* several *L. serriola*-like species, *L. saligna,* and *L. virosa*—are all annual or biennial herbaceous weeds.

Lettuce and most *Lactuca* spp. are self-fertile and possess floral structures that promote a high rate of self-pollination. Consequently, *Lactuca* populations are composed largely of homozygous plants. *L. serriola* is completely interfertile with lettuce, whereas its sexual compatibility with more distant relatives is limited (*L. saligna*) to nearly absent (*L. virosa*).

L. serriola is likely one of or the only direct ancestor of cultivated lettuce. Domestication of the earliest and most primitive forms likely originated through selection of variant forms of *L. serriola* or perhaps a hybrid between *L. serriola* and another *Lactuca* species that was more amenable to cultivation and consumption. The site of domestication was likely southwest Asia and probably within the Fertile Crescent region. Domestication in Egypt has also been proposed, as primitive, locally grown oil-seed-type lettuce similar to *L. serriola* is found in Egypt. In addition, tomb paintings in ancient Egypt dating to approximately 2500 BCE may represent the earliest known depictions of lettuce. They appear to show a stem-type lettuce that is still grown in Egypt. Some Egyptian stem-type lettuces closely resemble romaine lettuce, suggesting a common ancestry.

Regardless of its origin, lettuce was commonly grown throughout southwest Asia and around the Mediterranean Sea before spreading globally. Archeological evidence documents the ex-

Fig. 1. Morphological variation among different market types of lettuce: **A,** cultivar Imperial 850; **B,** modern crisphead cultivar Pacific; **C,** butterhead cultivar Dark Green Boston; **D,** romaine cultivar Hearts Delight; **E,** Great Lakes-type cultivar; **F,** Latin-type cultivar Little Gem; **G,** red leaf cultivar Sentry; **H,** green leaf cultivar Australian; **I,** green leaf cultivar Big Star; **J,** oil-seed lettuce plant introduction (PI) 251246; **K,** stem lettuce from Egypt; and **L,** Asian stem lettuce cultivar Da Ye Wo Sun. (Courtesy R. J. Hayes)

istence of lettuce in Persia in 550 BCE, Greece in 430 BCE, Rome in 42 CE, and China by the fifth century. It was mentioned in Chaucer's *The Canterbury Tales* (written in 1387–1400) and was brought on Columbus's second voyage to North America (1493–1496).

Evolution of the U.S. Lettuce Industry

Commercial lettuce production in the United States began in the early twentieth century and rapidly became concentrated in a few districts. By the 1920s, the western U.S. industry was already dominant. In 1998, California and Arizona accounted for 95% of U.S. production; the remaining 5% was spread across several other states, each harvesting less than 1,300 ha. In 2008, California and Arizona accounted for 99% of U.S. production. Within Arizona and California, production is further concentrated in a few regions (Fig. 2). In Arizona, nearly all the lettuce production occurs in Yuma County, and in California, more than half the state's production occurs in Monterey County, which includes the Salinas Valley.

Production in the United States was dominated by crisphead lettuce before the 1990s, when more than 80,000 ha of this type was harvested annually. Since then, the production of crisphead lettuce has steadily declined; in 2014, less than 51,000 ha was harvested. The amounts of leaf and romaine lettuce produced steadily increased during this time. In 1992, 19,800 and 38,600 ha of romaine and leaf lettuce were harvested, respectively; by 2014, these numbers had increased to 34,500 and 21,900 ha, respectively. Changes in production have reflected changes in consumer demand for more nutritious products, as well as improvements in postharvest technologies that have made available to consumers packaged salads containing romaine and leaf lettuce mixed with other vegetables.

The production of baby leaf lettuce for use in so-called spring mix and mesclun has also become increasingly popular. As many as 15–20 unique types of lettuce are used in these mixes. The lettuce portion is mixed with various other leafy green vegetables, such as endive (*Cichorium endivia*), radicchio (*C. intybus*), arugula (*Eruca vesicaria*), spinach (*Spinacia oleracea*), beet tops (*Beta vulgaris*) and red Swiss chard (*B. vulgaris* subsp. *cicla*), mache or cornsalad (*Valerianella locusta*), and mizuna (*Brassica rapa* subsp. *nipposinica*) and tatsoi (*Brassica rapa* subsp. *narinosa*), also known as "field mustard" and "spinach mustard," respectively. Based on production statistics from Monterey County, spring mix (which includes baby leaf lettuce) currently represents less than 10% of the harvested area.

Production Factors

Climate and Growing Season

Lettuce is grown as a home garden vegetable nearly everywhere in the United States. For successful commercial production, climate is the largest determinant of when and where lettuce is grown. The crop is best adapted to daytime temperatures of 18–25°C and nighttime temperatures of 10–15°C.

Year-round production within the United States has traditionally been achieved by rotating production around select locations within California and Arizona (Fig. 3). Summer harvests during April through October take place in three districts in coastal California: Salinas/Watsonville, Santa Maria, and Oxnard. During October and November, lettuce is harvested in the San Joaquin Valley of California. Winter harvests during November through March occur in the low desert regions of California (Imperial, Coachella, and Palo Verde Valleys) and Arizona (Yuma area). Harvesting occurs again in the San Joaquin Valley during March and April before it resumes in the coastal California districts.

Summer
• Coastal production

Fall/Spring
• San Joaquin Valley

Winter
• Low Desert

Fig. 2. Primary lettuce production districts in the United States. (Courtesy R. J. Hayes)

Fig. 3. Production schedules of major U.S. lettuce production areas. Black bars represent periods for planting, and gray bars represent periods for harvesting. (Reproduced, by permission, of California Leafy Greens Research Program)

Concerns over the availability of water in the San Joaquin Valley have resulted in a decrease of production there. Consequently, many producers have extended the growing season in coastal California and the low desert by planting earlier and later than historically normal. It is not clear whether this represents a temporary change or an emerging trend that will continue.

Cultivar Selection

Selection of an appropriately adapted cultivar is important for successful commercial production. Most modern cultivars are typically recommended for use in a particular planting slot, which is a range of recommended seeding dates for a specific location. The planting slot therefore represents the environment for which a cultivar is best adapted.

Cultivars are often bred with the intent of being adapted to a specific planting slot, which is confirmed through multiyear testing. Otherwise, the planting slot for a given cultivar is typically determined through widespread field testing by the developer or the company marketing the seed. Crisphead cultivars are in general more narrowly adapted than leaf and romaine cultivars; thus, crisphead cultivars have shorter-duration planting slots. In addition, crisphead cultivars adapted to winter production often have shorter planting slots than cultivars grown in the summer.

Planting slots encompass a wide range of photoperiods, soil conditions, and prevailing diseases, and some planting slots routinely experience suboptimal production conditions. In these cases, the cultivars bred for these planting slots are selected for tolerance or resistance to the particular biotic and abiotic stresses that commonly occur. Internationally but also increasingly in the northern and central United States, protected culture is used when temperatures are unfavorable for open field production or when protection is needed from adverse weather conditions, such as heavy wind and rain. A range of structures are used to provide varying degrees of control over the production environment. Plastic tunnels may be placed in production fields to capture solar radiation and increase the temperature, whereas greenhouses and growth rooms may offer control over temperature, light intensity, day length, and other factors.

Planting, Thinning, and Spacing

In open field production in California and Arizona, the most common method for establishing a crop is to sow pelleted lettuce seed on raised beds at intervals of 5–10 cm using precision planters. Preplant fertilizer may be applied before or during the shaping of beds. In other production regions, transplanting approximately 1-month-old seedlings is more common. In the western United States, soils are rarely moist enough to germinate seeds, and water is typically applied through overhead irrigation once a day until the seedlings emerge. In some desert production regions, seeds are germinated using furrow irrigation.

After 3–4 weeks of growth, the seedlings are thinned to the final plant density of the crop, which is a major factor in determining yield. The plant density is in turn determined by the bed configuration, the number of seed lines per bed, and the spacing between plants within seed lines.

In California and Arizona, typical beds are 10–25 cm high and have a narrow or a wide format. Narrow beds are 102–107 cm wide and have two seed lines 35 cm apart. In some cases, 107-cm beds may have three seed lines. Wide beds are 203–213 cm wide and have five or six seed lines. Using wide beds is advantageous because plant density can be increased 25–50% compared with narrow beds.

Spacing within seed lines ranges from 25 to 31 cm; the closer spacing is typically used for bulk-harvested lettuce destined for processing into packaged salads. Spacing as close as 13 cm within a seed line, with as many as eight seed lines in a wide bed, may be used for romaine hearts and other specialty types of lettuce. Baby leaf lettuce is grown on wide beds with 24 or 32 seed lines per bed, or approximately 4–6 million plants per ha; the crop is not thinned.

Irrigation

Most lettuce crops receive at least some supplemental irrigation after thinning. In the western United States, most if not all of a crop's water requirement is met through irrigation. The amount of water applied through the season depends on many factors, such as weather conditions, soil salinity, soil water-holding capacity, and other factors. Irrigation can also be used to cool crops during hot weather and to leach salts from the soil. Furrow, sprinkler, and drip irrigation are the primary methods used in lettuce production.

Fertilization and pH

Fertilization rates and materials vary widely depending on the type of production, the planting slot, the crop establishment method, the soil factors, and the type of lettuce being grown. In conventional production, most nutrient needs are met through applying a granular or liquid chemical fertilizer containing nitrogen (N), phosphorus (P), and potassium (K). Organic producers use pelletized chicken manure, blood meal, gypsum, compost, and various liquid organic fertilizers. Fertilizer may be applied preplant, side-dressed two or three times during the crop cycle, or applied through drip irrigation.

The requirement for N increases during crop development, whereas P is needed primarily for early growth. Consequently, preplant applications of fertilizer may contain little N, whereas later applications may be composed largely of N. Some soils in major western U.S. production districts have adequate levels of K, and additional K fertilization may not be necessary. Fertilization with micronutrients is typically not needed, although zinc (Zn) fertilization is practiced in some areas of coastal California, and copper (Cu) fertilization may be used on muck soils.

The optimum soil pH for lettuce production is 6.5–7.2. In some cases, acidic soils are treated with lime prior to planting.

Managing Weeds and Insect Pests

A wide variety of strategies are used to control weeds and insect pests. Reducing weed populations during the first 3–4 weeks after emergence is important for reducing yield losses caused by weeds. Preplant and pre-emergent herbicides are commonly used in conventional lettuce production. Hand weeding at thinning and at 2–3 weeks after thinning and cultivation is routine for conventional and organic production. Other weed management methods include preirrigation followed by shallow cultivation and propane flaming.

Insects damage lettuce crops in several ways: by vectoring disease-causing pathogens, by directly consuming plants, and by contaminating plants or causing blemishes (thus lowering the value of the crop). Applying insecticides is the most common method of insect management for conventionally produced lettuce, although other methods are becoming increasingly popular for both organic and conventional production. Alternative methods include planting resistant cultivars, applying biological controls, adjusting planting schedules, and using trap crops. Intercropping with insectary plants—typically alyssum (*Lobularia maritima*)—is common in organic and some conventional production to promote predator species that control the lettuce aphid (*Nasonovia ribisnigri*). In the lettuce production districts of Monterey County (California), growing the Lombardy poplar tree (*Populus nigra*) is prohibited, because it is the alternate host of the lettuce root aphid (*Pemphigus bursarius*).

Harvest and Postharvest Handling

Harvest practices depend on the end use of the product, although all harvesting includes cutting, packing, cooling, and shipping to market. A key goal of every harvest practice is to get the product to market quickly to maintain quality. Keeping the lettuce cool throughout the process (known as the "cold chain") is critical to achieving this goal. Because of this, most lettuce harvested in California and Arizona is vacuum-cooled after harvest to approximately 1°C and maintained at this temperature using cold storage and refrigerated trucks.

In fields harvested for whole heads or in bulk, mature plants of marketable size and quality are cut individually, and all the other plants are left in the field. Lettuce marketed as whole heads is packed into cartons or other types of containers. A typical carton holds 24 heads, although a wide variety of carton shapes and sizes are used depending on the type of lettuce grown and the intended market. Outer leaves with signs of disease and blemishes are removed, and each head is typically wrapped in film before being packed into the container. Once filled, the carton or container is closed and stacked on a pallet with other cartons/containers before being taken to the cooler. After cooling, the lettuce is moved to the retailer as quickly as possible. Growers are typically paid per carton or per container.

Lettuce for processing is harvested and bulked into palletized totes. Bulk-harvested lettuce often has blemished leaves trimmed off in the field, the core removed, or the top and bottom of the plant cut off entirely. Growers are paid by the weight of harvested lettuce or the area harvested. Most harvesting operations in California and Arizona involve mechanical assistance to some degree by using a harvesting rig that follows a harvesting crew. A conveyer belt moves heads into bins or cartons to a truck so they can be stacked on pallets. A harvest crew typically passes through a field once; only rarely does a crew return to a field for a second harvest.

Baby leaf lettuce is mechanically harvested 20–30 days after planting, when the leaves are 5–13 cm long. After cutting, the leaves are collected into bins and totes of various sizes. The different components of a salad mix may be harvested at the same time or at separate times. They are shipped to a central facility and combined to make the final product.

Bulk-harvested lettuce is moved to a processing plant, where it is chopped or shredded, washed, spun dry, and packaged. The cutting performed in processing substantially shortens the shelf life of lettuce. Maintaining the cold chain is the most critical factor in extending the shelf life of cut lettuce, although additional practices can extend shelf life, as well (see later in this "Introduction").

Many processing companies maintain production plants throughout North America, even though the lettuce being processed is supplied primarily from California and Arizona. Following this strategy shortens the distance that cut lettuce must travel postprocessing to reach the intended market. Modified atmosphere (MA) packaging is routinely used to extend the shelf life of cut lettuce. Low-oxygen and high-carbon dioxide environments are created inside packing film to retard oxidative browning and delay senescence. MA packaging is achieved by matching product respiration with the oxygen permeability of the packaging film and by flushing the package with a low-oxygen gas mixture before sealing the bag.

Selected References

Agricultural Commissioner, County of Monterey. 2013. 2013 Monterey County Crop Report. Agricultural Commissioner, Monterey, CA. Accessed Feb. 22, 2015, from http://cesantacruz.ucanr.edu/files/185447.pdf

de Vries, I. M. 1997. Origin and domestication of *Lactuca sativa* L. Genet. Resour. Crop Evol. 44:165-174.

Hochmuth, G., Hanlon, E., Nagata, R., Snyder, G., and Schueneman, T. 2009. Fertilization Recommendations for Crisphead Lettuce Grown on Organic Soils in Florida. Publ. SP153. University of Florida, Institute of Food and Agricultural Sciences, Gainesville. Accessed Feb. 22, 2015, from http://edis.ifas.ufl.edu/wq114

Kerns, D. L., Matheron, M. E., Palumbo, J. C., Sanchez, C. A., Still, D. W., Tickes, B. R., Umeda, K., and Wilcox, M. A. 1999. Guidelines for Head Lettuce Production in Arizona. IPM Series No. 12. Publ. az1099. University of Arizona, College of Agriculture and Life Sciences, Cooperative Extension, Tucson. Accessed Feb. 22, 2015, from http://cals.arizona.edu/crops/vegetables/cropmgt/az1099.html

Kim, J. G., Luo, Y., Tao, Y., Saftner, R. A., and Gross, K. C. 2005. Effect of initial oxygen concentration and film oxygen transmission rate on the quality of fresh-cut romaine lettuce. J. Sci. Food Agric. 85:1622-1630.

Lebeda, A., Ryder, E. J., Grube, R., Dolezalova, I., and Kristkova, E. 2007. Lettuce (Asteraceae; *Lactuca* spp.). Pages 377-472 in: Genetic Resources, Chromosome Engineering, and Crop Improvement Series. Vol. 3, Vegetable Crops. R. Singh, ed. CRC Press, Boca Raton, FL.

Ryder, E. J. 1999. Lettuce, endive and chicory. CAB International, New York.

Ryder, E. J., and McCreight, J. D. 2010. Lettuce (A–L). Vegetable Cultivar Descriptions for North America. U.S. Agricultural Research Station, Salinas, CA. Accessed Feb. 22, 2015, from http://cuke.hort.ncsu.edu/cucurbit/wehner/vegcult/lettuceal.html

Ryder, E. J., and McCreight, J. D. 2010. Lettuce (M–Z). Vegetable Cultivar Descriptions for North America. U.S. Agricultural Research Station, Salinas, CA. Accessed Feb. 22, 2015, from http://cuke.hort.ncsu.edu/cucurbit/wehner/vegcult/lettucemz.html

Simko, I., Hayes, R. J., Mou, B., and McCreight, J. D. 2014. Lettuce and spinach. Pages 53-85 in: Yield Gains in Major U.S. Field Crops. S. Smith, B. Diers, J. Sprecht, and B. Carver, eds. American Society of Agronomy, Crop Science Society of America, and Soil Science Society of America, Madison, WI.

Smith, R., Cahn, M., Daugovish, O., Koike, S., Natwick, E., Smith, H., Subbarao, K., Takele, E., and Turini, T. 2011. Leaf Lettuce Production in California. Publ. 7216. University of California, Division of Agriculture and Natural Resources, Oakland.

Tourte, L., Smith, R. F., Klonsky, K. M., and De Moura, R. L. 2009. Sample Costs to Produce Organic Leaf Lettuce. Publ. LT-CC-09-O. University of California, Cooperative Extension, Davis.

Turini, T., Cahn, M., Cantwell, M., Jackson, L., Koike, S., Natwick, E., Smith, R., Subbarao, K., and Takele, E. 2011. Iceberg Lettuce Production in California. Publ. 7215. University of California, Vegetable and Research and Information Center, Davis.

University of California, Integrated Pest Management (UC IPM). 2009. Lettuce: Irrigation of head and romaine lettuce. How to Manage Pests: UC Pest Management Guidelines. Accessed Feb. 22, 2015, www.ipm.ucdavis.edu/PMG/r441311511.html

U.S. Department of Agriculture, National Agricultural Statistics Service (USDA-NASS). n.d. 1998-2012, Lettuce production data, USDA-NASS, Washington, DC. Accessed Feb. 22, 2015, from http://quickstats.nass.usda.gov

U.S. Department of Agriculture, National Agricultural Statistics Service (USDA-NASS). 2014. USDA Census of Agriculture. 2012 Census Volume 1, Chapter 2: County Level Data—Arizona. Accessed Feb. 22, 2015, from www.agcensus.usda.gov/Publications/2012/Full_Report/Volume_1,_Chapter_2_County_Level/Arizona/

U.S. Department of Agriculture, National Agricultural Statistics Service (USDA-NASS). 2014. USDA Census of Agriculture. 2012 Census Volume 1, Chapter 2: County Level Data—California. Accessed Feb. 22, 2015, from www.agcensus.usda.gov/Publications/2012/Full_Report/Volume_1,_Chapter_2_County_Level/California/

Wallace, R. W., Wszelaki, A. L., Miles, C. A., Cowan, J. S., Martin, J., Roozen, J., Gundersen, B., and Inglis, D. A. 2012. Lettuce yield and quality when gown in high tunnel and open-field production systems under three diverse climates. HortTechnology 22:659-668.

(Prepared by R. J. Hayes)

Lettuce Breeding

Growing improved cultivars can increase the efficiency of crop production and the value of the harvested crop. In short, crop breeding entails moving or accumulating genes that confer desirable traits or superior performance into a new, genetically stable cultivar.

Breeding for the continual improvement of lettuce is conducted by publicly funded institutions and private seed companies. Public institutions largely conduct enhancement breeding, in which new lettuce types are developed or new economically valuable traits are introgressed into the cultivated gene pool. This germplasm is typically released with no intellectual property protection and freely given to private seed companies for further breeding and commercialization. Publicly funded programs often conduct research on new breeding methods, the inheritance of specific traits, and the genomics of lettuce. This research can be used to increase the rate at which new cultivars are developed.

The characteristics of modern lettuce cultivars are strongly influenced by a handful of landmark cultivars. Because of this, modern cultivars of these types tend to be closely related. Publicly funded lettuce breeding within the U.S. Department of Agriculture (USDA) began in 1922 to deal with a disorder known as "brown blight" that occurred in southern California. The breeder, I. C. Jagger, selected a few healthy plants of the cultivar New York being grown in an afflicted field. These plants gave rise to a series of cultivars under the name Imperial and with additional crossing and selection gave rise to a series of Imperial-type cultivars. New York and Imperial cultivars are similar to modern-day Batavia cultivars.

T. W. Whitaker crossed the cultivar Imperial 152 with the European cultivar Brittle Ice to develop the cultivar Great Lakes—the first iceberg-type crisphead cultivar, which was released in 1941. Numerous selections were made from within the Great Lakes cultivar, and this group of cultivars was widely grown into the mid-1970s. One of the most popular of these was the cultivar Calmar, which was bred using Great Lakes-type parents to incorporate downy mildew resistance.

R. C. Thompson developed the cultivar Vanguard, which was the first lettuce cultivar developed using interspecific hybridization. This cultivar was developed from a cross between a complex line incorporating *Lactuca virosa* and *L. serriola* to a numbered line that would eventually be named Climax. Climax and Vanguard are best adapted to winter production and occur in the pedigrees of cultivars adapted for winter production.

Among the historically important cultivars for desert production are Merit and Empire. Empire and its descendants are particularly valued for their bolting resistance in fall plantings in the low desert of California. The cultivar Salinas was developed by E. J. Ryder and released in 1975; it was selected from a cross between a Vanguard-like breeding line and Calmar. Salinas is adapted to spring and summer production in coastal California and has improved shipping qualities, better tipburn resistance, and higher yields compared with other cultivars grown at the time. Most crisphead cultivars adapted to coastal California are derived from Salinas or bred to resemble Salinas. Vanguard served an important function in the development of modern crisphead cultivars. Vanguard was released after three generations of self-pollination and selection and possessed enough genetic variation for numerous desert-adapted cultivars to be selected from it. Through its contribution to Salinas, Vanguard resides in the pedigrees of many cultivars adapted to coastal California, as well.

Many modern romaine cultivars used for commercial production are derived from the cultivars Parris Island Cos and Tall Guzmaine. Parris Island Cos was released in the 1950s by the Clemson College Truck Experiment Station—reportedly from a cross between plant introduction (PI) 120965 and the cultivar Dark Green. Tall Guzmaine was developed by V. L. Guzman at the University of Florida from a cross between the cultivars Parris White and Short Guzmaine. Tall Guzmaine is slow bolting and has resistance to important diseases. Many new romaine cultivars have been developed by selecting slightly improved versions from within these cultivars or from intercrossing Parris Island Cos and Tall Guzmaine.

Objectives of Lettuce Breeding

In the beginning stages of a breeding program, the breeder determines the objectives. Plant breeding is a long-term endeavor, and breeding objectives typically include improvement of the plant characters that are currently important along with those that are likely to be important in the future.

The horticultural characters considered desirable are often unique for each lettuce type. These characters represent a specific combination of head architecture and leaf color, shape, texture, and flavor. Earliness, slow bolting, short cores, and reliable and rapid seed germination are generally desirable for all types. High yield is also desirable for all types, although the traits that contribute to high yield depend on whether the lettuce is harvested for sale as whole heads or for processing. Plant density after thinning is an important determinant of yield; thus, breeding cultivars with high rates of survival from common diseases and pests is important.

Uniformity of maturity and of horticultural type are both critical in all cases. The popularity of the cultivar Salinas is largely attributed to an increased uniformity of head maturity, which substantially increased its yield compared with the yields of previous cultivars. Head weight and size above a minimum standard are important for lettuce marketed as whole heads, although breeding heads with ever-increasing head size is not necessarily desirable. Heads that are too large will not fit into their designated containers or may be considered abnormal for a given lettuce type. However, the yield of bulk-harvested lettuce for processing can be increased by breeding for larger heads.

Diseases and insect pests reduce yield and quality by reducing plants' vigor and harvest weight, increasing the number of leaves that need to be trimmed off at harvest, rendering plants unsightly and unmarketable, and outright killing plants before harvest. When bred into adapted cultivars, complete and incomplete genetic resistance to diseases and pests can effectively reduce losses. Numerous major genes that confer high levels of resistance have been deployed against plant pathogens and insects. Typically, these resistances are inherited and amenable to rapid backcross breeding approaches.

In the case of downy mildew, more than 30 resistance loci have been identified. Major genes for resistance to downy mildew are rapidly defeated by new strains of the pathogen; consequently, new genes must be routinely identified and introgressed into adapted cultivars. Other major resistance genes commonly bred into lettuce cultivars include *cor* (resistance to corky root) and *Tvr1* (resistance to *Tombusvirus* species). The *Vr1* gene confers resistance to race 1 isolates of *Verticillium dahliae* and will likely become widespread among crisphead cultivars. Incomplete resistance to several diseases is known in lettuce and may be useful for reducing losses. Resistance that limits damage to the lower leaves, which are trimmed off as part of normal harvest operations, is known for downy mildew and bacterial leaf spot. Lettuce is harvested at a vegetative stage, and genes that delay disease symptoms past harvest may be useful in resistance breeding. Resistance to big-vein disease in the cultivar Pacific is attributed to this mechanism, as is resistance to lettuce drop in some *Lactuca* accessions.

The development and use of cultivars with improved resistance or tolerance to abiotic stresses can increase the reliability of crop yields and quality. Cultivars are routinely bred for resistance to physiological defects that render plants unmarketable, such as tipburn, rib discoloration, and premature bolting. Other traits are being pursued to improve the crop's ability to withstand extreme fluctuations in weather conditions. For example, the germination of lettuce seed can be inhibited by high temperatures. Identification of a major quantitative trait locus (QTL) for high-temperature germination (*Hgt6.1*) in an *L. serriola* accession may lead to the development of cultivars that

successfully germinate under hot conditions. Developing cultivars that use water and other nutrients more efficiently is a priority for the lettuce industry, although little is known about these traits. Lettuce cultivars bred for production under protected culture may be selected for low nitrate content. Selection for improved nutritional content, particularly vitamins and antioxidants, is underway to develop cultivars that are more desirable to consumers.

Breeding cultivars with improved shelf life for salad-cut lettuce is increasingly important given the increased popularity of these products and growing concerns over food waste. Salad products are popular with consumers, and the lettuce component commonly has the shortest shelf life of the vegetables used in the mix. Modified atmosphere (MA) packaging is used to control wound-induced oxidation, which causes browning or pinking of cut surfaces. Nevertheless, lettuce cultivars exhibit genetic variation for decay (e.g., tissue darkening, waterlogging, and complete breakdown) in MA packaging, which limits its usefulness. A major QTL, *qSL4,* exerts a large degree of control over the decay rate of salad-cut lettuce across diverse production and packing environments. Several primitive accessions and heirloom cultivars with resistance to Verticillium wilt and *Tombusvirus* species carry the *qSL4* allele for fast decay. Modern germplasm with resistance to these diseases was developed by selecting for resistance and against fast decay. Several minor QTLs that control leaf development and biophysical traits also appear to influence shelf life. Lettuce breeders can likely use this variation to develop cultivars that decay slowly. The severity of browning and pinking on cut surfaces is also under genetic control, indicating the possibility of breeding cultivars that are less reliant on MA for good quality.

Methods of Lettuce Breeding

Lettuce is diploid ($2n = 2x = 18$) and a near-obligate, self-pollinating crop that tolerates inbreeding depression. Consequently, cultivars are inbred lines, and the breeding methods used for lettuce are those devised for inbred crops. No commercially successful hybrid cultivars are known. Hand cross-pollination between normally self-fertile plants is time consuming and regularly produces seed lots that are a mixture of hybrid seed and seed from unwanted self-pollination. Genetic male sterility has been identified, but lettuce pollen is not adapted for movement by wind. Insect pollination may occur but has not been widely tested.

Genetic variation is required for plant breeding, and several sources of genetic variation are available in lettuce. Production of unique types of lettuce in various regions of the world has created substantial genetic variation within cultivated lettuce, particularly for horticultural characters. Even greater amounts of genetic diversity can be found in *L. serriola, L. saligna,* and *L. virosa.* Related wild species have also been an important source of genes for disease and insect resistance. These wild species share the same number of chromosomes as lettuce but differ in their sexual compatibility with the crop. *L. serriola* and all types of cultivated lettuce intercross freely. Lettuce and *L. saligna* have limited sexual compatibility, although hybridization and seed production through self-pollination of the resulting hybrid plants is typically feasible. Interspecific hybridization between lettuce and *L. virosa* requires specialized techniques, such as in vitro culture of embryos, bridge crossing, and chromosome doubling of hybrids. Although protoplast fusion has been used to create somatic hybrids between lettuce and its more distant relatives, no cultivars have been produced using this approach. Chemical mutagenesis was used to create genes that reduce plant size by approximately half. These genes were subsequently used to breed mini-crisphead lettuce. Radiation mutation has been used in an effort to develop plants with herbicide resistance. Transformation is a technically feasible breeding method in lettuce, and lettuce has been successfully transformed with both plant and nonplant genes.

The most commonly used breeding procedures in lettuce are pure-line selection, pedigree breeding, and backcross breeding. Single-seed descent is not widely used as a breeding procedure in lettuce, but it is routinely used for the development of recombinant inbred-line populations for genetic analysis (QTL mapping) of complex traits. Occasionally, a particular recombinant inbred line from a population originally used for genetic analysis may be released as germplasm. Newer selection methods, such as genomic selection, are experimental in lettuce but hold great promise.

Pure-Line Selection

Pure-line selection is practiced by identifying and selecting variant plants (often with subtle differences) from a population of inbred plants (typically within an existing cultivar). Progeny from the selected plants are compared with the original population to determine if the differences observed in the previous generation were heritable and of sufficient value to warrant release as a cultivar. Mass selection follows to generate enough seed for multienvironment testing and release.

This approach has been widely used in lettuce breeding. A relevant example includes the selection of brown blight-free plants from within the cultivar New York, which eventually resulted in the Imperial-type cultivars. Additionally, numerous strains have been selected from within Great Lakes, Vanguard, Salinas, Parris Island Cos, and Tall Guzmaine.

Pedigree Breeding

Pedigree breeding begins by using conventional hybridization of parents with complementary characters to generate hybrid progeny. In many cases, biparental crosses are made between inbred plants. The method uses successive rounds of self-pollination and selection. The generations of self-pollination are often designated using the notation F_2 (second filial generation), F_3, and so on for each additional round of self-pollination. The F_2 seed, which results from self-pollination of the F_1 plant, is the first generation in which recombination and segregation are observed. Therefore, evaluation and selection for desirable plants begins in this generation. The selected F_2 plants are allowed to self-pollinate. The F_3 and later generations are subjected to successive rounds of selection between and within families or lines for desirable progeny followed by self-pollination. The inbreeding process reduces variability within lines while increasing the differences between lines.

Selection in early generations (F_2 through F_4) focuses on highly heritable traits, such as plant morphology and color. In later generations (F_4 and beyond), selection is typically between lines and focuses on traits with low heritability, such as head size and uniformity. At some point, the differences between plants within a line become imperceptible, and the line appears uniform. The breeder will select between lines and bulk the seed from multiple plants within a line.

The pedigree approach can be modified to suit a broad range of breeding objectives and situations. For example, more complex crossing strategies can be used, such as crosses using F_1 plants originating from three or more inbred lines and crossing using early generation plants. In field experiments with the progeny, selected plants are dug up from the field and repotted in a greenhouse for seed production. In cases in which evaluations use destructive assays or involve soil- or seedborne pathogens, separate plantings may be needed for evaluations and seed production. For example, when breeding lettuce for resistance to Verticillium wilt and lettuce drop, congruent field experiments in infested and noninfested field experiments are used. Within F_3 and later generations, disease-resistance evaluations are conducted in infested soil to identify families with high levels of resistance. In the noninfested field site, plants

Fig. 4. Lettuce drop in romaine lettuce in a Spreckels, California (United States), grower field experiment: **A**, cultivar Hearts Delight; **B**, cultivar Green Towers; **C** and **D**, inbred breeding lines from Hearts Delight × Eruption selected for resistance to lettuce drop. (Courtesy R. J. Hayes)

with superior horticultural characters are selected for seed production from only the resistant families. This approach has developed romaine breeding lines with lettuce drop resistance (Fig. 4) and crisphead lines with Verticillium wilt resistance.

Backcross Breeding

Backcross breeding is used to transfer one to a few genes from a donor parent to a recipient, which is a horticulturally elite cultivar. The goal of this approach is to develop a new cultivar that is the same as the original recipient cultivar but with a new trait. Plants are simultaneously selected for the new trait and for the horticultural characters of the recipient parent. Selected plants are then crossed back to the recipient parent, and the process is repeated several times. The number of backcrosses needed depends on a range of genetic considerations. The use of molecular markers to select for the recipient genetic background can substantially reduce the number of backcrosses. In lettuce, early flowering genes can be used that reduce the time needed to complete each cycle of selection and backcrossing. After a sufficient number of backcrosses, plants are self-pollinated and seed is bulked from multiple plants for use in field testing.

Numerous modifications can be made to the basic backcrossing scheme that depend largely on the inheritance of the trait coming from the donor parent. However, the trait from the donor parent is typically simply inherited, accurately selected for using phenotypic or marker assays, and not strongly influenced by the environment.

Disease-resistance traits conferred by single major genes are commonly bred into new cultivars using backcross breeding. An example in lettuce includes the development of cultivars resistant to *Lettuce mosaic virus* in the United States using the $mo1^2$ gene derived from the oil-seed lettuce PI 251245. Dominant genes conferring race-specific resistance to downy mildew have been bred into many new lettuce cultivars using backcrossing.

Genomic Selection

Molecular markers have numerous uses in plant breeding, including marker-assisted breeding. Marker-assisted breeding can shorten the length of each selection cycle and accelerate genetic improvement. It can be particularly advantageous for traits that are measured using destructive assays, because the marker test can be applied to individual plants in early generations without destroying them. Traditional marker-assisted selection (MAS) uses a few markers that are closely linked to important loci; this approach is typically effective for traits controlled by one to a few genes.

A different approach, termed "genomic selection," has been more effective than MAS for selection of polygenic traits in cereal crops. In genomic selection, genome estimated breeding values (GEBVs) are calculated using a large number of markers spread across the genome. This practice is applied to individuals with only genotypic (marker) data; those with the most favorable GEBVs are selected for advancement. The calculation of GEBVs employs a model that is developed using a population that has both phenotypic (trait) and genotypic data. Genomic selection is still being tested in lettuce (as of early 2017) but may be useful for accelerating the genetic improvement of lettuce.

Field Testing

Extensive field testing is required to characterize new inbreds regardless of the breeding scheme used to develop them. This testing is done through multienvironment field experiments conducted in the late stages of a breeding program, when only a few elite lines remain. The results of these experiments are used to determine whether a line should be released as a cultivar or as germplasm and whether a line is suitable for whole heads, processing, or both. Numerous experiments are usually needed to characterize a line's resistance to physiological defects (e.g., tipburn), which require unpredictable environmental conditions for expression. Information that is critical to growers is also gathered during these experiments, such as appropriate planting slots, unusual susceptibilities, and time to harvest.

Selected References

Atkinson, L. D., McHale, L. K., Truco, M. J., Hilton, H. W., Lynn, J., Schut, J. W., Michelmore, R. W., Hand, P., and Pink, D. A. C. 2013. An intraspecific linkage map of lettuce (*Lactuca sativa*) and genetic analysis of postharvest discolouration traits. Theor. Appl. Genet. 126:2737-2752.

Frisch, M., Bohn, M., and Melchinger, A. E. 1999. Comparison of selection strategies for marker-assisted backcrossing of a gene. Crop Sci. 39:1295-1301.

Guzman, V. L. 1986. Short Guzmaine, Tall Guzmaine and Floriglade: Three Cos Lettuce Cultivars Resistant to Lettuce Mosaic Virus. Publ. S-326. University of Florida, Institute of Food and Agricultural Sciences, Gainesville.

Hayes, R. J., Maruthachalam, K., Vallad, G. E., Klosterman, S. J., Simko, I., Luo, Y., and Subbarao, K. V. 2011. Iceberg lettuce breeding lines with resistance to Verticillium wilt caused by race 1 isolates of *Verticillium dahliae*. HortScience 46:501-504.

Hayes, R. J., Galeano, C., H., Luo, Y., Anotonise, R., and Simko, I. 2014. Inheritance of decay of fresh-cut lettuce in a recombinant inbred line population from Salinas 88 × La Brillante. J. Am. Soc. Hortic. Sci. 139:388-398.

Lebeda, A., Ryder, E. J., Grube, R., Dolezalova, I., and Kristkova, E. 2007. Lettuce (Asteraceae; *Lactuca* spp.). Pages 377-472 in: Genetic Resources, Chromosome Engineering, and Crop Improvement Series. Vol. 3, Vegetable Crops. R. Singh, ed. CRC Press, Boca Raton, FL.

Lebeda, A., Křístková, E., Kitner, M., Mieslerová, B., Jemelková, M., and Pink, D. A. C. 2014. Wild *Lactuca* species, their genetic diversity, resistance to diseases and pests, and exploitation in lettuce breeding. Eur. J. Plant Pathol. 138:597-640.

Mikel, M. A. 2007. Genealogy of contemporary North American lettuce. HortScience 42:489-493.

Mikel, M. A. 2013. Genetic composition of contemporary proprietary U.S. lettuce (*Lactuca sativa* L.) cultivars. Genet. Resourc. Crop Evol. 60:89-96.

Mou, B. 2011. Mutations in lettuce improvement. Int. J. Plant Genomics. Vol. 2011, Article ID 723518. doi.org/10.1155/2011/723518

Ryder, E. J. 1979. 'Salinas' lettuce. HortScience 14:283-284.

Ryder, E. J. 1999. Lettuce, endive and chicory. CAB International, New York.

Simko, I. 2013. Marker-assisted selection for disease resistance in lettuce. Pages 267-289 in: Translational Genomics for Crop Breeding.

Vol. 1, Biotic Stresses. R. K. Varshney and R. Tuberosa, eds. Wiley-Blackwell, New York.

Simko, I., Hayes, R. J., Mou, B., and McCreight, J. D. 2014. Lettuce and Spinach. Pages 53-85 in: Yield Gains in Major U.S. Field Crops. S. Smith, B. Diers, J. Sprecht, and B. Carver, eds. American Society of Agronomy, Crop Science Society of America, and Soil Science Society of America, Madison, WI.

Thompson, R. C., and Ryder, E. J. 1961. Descriptions and Pedigrees of Nine Varieties of Lettuce. Tech. Bull. 1244. U.S. Department of Agriculture, Washington, DC.

Varshney, R. K., Terauchi, R., and McCouch, S. R. 2014. Harvesting the promising fruits of genomics: Applying genome sequencing technologies to crop breeding. PLoS Biol. 12:e1001883.

Zhang, F. Z., Wagstaff, C., Rae, A. M., Sihota, A. K., Keevil, C. W., Rothwell, S. D., Clarkson, G. J. J., Michelmore, R. W., Truco, M. J., Dixon, M. S., and Taylor, G. 2007. QTLs for shelf life in lettuce co-locate with those for leaf biophysical properties but not with those for leaf developmental traits. J. Exp. Bot. 58:1433-1449.

(Prepared by R. J. Hayes)

Applications of Biotechnology and Genomics to Disease Resistance in Lettuce

Our ability to identify and manipulate genetic variation in crop plants has been revolutionized since the early 1980s. Lettuce has benefited from the applications of several technologies to characterize the genetic basis of disease resistance and to deploy resistance genes. These have resulted in ultradense maps with numerous resistance genes mapped relative to other agriculturally important phenotypes and have provided molecular markers for marker-assisted selection (MAS) in breeding programs. Rapid genetic analysis of disease-resistance phenotypes and MAS are becoming routine, and even bigger advances are on the horizon. These approaches provide opportunities for developing durable disease resistance to multiple pathogens and pests of lettuce that will remain effective over long periods of widespread agricultural use.

Tissue Culture

Lettuce (*Lactuca sativa*) is amenable to several tissue culture approaches. Embryo rescue has been used on multiple occasions to enable wide crosses to the secondary gene pool and transfer of disease resistance from *L. saligna* and *L. virosa* to cultivated *L. sativa*. Protoplast fusions between sexually incompatible *Lactuca* species has been reported but not yet resulted in the transfer of useful genetic variation to cultivated lettuce from outside the sexually compatible gene pool (as of early 2017). Anther culture and generation of haploids has been attempted but not been successful.

Molecular Markers and Genome Sequencing

A series of technological advances and marker types has resulted in the development of increasingly dense genetic maps of lettuce. More than 50 genes for resistance to seven diseases have been placed relative to horticultural traits on a consensus map of lettuce that integrates information from multiple populations. Most but not all major resistance phenotypes map to complex major resistance clusters (MRCs) that encode nucleotide binding site–leucine-rich repeat (NB–LRR) proteins. MRCs are not highly recombinagenic in biparental populations, probably because of structural hybridity between the parents of the cross; thus, it is challenging to generate haplotypes that combine multiple resistance genes in *cis*. It is relatively easy to assign specificities to an NB–LRR-encoding gene family using RNA interference (RNAi); however, it remains difficult to identify individual causal genes. NB–LRR-encoding gene families and cloned resistance genes are excellent molecular markers for MAS. Saturated genetic maps with informative markers distributed along each chromosome enable the dissection of polygenic resistance phenotypes and the identification of underlying quantitative trait loci (QTLs).

One of the major transformative technologies since the early 2000s has been DNA sequencing, for which the cost has decreased rapidly while the level of throughput has increased dramatically. Productive collaborations between academia and the commercial sector have allowed the sequencing and assembly of the lettuce genome and the genome of one of the major pathogens of lettuce, *Bremia lactucae,* the causal agent of downy mildew. The reference genome of lettuce was generated for the crisphead cultivar Salinas and for an accession of the wild likely progenitor species, *L. serriola*. Low-pass, whole-genome sequencing of recombinant inbred lines (RILs) validated the quality of the genome assemblies and assigned approximately 97% of the assemblies to genetic bins ordered along the nine chromosomal linkage groups. Both genomes contain several hundred NB–LRR-encoding genes that cluster mainly at one of the five MRCs. NB–LRR-encoding genes can be grouped into 40 families; in the genome of the cultivar Salinas, 14 are single-copy genes, whereas the remainder belong to multigene families of up to 60 copies. Each MRC spans multiple megabases and often contains members of different families of NB–LRR-encoding genes, as well as genes not obviously related to resistance.

The sequencing of additional diverse cultivars and wild accessions is revealing a large diversity of resistance-gene candidates. Every genotype contains hundreds of resistance-gene candidates, even if only a few are recognized as effective. Therefore, backcrossing to introduce a resistance gene results in one MRC haplotype being replaced by another, and it is possible that useful resistance genes are being inadvertently deleted. The sequencing of multiple isolates of *B. lactucae* has uncovered the diversity of effector repertoires between isolates that will enable monitoring pathogen populations to guide resistance-gene deployment.

Genotyping by sequencing (GBS) of experimental populations means that generating genomewide marker data is no longer limiting; however, generating informative populations and phenotyping can be. GBS can identify polymorphisms even within types with a narrow genetic base, such as the crisphead cultivars. It is necessary to anticipate what populations will be informative and to make crosses to access resistance from wild germplasm. GBS also allows comprehensive surveys of haplotype diversity at MRCs in germplasm in the primary, secondary, and tertiary gene pools of lettuce.

Molecular markers are being used increasingly in commercial breeding programs. Markers can be used for cultivar identification and registration, although it is easier to demonstrate differences than to prove identity. MAS can greatly accelerate introgression of disease-resistance genes into cultivated lettuce. Markers based on the causal genes minimize the possibility of recombination between markers and resistance phenotypes. The use of markers enables pyramiding of genes that are effective against all known strains of a pathogen such as *B. lactucae,* which is not possible using phenotypic screens alone. Selec-

tion of recombinants using flanking markers can reduce linkage drag, which can be particularly important when resistance is introgressed from wild species. Background selection using markers unlinked to resistance can accelerate the return to the genotype of the recurrent parent.

The efficient identification of markers for large numbers of resistance genes in lettuce and diagnostic markers for strains of pathogens enables data-driven deployment of resistance genes. A variety of strategies can be implemented that fragment selection pressure on pathogen populations in space and time and that maximize the evolutionary hurdle required for a pathogen to become virulent. Pipelines should be developed for the continual introgression of new resistance genes from wild germplasm into cultivated lettuce. Different resistance genes should be deployed in different lettuce types so that epidemics of newly virulent strains do not spread from one type to another. A minimum of three genes that are effective against all strains in the target production areas should be pyramided in a single genotype. Pyramids of linked genes in *cis* are difficult to generate. Flanking markers can be utilized to select recombinants; however, an assay is needed to identify when effective genes are in *cis*. *Agrobacterium*-mediated transient expression of effector genes from the pathogen that are recognized by specific resistance genes may allow this. Once in *cis,* pyramided genes can be selected as a single Mendelian unit, avoiding the problem of pyramids of unlinked loci breaking down when crosses are made and resulting in exposure of the resistance genes individually, which invites sequential events in the pathogen to overcome resistance.

Status of Molecular Markers for Resistance to Specific Diseases

Downy Mildew

Downy mildew, caused by the oomycete *B. lactucae,* is the most important disease affecting lettuce both in the United States and worldwide. Although major genes for resistance to downy mildew (*Dm* genes) are highly effective and have been widely used, they have had limited lifespans because they have been rendered ineffective by changes in virulence of the pathogen.

The interaction between lettuce and *B. lactucae* is one of the most extensively genetically characterized gene-for-gene plant–pathogen relationships. At least 52 major *Dm* genes and resistance factors are known that provide complete resistance against specific isolates of *B. lactucae* in a gene-for-gene manner and that are located predominantly in five MRCs in the lettuce genome. The major resistance cluster (MRC2) contains more than nine genetically separable *Dm* specificities, as well as resistance to the lettuce root aphid (*Pemphigus bursarius*). Another large cluster contains several *Dm* genes, resistance genes to the root-infecting downy mildew pathogen (*Plasmopara lactucae-radicis*), and genes associated with the hypersensitive reaction to *Turnip mosaic virus* (TuMV). Several *Dm* specificities have been shown by RNAi to be determined by particular families of NB–LRR-encoding genes. However, isolating the causal genes remains challenging, and only *Dm3* and *Dm7* have been assigned to individual *Dm* genes. These genes and gene families are excellent markers for resistance. There are numerous MRC haplotypes, and it is likely that hundreds of *Dm* genes with efficacy against *B. lactucae* are present in wild germplasm and await characterization.

Several QTLs have been identified that determine partial adult plant resistance in some old lettuce cultivars. Molecular markers will facilitate the introgression of major QTLs for adult plant resistance; however, such QTLs are not necessarily race-non-specific and may not be more durable than *Dm* genes.

Markers will allow these QTLs to be combined with *Dm* genes, potentially increasing the latter's durability.

Corky Root

Corky root, caused by the bacterium *Rhizorhapis suberifaciens,* is another worldwide disease of lettuce. Resistant cultivars are available, in which resistance is determined by a single recessive gene, *cor.* Screening for resistance to corky root is difficult, making marker-assisted selection desirable. Flanking molecular markers can be used to select for resistance; however, there was only a paucity of markers closely linked to *cor* until fine mapping of the region localized *cor* to a single genomic region. Additional nonallelic sources of resistance to corky root exist that have yet to be characterized genetically.

Lettuce Mosaic

Lettuce mosaic virus (LMV), which is controlled mainly by seed-indexing programs, is potentially a major constraint to lettuce production worldwide. Several dominant genes for resistance have been identified, but they have yet to be mapped and used for crop protection. The recessive *mo1* gene confers resistance to many but not all strains of LMV, but only two alleles of this gene have been used commercially. The *mo1* gene, which encodes the eukaryotic translation initiation factor 4E (eIF4E), has been cloned. At least one copy of the wild-type *eIF4E* gene is required for virus accumulation in lettuce. The single nucleotide polymorphism (SNP) responsible for resistance provides an excellent marker for resistance.

Verticillium Wilt

Verticillium wilt, caused by the fungus *Verticillium dahliae,* is an increasingly important disease in California and worldwide. A single dominant gene—*Verticillium resistance 1* (*Vr1*), for resistance to race 1—maps to a small cluster of genes that encode receptorlike kinases with sequence similarity to the *Ve* gene that confers resistance to *V. dahliae* in tomato. A small indel in one of these candidate genes provides a restriction-site polymorphism that is diagnostic of resistance. No accessions have been identified that have high levels of resistance to race 2 of the pathogen, despite extensive screening of germplasm. Lines with reduced symptoms have been identified, and genetic analysis is ongoing.

Dieback

Dieback is a soilborne disease caused by two species of *Tombusvirus.* Susceptibility is widespread in romaine and leaf-type lettuces, whereas modern crisphead cultivars are resistant. Resistance is conferred by a single dominant gene, *Tvr1,* that maps close to the *Vr1* locus. Care is needed to ensure that the introduction of genes for resistance to dieback does not result in susceptibility to Verticillium wilt and vice versa. Markers can be used to select resistance haplotypes with the *Tvr1* and *Vr1* genes in *cis* and their subsequent selection as a closely linked Mendelian unit.

Fusarium Wilt

Fusarium wilt is caused by the fungus *Fusarium oxysporum* f. sp. *lactucae.* Resistance to several races of this pathogen is known. Multiple QTLs have been identified for resistance to race 1, providing markers for their introgression and pyramiding.

Other Diseases

The genetic bases for resistance to other diseases of lettuce—such as lettuce drop (or Sclerotinia rot), lettuce big vein, and gray mold—are not well characterized, and markers have yet to be developed. However, the development of markers linked to resistance to these diseases will likely occur as soon as populations that segregate for resistance have been phenotyped and then analyzed by GBS.

Transgenic Approaches

Lettuce is readily transformed using co-cultivation with *Agrobacterium tumefaciens.* Genotype-specific differences in transformation efficiencies exist; for example, butterhead cultivars tend to be easier to transform than crisphead types. *Agrobacterium*-mediated transient assays are also facile but have yet to be used for testing resistance (*R*) genes. Although it is easy to generate transgenic plants, transgenes are often silenced, and generating inbred lines with stable, effective levels of expression is more difficult. The phenomenon of gene silencing has not been extensively explored, and more research is needed before transgene deployment is routinely applied in lettuce.

The deployment of transgenes offers the possibility for resistance against challenges for which there are no natural resistance genes and may provide the only alternatives to chemical protectants. In particular, genes encoding the δ-endotoxins produced by *Bacillus thuringiensis* could be highly effective against a range of insects that attack lettuce. These endotoxins are the active agents in biological, organically approved pesticides that have been used on lettuce for many years. Several antiviral strategies, such as coat protein-mediated approaches and RNAi, also have protectant potential against viruses such as LMV, TuMV, and *Tomato spotted wilt virus* (TSWV), as well as the virus that causes lettuce big vein. There have been reports of transgenic resistance, but they have not been sustained, possibly because of gene silencing.

Host-induced gene silencing (HIGS) has been demonstrated in diverse pathosystems. HIGS is an RNAi-based approach to disease resistance in which small interfering RNAs (siRNAs) are produced in the host plant and subsequently move into the pathogen or pest to silence vital genes of the pathogen/pest. Stable transgenic lettuce plants expressing siRNAs targeting two of the six genes of *B. lactucae* tested specifically suppressed expression of these two genes, resulting in greatly reduced growth and inhibition of sporulation of the pathogen. These results are consistent with the movement of small RNA molecules from lettuce across the haustorial interface leading to RNAi within *B. lactucae.* HIGS presents a radically different evolutionary hurdle for *B. lactucae* compared with *Dm* genes. Because the RNAi trigger sequences are several hundred bases long and target vital genes, a major change will be required in *B. lactucae* to overcome HIGS. Consequently, resistance based on HIGS will likely be more durable than that conferred by *Dm* genes. In addition, because the active agent of HIGS is RNA rather than protein, regulatory concerns may be reduced.

Given the potential for consumer concerns and the expense involved in gaining regulatory approval, the production of commercial transgenic lettuce is not anticipated in the near future (as of early 2017). There is no "must have" consumer-desired trait that motivates the development and deployment of transgenic lettuce. Patent issues also constrain deployment. It would be helpful if enabling patents could be pooled to allow the freedom to operate in breeding programs until commercial cultivars are ready for release; however, liability and issues of gene custody obstruct such a scheme.

Genome Editing

Genome editing will be a disruptive breeding technology. Advances are rapidly being made in the molecular aspects of precisely editing genomic DNA sequences mediated by the clustered regularly interspaced short palindromic repeats (CRISPR)/Cas9 technology. It has become relatively easy to knock out genes. In fact, doing so is so efficient that often both copies of a gene are knocked out simultaneously. Also, multiple genes can be targeted and knocked out at the same time. Allelic replacements and gene insertions are more difficult but likely to become routine in the future. CRISPR/Cas9-mediated genome editing has been demonstrated in many crops, including lettuce.

One limitation to efficient genome editing is the necessity to use tissue culture. Passage through tissue culture is mutagenic at both the DNA sequence and epigenomic levels. Germline modification without tissue culture is needed so that elite cultivars can be precisely modified with predictable and reliable results.

A second limitation to genome editing is the lack of knowledge of genes to edit. It is no longer sufficient just to have markers linked to phenotypes. The actual genes that determine agriculturally important phenotypes, such as disease resistance, must be identified. Unfortunately, only a few such genes have been cloned and are available for editing. Renewed emphasis is therefore needed on cloning the causal genes that determine disease resistance. Genome editing to precisely knock out candidate genes will be an important component of efficient map-based cloning strategies. Genes that when knocked out may provide useful resistance include *DMR6-like oxygenase,* which was identified as conferring resistance to downy mildew after mutagenesis of a susceptible cultivar, and homologs of the *Mlo* gene, which confers resistance to powdery mildew.

Genome editing provides the opportunity to stack beneficial genes at tightly linked locations in the genome. As more advantageous chromosomal regions and genes are identified, it becomes increasingly difficult to accumulate them in a single genotype by conventional breeding. Therefore, stacking as many monogenic traits as possible at a single locus will become increasingly useful, because beneficial combinations of genes will be inherited as a single Mendelian locus and will not dissipate when crosses are made as part of a breeding program. This will greatly simplify breeding for disease resistance, allowing breeders to focus on more complex traits, such as water- and nitrogen-use efficiencies and nutritional quality. Gene stacks will also protect pyramids of multiple resistance genes that are effective against all known pathotypes of a particular pathogen, enhancing their durability.

It is possible to envision stacks of genes at a single locus in the lettuce genome that together confer resistance to all known pathotypes of *B. lactucae* because of a pyramid of *Dm* genes, plus genes for resistance to other diseases and genes conferring HIGS against multiple viral, bacterial, and fungal diseases, as well as insect pests and nematodes. Such gene stacks would be inherited as single Mendelian units, facilitating their management in breeding programs; selection could be further aided by the addition of an herbicide-resistant gene (e.g., *Acetolactate Synthase*) as a selectable marker. Gene stacks could be expanded as more resistance genes are cloned, and genes in the stack could be replaced when they are overcome by changes in the pathogens.

It is not clear whether the products of genome editing will be regulated as genetically modified organisms (GMOs). Some products, particularly gene knockouts, will be indistinguishable from the products of conventional mutagenesis, although considerably more precise. Hopefully, the 2016 decision by the U.S. Department of Agriculture (USDA) that button mushrooms with a gene knockout mediated by genome editing are not subject to regulation means that similar gene knockouts in lettuce will not be regulated as GMOs. The regulatory decision that is made may be influenced by the method through which editing is achieved and whether any components of a pathogen are involved. Regulation may vary across the globe because of differences in regulatory approaches in Europe and in the United States, in which the former is more concerned with the process and the latter, with the product. Hopefully, regulatory barriers will not obstruct the application of this very powerful technology to generate disease-resistant lettuce cultivars.

Opportunities from Model and Other Species

The paradigm of how disease resistance works in plants is being worked out in detail using model species, particularly *Arabidopsis*. Unsurprisingly, the lettuce genome encodes the same classes of recognition, signal transduction, and response genes as those shown to act in other species. The majority of resistance phenotypes co-segregate with NB–LRR-encoding recognition genes. None have co-segregated with signal transduction or response genes.

Genomic approaches are reducing the reliance on model species, thereby providing inferences across diverse plant species. Analysis of the *RGC2* gene cluster at MRC2 led to the discovery of heterogeneous rates of evolution on NB–LRR-encoding resistance genes that were subsequently validated in other species. Although defenses in lettuce seem to function in similar manners to the current paradigm, there is evidence that the resistance signal transduction networks in lettuce are more complex than those described by current models developed from studies of a limited number of model species.

Metagenomics

There is a growing appreciation of the importance of the microbiome in plant health and disease. The microbial composition of the phylloplane likely influences susceptibility to foliar pathogens and impacts food safety by antagonizing the growth of human-pathogenic bacteria. Microbial populations in the plant rhizosphere are poorly understood but certainly influence nutrient uptake and susceptibility to root pathogens and pests. High-throughput sequencing has the potential to characterize and dissect these complex communities, ultimately leading to the development of strategies for manipulating the microbiome to improve lettuce performance.

Conclusions

Genomic approaches provide a rapidly changing landscape of opportunities for improving disease resistance in lettuce. An increasing number of genes for resistance for most of the major pathogens of lettuce will be identified in wild germplasm and deployed in cultivars, initially using MAS and later using genome editing after they have been cloned. The cloning of resistance genes will provide genic markers for resistance phenotypes and in some cases the causal genetic polymorphisms. Genomic knowledge of the pathogens and pests of lettuce will provide multiple opportunities for HIGS. Integration of these conventional and novel approaches will lead to an increased likelihood of durable disease resistance.

There are several bottlenecks and challenges in the quest to exploit these opportunities. It will be challenging to focus and prioritize goals to allow the effective allocation of finite resources, people, and funds. Genomic approaches and their application generate unprecedented amounts of data; tools for efficient data analysis and management in a breeding context are required. Informative segregating populations take time to generate, and populations that are suitable for genetic analysis may not be maintained or prioritized in breeding programs. Useful variation may not be present in sexually compatible gene pools; further collection and characterization of germplasm should be a high priority for lettuce improvement. In order to fully realize the potential of genome editing, methods for delivery of CRISPR/Cas9 technology are needed for germline modification without tissue culture.

As resistance genes become characterized at the sequence level, it will become possible to name the resistance genes present in cultivars. Doing so is preferable to characterizing cultivars on the basis of the pathogen isolates to which they are resistant, as is currently the case for downy mildew.

Several technological advances can be anticipated that will impact breeding for disease resistance in lettuce. There will be increasingly inexpensive high-throughput genotyping, sequencing machines with even higher throughput and lower costs, and sequencing machines with even longer reads, as well as nanopore and other platforms that will provide rapid diagnostics in the field. Increased and probably "cloud"-based computational capabilities will allow real-time processing of breeding data so as to enable data-driven breeding decisions. Genome editing will become increasingly efficient and an integral component of gene identification and gene stacking. The parameters determining the effectiveness of HIGS will be worked out to provide strategies for controlling diverse pathogens and pests. Metagenomics will provide the information for beneficial manipulation of the microbiome.

Disease resistance is only one breeding objective. Integration is needed with other objectives, such as response to abiotic stresses induced by climate change, changing consumer preferences, improved postharvest attributes, and enhanced nutritional quality. The genomic approaches described earlier in this section are also applicable to these other objectives and will facilitate their integration for the overall improvement of lettuce.

Selected References

Bonnier, F. J. M., Reinink, K., and Groenwald, R. 1994. Genetic analysis of *Lactuca* accessions with new major gene resistance to lettuce downy mildew. Phytopathology 84:462-468.

Chin, D. B., Arroyo-Garcia, R., Ochoa, O., Kesseli, R. V., Lavelle, D. O., and Michelmore, R. W. 2001. Recombination and spontaneous mutation at the major cluster of resistance genes in lettuce (*Lactuca sativa*). Genetics 157:831-849.

Christopoulou, M., McHale, L. K., Kozik, A., Reyes-Chin Wo, S., Wroblewski, T., and Michelmore, R. W. 2015. Dissection of two complex clusters of resistance genes in lettuce (*Lactuca sativa*). Mol. Plant Microbe Interact. 28:751-765.

Christopoulou, M., Reyes-Chin Wo, S., Kozik, A., McHale, L. K., Truco, M.-J., Wroblewski, T., and Michelmore, R. W. 2015. Genome-wide architecture of disease resistance genes in lettuce. G3: Genes Genomes Genet. 5:2655-2669.

Crute, I. R., and Johnson, A. G. 1976. The genetic relationship between races of *Bremia lactucae* and cultivars of *Lactuca sativa*. Ann. Appl. Biol. 83:125-137.

De Cremer, K., Mathys, J., Froenicke, L., Michelmore, R. W., Cammue, B. P. A., and De Coninck, B. 2013. RNAseq-based transcriptome analysis of *Lactuca sativa* infected by the fungal necrotroph *Botrytis cinerea*. Plant Cell Environ. 36:1992-2007. doi: 10.1111/pce.12106

den Boer, E., Zhang, N. W., Pelgrom, K., Visser, R. G., Niks, R. E., and Jeuken, M. J. 2013. Fine mapping quantitative resistances to downy mildew in lettuce revealed multiple sub-QTLs with plant stage dependent effects reducing or even promoting the infection. Theor. Appl. Genet. 126:2995-3007.

den Boer, E., Pelgrom, K. T., Zhang, N. W., Visser, R. G., Niks, R. E., and Jeuken, M. J. 2014. Effects of stacked quantitative resistances to downy mildew in lettuce do not simply add up. Theor. Appl. Genet. 127:1805-1816.

Govindarajulu, M., Epstein, L., Wroblewski, T., and Michelmore, R. W. 2014. Host-induced gene silencing inhibits the biotrophic pathogen causing downy mildew of lettuce. Plant Biotech. J. 13:875-883. doi:10.1111/pbi.12307

Hayes, R. J., McHale, L. K., Vallad, G. E., Truco, M.-J., Michelmore, R. W., Klosterman, S. J., Maruthachalam, K., and Subbarao, K. V. 2011. The inheritance of resistance to Verticillium wilt caused by race 1 isolates of *Verticillium dahliae* in the lettuce cultivar La Brillante. Theor. Appl. Genet. 123:509-517. doi:10.1007/s00122-011-1603-y

Hayes, R. J., Trent, M. A., Truco, M.-J., Michelmore, R. W., and Bull, C. T. 2014. The inheritance of resistance to bacterial leaf spot of lettuce caused by *Xanthomonas campestris* pv. *vitians* in three lettuce cultivars. Hortic. Res. 1:14066. doi:10.1038/hortres.2014.66

Kuang, H., Woo, S.-S., Meyers, B., Nevo, E., and Michelmore, R. W. 2004. Multiple genetic processes result in heterogeneous rates of evolution within the major cluster of disease resistance genes in lettuce. Plant Cell 16:2870-2894.

Kuang, H., van Eck, H. J., Sicard, D., Michelmore, R. W., and Nevo, E. 2008. Evolution and genetic population structure of prickly lettuce (*Lactuca serriola*) and its *RGC2* resistance gene cluster. Genetics 178:1547-1558.

McHale, L. K., Truco, M. J., Kozik, A., Lavelle, D. O., Ochoa, O. E., Wroblewski, T., Knapp, S. J., and Michelmore, R. W. 2009. Genomic architecture of disease resistance in lettuce. Theor. Appl. Genet. 118:565-580.

Moreno-Vaquez, S., Ochoa, O., Faber, N., Chao, S., Jacobs, J. M. E., Maisonneuve, B., Kesseli, R., and Michelmore, R. W. 2003. SNP-based codominant markers for a recessive gene conferring resistance to corky root rot (*Rhizomonas suberifaciens*) in lettuce (*Lactuca sativa*). Genome 46:1059-1069.

Moretti, M., Minerdi, D., Gehrig, P., Garibaldi, A., Gullino, M. L., and Riedel, K. 2012. A bacterial-fungal metaproteomic analysis enlightens an intriguing multicomponent interaction in the rhizosphere of *Lactuca sativa*. J. Proteome Res. 11:2061-2077.

Nicaise, V., German-Retana, S., Sanjuan, R., Dubrana, M. P., Mazier, M., Maisonneuve, B., Candresse, T., Caranta, C., and LeGall, O. 2003. The eukaryotic translation initiation factor 4E controls lettuce susceptibility to the Potyvirus *Lettuce mosaic virus*. Plant Physiol. 132:1272-1282.

Parra, L., Maisonneuve, B., Lebeda, A., Schut, J., Christopoulou, M., Jeuken, M., McHale, L., Truco, M.-J., Crute, I., and Michelmore, R. W. 2016. Rationalization of genes for resistance to *Bremia lactucae* in lettuce. Euphytica 210:309-326.

Shen, K. A., Chin, D. B., Arroyo-Garcia, R., Ochoa, O. E., Lavelle, D. O., Wroblewski, T., Meyers B. C., and Michelmore, R. W. 2002. *Dm3* is one member of a large constitutively expressed family of nucleotide binding site–leucine-rich repeat encoding genes. Mol. Plant Microbe Interact. 15:251-261.

Simko, I., Pechenick, D. A., McHale, L. K., Truco, M.-J., Ochoa, O. E., Michelmore, R. W., and Scheffler, B. E. 2010. Development of molecular markers for marker-assisted selection of dieback disease resistance in lettuce (*Lactuca sativa*). Acta Hortic. 859:401-406.

Simko, I., Atallah, A. J., Ochoa, O. E., Antonise, R., Galeano, C. H., Truco, M.-J., and Michelmore, R. W. 2013. Identification of QTLs conferring resistance to downy mildew in legacy cultivars of lettuce. Sci. Rep. 3:2875. doi:10.1038/srep02875

Stassen, J. H. M., den Boer, E., Vergeer, P. W. J., Andel, A., Ellendorff, U., Pelgrom, K., Pel, M., Schut, J., Zonneveld, O., Jeuken, M. J. W., and Van den Ackerveken, G. 2013. Specific in planta recognition of two GKLR proteins of the downy mildew *Bremia lactucae* revealed in a large effector screen in lettuce. Mol. Plant Microbe Interact. 26:1259-1270.

Truco, M.-J., Ashrafi, H., Kozik, A., van Leeuwen, H., Bowers, J., Reyes Chin Wo, S., Stoffel, K., Xu, H., Hill, T., van Deynze, A., and Michelmore, R. W. 2013. An ultra high-density, transcript-based, genetic map of lettuce. G3: Genes Genomes Genet. 3:617-631. doi:10.1534/g3.112.004929

Wroblewski, T., Piskurewicz, U., Tomczak, A., Ochoa, O., and Michelmore, R. W. 2007. Silencing of the major family of NBS-LRR-encoding genes in lettuce results in the loss of multiple resistance specificities. Plant J. 51:803-818.

(Prepared by R. W. Michelmore)

Lettuce Seed Germination Under Environmental Stress

The efficiency of commercial lettuce production begins with seed that germinates in the field both rapidly and uniformly.

The hallmark of a high-quality seed lot is its ability to germinate under abiotic stress. This ability is conditioned by the environment of the maternal plant during seed development and the genetic composition of the plant, and it is affected significantly by environmental–genomic interactions. Seed germination is a genetically complex trait, and the genetic components are slowly being identified that sense and transmit multiple environmental signals as seed either commits to germination or remains in a quiescent state.

A comprehensive understanding of this basic information will be necessary to improve the ability of lettuce seed to germinate under stress. In the meantime, seed treatments are commonly used to overcome both temperature- and light-induced dormancy and to improve seed germination under stress, which is especially important in desert production areas.

Maternal Environment During Seed Maturation

The germination capacity of lettuce seed is affected by the maternal environment under which the seed develops and matures on the plant. The primary environmental factors that affect seed vigor are temperature, light, and mineral nutrition. Lettuce plants produced under low-temperature regimes (defined as 20°C/10°C, day/night) produce fewer but larger seeds compared with plants grown in high-temperature regimes (30°C/20°C). Lettuce seed produced under high- or moderate- (25°C/15°C) temperature regimes has greater germination capacity at high temperatures (30°C) than seed produced under low temperatures. Furthermore, seed produced at lower temperatures is less tolerant to osmotic stress than seed produced at high or moderate temperatures.

Light quality during seed development also affects the subsequent germination behavior. Lettuce seed produced in a low red:far red (R:FR) ratio light environment has lower germination and a higher abscisic acid (ABA) content compared with seed produced in a higher R:FR ratio light environment. Higher endogenous ABA content is often associated with increased dormancy and sensitivity to environmental stresses.

Although a small portion of the lettuce seed crop is produced in glasshouses, most production occurs in the field. Seed producers who grow crops in the field can decide when to plant the crop but otherwise have limited to no control over temperature. However, seed production fields are often located in regions in which there is little probability for rain, which can be detrimental to seed as it develops and matures in the field. Thus, water and mineral nutrition are two inputs that seed producers can manipulate to affect seed quality. If lettuce plants are not sufficiently watered during the reproductive phase of bolting and early seed maturation, the seed they produce will be more sensitive to exogenous ABA and to osmotic stress.

Seed quality is also affected by the availability and uptake of nitrate. A low level of nitrate in lettuce plants has been associated with primary seed dormancy and increased sensitivity of germination to high temperatures and light quality (dark and FR).

Sensitivity to Temperature and Salinity Stress

As noted earlier, lettuce cultivars are planted year-round in the commercial production areas of California and Arizona (United States)—with spring and summer plantings in the coastal regions and fall and winter plantings in the inland valleys and low desert regions. Soil and air temperatures are quite different between coastal and desert production areas, and few cultivars are suitable for planting in both. Depending on the season, day lengths differ between these regions, as well; this is another factor for growers to consider, since the interaction between day length and high temperatures may stimulate bolting. High temperatures also have the potential to negatively impact germination and stand establishment.

In the desert production regions of southern California and Arizona, air and soil temperatures vary widely during the growing season. Lettuce is planted in the low desert in late August and early September. During this period, the daily high temperature in Yuma, Arizona, for example, is typically 40–42°C, whereas the soil temperature at seed level may exceed 60°C (Fig. 5). In contrast, the air and soil temperatures in early December are typically 21°C and 12°C, respectively. Conversely, soil temperatures in California's coastal production regions are relatively stable and mild year-round.

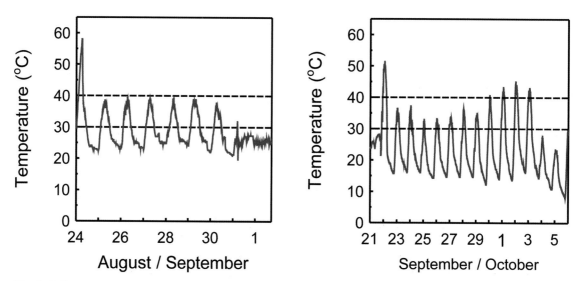

Fig. 5. Soil temperatures in the low desert production region of Yuma, Arizona (United States), during the beginning of the production season: late August and early September (left) and late September through early October (right). On 24 August, the soil temperature at seed level was 58°C. Overhead irrigation was turned on in the afternoon and remained on for the next 6 days. The maximum soil temperature was 40°C at seed level under the sprinklers during the day but dropped to 24°C at night. Primed seed progresses from germination to radicle emergence within 10–12 h at sustained temperatures below 30°C. (Courtesy D. W. Still—© APS)

The sensitivity of lettuce seed to high temperatures during germination depends on the genetics of the cultivar and the seed storage conditions. The regulation of seed germination is complex and not fully understood. Signals from multiple pathways—including but not limited to light perception and signaling, water (hydration) sensing and signaling, hormonal synthesis, and hormonal catabolic pathways—function independently but are also integrated at key points to ultimately modulate levels of ABA and gibberellic acid (GA). ABA maintains seed dormancy and inhibits germination, whereas GA promotes germination. In seed that ultimately germinates, ABA is catabolized to an inactive form before germination (i.e., radicle emergence) occurs.

Seed planted in the early (late August to early September) slots of the desert production area are sown at temperatures that normally inhibit germination. Furthermore, high ambient air temperatures increase the potential of the radicle to dehydrate within hours if it remains on top of the soil instead of penetrating the soil (Fig. 6). When seed is exposed to high temperatures and fails to germinate, it is said to be "thermos inhibited." If seed fails to germinate when returned to temperatures normally conducive to germination, it is said to be "thermos dormant." Thermos dormancy rarely if ever occurs in the field or in laboratory tests. Seeds of most lettuce cultivars exposed to temperatures ranging from 28 to 32°C during imbibition fail to germinate. In the desert, overhead sprinkler irrigation is used to germinate seed. The water absorbs the heat and then evaporates, which results in lowering the soil temperature. At night but not during the day, the soil temperature is below 30°C for 8–10 h, and this provides enough time for the radicle to emerge (Fig. 5). Sprinklers are run for several days to ensure that seedlings do not dry out as the radicles penetrate the soil.

High temperatures during germination increase ABA synthesis but not catabolism, and the endogenous level of ABA increases and germination is inhibited. High temperatures appear to increase the sensitivity of seed to other factors that inhibit germination. For example, if lettuce seed is germinated under high temperatures, the seed becomes more sensitive to ABA. That is, concentrations of ABA that do not inhibit seed germination at 20°C will inhibit germination at 30°C. In addition, high temperatures increase the sensitivity of germination to osmotic stress and increase the sensitivity to dark and far-red light.

Light is another environmental factor that controls endogenous GA and ABA levels during seed germination. During germination, red light promotes germination by increasing GA synthesis, whereas far-red light inhibits germination by increasing the synthesis of ABA but not its catabolism; subsequently, endogenous concentrations of ABA increase.

Seed Technology Enhances Germination—but at a Price

The seeds of many lettuce cultivars require exposure to red light to stimulate germination. But regardless of genotype, the germination of lettuce seed is inhibited by even a brief exposure to far-red light. If the exposure is prolonged, secondary dormancy may be induced. Far-red-rich environments occur in the first few millimeters under the soil, as well as underneath the leaf canopy and in leaf litter. To increase the upper temperature limit for germination and/or to reduce the sensitivity to light, lettuce seed is often preimbibed (primed) under light to stimulate GA synthesis and increase germination under stress.

Much lettuce seed is pelleted (i.e., coated or encrusted to facilitate machine planting) prior to planting to enable precision placement of seeds in beds. Before priming, each seed technology company tests the suitability of the seed lot for priming and decides which priming treatment to apply. Both pelleting and priming treatments have the potential to reduce the vigor of the seed lot, although this does not frequently occur. Each technology company uses different suitability tests, formulations, and procedures for pelleting and priming. When technology companies are supplied with identical seed, they report differences in the germination performance of the pelleted and the primed seed.

Although priming is mainly a treatment for overcoming temperature and light stress, it can also increase the capacity of seed to germinate under an osmotic stress, such as high levels of saline. When there are no obvious environmental field stresses, priming treatments do not appear to confer significant advantages in germination and stand establishment. However, priming has clear advantages when stress occurs, particularly when many environmental factors are out of the grower's control. As noted previously, as the temperature increases, seed sensitivity to light (dark or far-red) and ABA and osmotic stresses increase, as well. Thus, at higher temperatures, seed will likely experience compound stress, and germination will be further inhibited.

Given the effects of global warming and the increased frequency of unpredictable and extreme weather events, applying priming treatments offers a hedge against individual and compound stresses. These seed treatments, however, are expensive

Fig. 6. Lettuce seed may be primed and pelleted before planting in the early slots of desert production areas to increase the capacity to geminate at high temperatures and enable the precision planting of the seed, respectively. **A,** Establishment of a lettuce seed that has been primed and pelleted and planted into soil at temperatures depicted in Figure 5. Note that the expanded cotyledons, the first true leaves, are emerging, and the radicle has elongated and penetrated the soil—a process called "pegging." **B,** A lettuce seed planted in the same field has failed to establish a seedling. Note that the radicle has not elongated and penetrated the soil. The soil in this area of the field had relatively high salt content, which allowed germination but not establishment of the seedling. (Courtesy D. W. Still—© APS)

and significantly lower the shelf life of the seed. Normally, lettuce seed is planted in the field soon after being primed. Primed seed that is stored and planted the next year generally does not perform as well as it did the first year. For this reason, seed technology companies generally advise against planting primed seed carried over from the previous growing season.

The rate of seed germination is a highly sensitive indicator of the vigor of a seed lot and can be used to evaluate stored seed. As vigor is lost, the germination rate declines. Once planted, seed that remains in the field without germinating is increasingly likely to be subjected to inhibitory conditions as part of diurnal cycles (e.g., light and/or temperature) that can induce secondary dormancy. The extended time also increases the seed's exposure to pathogens that may further reduce seed vigor, resulting in poor stand establishment. To preserve the vigor of the seed lot, seed should be dried to low moisture content (~7%) and stored under cool, dry conditions. As a general rule, seed will lose half of its storage life for every 1% increase in seed moisture between 5 and 14% and for every 5°C increase in storage temperature between 0 and 50°C. Low moisture content is the key for successful long-term seed storage.

Breeding for improved seed vigor and germination under stress has not been a priority for most industry and public breeding programs. Instead, seed technology has been used to overcome obstacles that would otherwise limit lettuce production in environmentally challenging production areas. Several studies, however, have identified key genes that improve the germination of seed under stress, and in doing so, these studies have established the genetic basis by which to improve germination traits in lettuce. Obvious goals are to improve the thermotolerance and photosensitivity of germination. In both cases, the hormone ABA plays a pivotal role in establishing sensitivity to these environmental cues.

An allele from the wild progenitor of lettuce, *Lactuca serriola,* is being backcrossed into commercial germplasm that is suitable for desert production areas. Specifically, the *L. serriola* allele from a key gene in the ABA synthesis pathway (*NCED4*) introgressed into commercial cultivars improves high-temperature germination capacity by several degrees Celsius. The wild allele does not respond to high temperatures by synthesizing more ABA, and seed is able to germinate under higher temperatures—an effect similar to priming. These results are encouraging, but other research has shown that different genes are needed to improve the ability of seed to germinate in response to other environmental stimuli. Another goal is to understand the influence of the environment during seed development so that the negative effects can be minimized and seed vigor can be better managed by seed producers.

Selected References

Argyris, J., Dahal, P., Hayashi, E., Still, D. W., and Bradford, K. J. 2008. Genetic variation for lettuce seed thermoinhibition is associated with temperature-sensitive expression of abscisic acid, gibberellin and ethylene biosynthesis, metabolism and response genes. Plant Physiol. 148:926-947.

Contreras, S., Bennett, M. A., Metzger, J. D., and Tay, D. 2008. Maternal light environment during seed development affects lettuce seed weight, germinability, and storability. HortScience 43:845-852.

Hayashi, E., Aoyama, N., and Still, D. W. 2008. Quantitative trait loci associated with lettuce seed germination under different light and temperature environments. Genome 51:928-947.

Huo, H., Dahal, P., Kunusoth, K., McCallum, C. M., and Bradford, K. J. 2013. Expression of *9-cis-EPOXYCAROTENOID DIOXYGENASE4* is essential for thermoinhibition of lettuce seed germination but not for seed development or stress tolerance. Plant Cell 25:884-900.

Lafta, A., and Mou, B. 2013. Evaluation of lettuce genotypes for seed thermotolerance. HortScience 48:708-714.

(Prepared by D. W. Still)

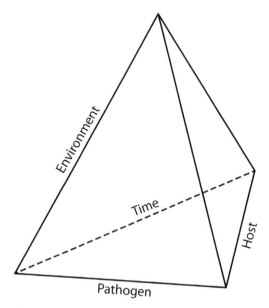

Fig. 7. The disease pyramid. Whether a disease occurs depends on the nature of the interactions among the pathogen, plant host, environment, and time. (Based on Francl, 2001—© APS).

Lettuce Diseases and Disorders

Diseases play a significant role in limiting lettuce production when resistant cultivars are not available. Approximately 75 lettuce diseases have been identified, but whether a given disease occurs depends on the nature of the interactions among the pathogen, plant host, environment, and time. For a disease outbreak to occur, time can be a critical component, since a lettuce plant at particular growth stages may be more susceptible to certain diseases and the transmission of some pathogens may be influenced by seasonal fluctuations. The interactions among these four factors are depicted in the disease pyramid shown in Figure 7.

Biotic diseases on lettuce are caused by the pathogenic organisms shown in Figure 8, including bacteria, viruses, fungi and oomycetes, phytoplasmas, parasitic higher plants, and nematodes. Diseases and disorders of abiotic origin can occur in the absence of a pathogen, such as those that result from an excess or lack of soil nutrients. Although lettuce requires considerably high and constant soil moisture, excessive watering may also promote abiotic diseases.

Lettuce cultivars vary in their response to biotic and abiotic diseases and disorders; hence, resistance under local conditions is an important criterion for cultivar selection. Some lettuce pathogens also vary according to pathotypes or races, in which strains of the pathogen may be morphologically identical but cause disease in only one or a subset of cultivars.

Infectious Agents

Fungi and Oomycetes

Fungi are organisms that generally have elongated filaments, or mycelia (Fig. 8), that range from 0.5 to 100.0 μm in diameter, and most can be readily observed using light microscopy. Oomycetes, also known as "water molds," are a group of organisms that cause late blight, damping-off, downy mildews, sudden oak death, and other diseases. Mycelia can be branched or continuous and with or without cross-walls (septa). Filaments that lack cross-walls are often referred to as "coenocytic," in which the entire filament is one continuous or branching cell that may be multinucleate.

Approximately 100,000 fungal species have been identified, and of these, almost 8,000 species can cause plant diseases. Classification of fungi into species has traditionally been based on the types of asexual or sexual spores produced, but technological advances have made it possible to apply molecular methods to develop a stable classification system. Asexual fungal and oomycete spores include conidia, chlamydospores, sclerotia, sporangia, and zoospores. Asexual spores are generally microscopic, vary considerably in shape, and may be pigmented or hyaline. Sexual spores—such as zygospores, oospores, and ascospores—may be heavily pigmented or hyaline, and the outer walls may be smooth or ornamented with spines, spikes, or grooves. Sexually produced spores are often resistant to desiccation and temperature extremes, allowing the organisms to survive or overwinter in soil or plant debris even in the absence of a live host. Because sexual spores may be dormant for years, these structures are sometimes referred to as "resting bodies." Some fungi, such as those that cause powdery mildews, require a live host to complete sexual reproduction; thus, the formation of these resistant sexual spores may be restricted by host availability. Fungal spores can be disseminated via wind and windblown soil particles, irrigation water, soil on equipment, rain, vegetative plant material, animals, and seed.

Approximately 25 species of fungi cause serious diseases on lettuce.

Nematodes

Nematodes are eel-shaped roundworms (Fig. 8) and often nearly 1 mm in length. Their bodies are semihyaline and smooth and up to 35 μm in diameter. Nematodes may be soilborne or aquatic. Nearly 17% of all the described nematodes are parasitic on plants.

A nematode may spend most of its life within plant tissues or on the outside surfaces of plants, often feeding on and deriving nutrition from the roots. The majority of soilborne nematodes are found in the top 15–30 cm of soil, although they may reach depths of 150 cm.

Nematodes may cause plant diseases directly as plant parasites and/or indirectly as vectors of plant-parasitic viruses. Furthermore, secondary plant colonizers, including fungi and bacteria, may enter the roots where nematodes have fed and injured root tissue, leading to other root diseases.

Although nematodes can travel only short distances, they can be dispersed over long distances by wind and windblown soil, equipment, irrigation water, and animals. A variety of factors determine the type or types of nematode species that occupy a particular geographical niche, such as soil temperature and moisture, soil composition, availability of nutrients, and competition with other microbes for feeding sites.

Bacteria

Bacteria are unicellular, microscopic organisms (typically 0.2–10 μm long) that lack membrane-bound organelles and a true nucleus. As a group, bacteria are highly beneficial as saprophytes, allowing the decomposition of organic matter, but some also serve an important function in nitrogen acquisition through fixation of atmospheric nitrogen in legumes and other plants. There are also numerous plant-pathogenic bacterial species, which can cause serious plant diseases accompanied by substantial economic losses.

Among the bacteria that cause plant diseases, the majority fall into five genera: *Agrobacterium, Clavibacter, Erwinia, Pseudomonas,* and *Xanthomonas.* The plant-pathogenic bacteria within these genera are generally rod shaped and motile and do not form spores (Fig. 8). Bacteria are often distinguished from one another using biochemical tests that assess pigment production, sugar utilization, and serological relationships in

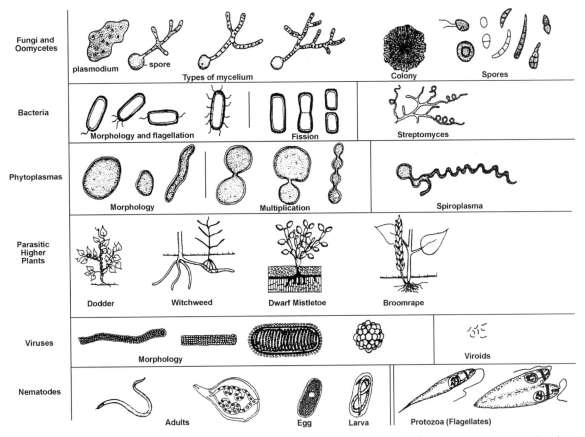

Fig. 8. Morphology and multiplication of some of the major groups of plant pathogens. (Reproduced, by permission, from Agrios, 1988)

17

addition to morphological characteristics, such as the position and number of flagella.

Bacteria gain entry to the plant through wounds and natural openings on the plant surface, and they can survive in plant debris and seeds and in soil and water. Bacteria are commonly spread via infected or infested seed, as well as by insects, nematodes, and soil particles carried by driving winds, splashing rain, and mechanical means.

Plant-pathogenic bacteria generally produce water-soaked symptoms caused by the extensive enzyme-mediated breakdown of plant host tissues. There are at least five serious bacterial diseases in lettuce.

Viruses

Viruses are responsible for causing more than 600 plant diseases, and new viruses and the diseases they cause are continually reported. Unlike plant-pathogenic fungi, nematodes, and bacteria, viruses are submicroscopic.

Virus particles are often long and rod shaped, but they may also be spherical bodies or short bacilliform rods (Fig. 8). A virus is composed of a protein coat (also known as a "capsid"), which encapsulates the genetic material (RNA or DNA). Most plant-pathogenic viruses are RNA-type viruses, although some important diseases in plants are caused by DNA-type viruses.

Viruses are obligate pathogens and can replicate themselves only in living organisms; hence, the identification and classification of a virus often depends on the host. Additional features of viruses that are commonly used for classification include mode of transmission, morphology of the capsid, electrophoretic and purification properties, nucleic acid size, and serology.

Plant-pathogenic viruses can be transmitted to plants by insects, mites, nematodes, fungi, grafting, and even parasitic plants (e.g., dodder, broomrape). Some viruses are also seedborne.

Phytoplasmas

The phytoplasmas, which were previously called "mycoplasmalike organisms (MLOs)" (Fig. 8), are responsible for a group of plant diseases known as "yellows." Like viruses, phytoplasmas are generally submicroscopic, but their cells are highly variable in shape, ranging from 70 to 1,000 nm in diameter. Phytoplasmas can be found in plant phloem tissue and can be transmitted between plants by grafting, dodder, and insects (especially leafhoppers). Unlike viruses, phytoplasmas are not mechanically transmitted.

Phytoplasmas are identified by the types of symptoms they cause, as well as host specificity, insect vector relationships, and the use of molecular markers. Phytoplasmas are sensitive to some antibacterial antibiotics.

Abiotic Diseases and Disorders

Abiotic diseases and disorders are caused by environmental factors, such as an excess or lack of nutrients, moisture, light, and salinity. Certain herbicides and pesticides can cause foliar and root damage, and these types of damage may be exacerbated by water stress, soil type, and improper fertilization. Abiotic diseases may also be caused by temperature extremes; lettuce cultivars differ in heat tolerance. In addition, inadequate soil structure can hinder root development.

Because these diseases are abiotic in origin, they are not transmitted between plants or between fields. But like infectious diseases, abiotic diseases may cause symptoms at any stage of crop development. Moreover, abiotic diseases are sometimes difficult to diagnose, especially since the symptoms they cause on lettuce can closely resemble those caused by root pathogens, phytoplasmas, and viruses.

Remedial measures can be effective for treating abiotic diseases, but diagnosing them early is important to minimize losses. It is also equally important to apply remedial measures quickly following diagnosis, because some pathogens exploit nonparasitic damage to the plant to cause disease, through either a generally weakened immunity or entry through injured plant tissue.

Abiotic diseases can affect both the quantity and the quality of the yield in lettuce. As a result, serious economic losses can occur.

Management of Lettuce Diseases and Disorders

Management of diseases and disorders depends on having thorough knowledge of all the local factors represented in the disease pyramid (Fig. 7), including the pathogens present, the host cultivars, the environmental conditions, and the interplay among these factors over time. The first step in disease management is to correctly diagnose the causal agent of the disease or the cause of the disorder. Once the causal agent or cause has been identified, the appropriate disease-resistant cultivar can be deployed, if available, or the appropriate chemical (i.e., fungicide application), cultural, or biological management strategy can be implemented.

In some instances, however, a new or emerging pathogen requires the development and implementation of management approaches before the pathogen involved has been fully characterized. Until a new approach can be developed, basic cultural practices for disease management can be applied, such as eliminating potential inoculum sources through sanitation, crop rotation, and careful seed selection (i.e., from areas in which the disease is not present). Experimental fungicide applications may also be warranted until new management approaches can be devised and tested.

A major consideration in the selection of any disease management strategy is economic feasibility. That is, the cost of managing the disease should be much less than the value of the crop. For this reason, accurate assessments of disease incidence and yield loss are critically important for determining whether a disease management approach will be cost effective. A secondary consideration is that the treatment options should be simple, safe, and easy to apply. The use of resistant cultivars is especially desirable, since this type of resistance can be complete and not require additional costly inputs.

An integrated disease management strategy that relies on a combination of resistant cultivars and chemical, biological, and cultural practices may be required to eliminate the pathogen or to reduce the inoculum level. Biological controls by themselves are typically not effective against most pathogens and therefore are often combined with other control strategies. Similarly, chemical controls can be more effective when applied as part of an integrated disease management strategy. Cultural practices can be very effective for disease management, especially since few if any regulatory constraints are associated with using them. For example, rotation to a nonhost crop can reduce or eliminate the inoculum level, since many pathogens do not survive more than one growing season in the absence of an adequate host. Management of weeds is also important. Weeds can serve as reservoirs for fungi and viruses that cause diverse diseases and should be controlled within and around fields to minimize the transmission of these pathogens to lettuce. Some of the pathogens that affect lettuce are also seedborne and can be carried on the seeds of weeds and other crops grown in rotation with lettuce. If seeds are produced at sites other than the site of lettuce production, new and perhaps more virulent forms of pathogens can be introduced by infested seed. The use of clean seed for both the rotation crop and the current crop may therefore reduce the amount of inoculum introduced into the system. Finally, changes in the timing or the amount of irrigation may reduce the inoculum levels of some pathogens.

Disease management strategies follow principles that may be curative and/or preventive. Host resistance relies on the selection of lettuce cultivars that are immune, tolerant, or resistant to one or more diseases. Preventive strategies may employ regulatory measures for plant quarantines and lettuce-free periods and for eliminating pathogens from equipment, removing weeds, and so on through sanitation practices. Chemical control measures may be both preventive by forming a protective layer over the plant surfaces, thereby preventing pathogen entry, and curative by destroying the pathogen following infection.

Selected References

Agrios, G. N. 1988. Plant Pathology. 3rd ed. Academic Press, San Diego, CA.

Francl, L. J. 2001. The Disease Triangle: A Plant Pathological Paradigm Revisited. The Plant Health Instructor. doi:10.1094/PHI-T-2001-0517-01 (Reviewed, 2007)

(Prepared by S. J. Klosterman and K. V. Subbarao)

Lettuce-Associated Microbiota

An important element that must be considered in discussing diseases and disorders of lettuce is the microbial communities, or microbiota, that naturally associate with lettuce. The term "microbiota" is used to mean the microbial biota—bacteria, fungi, yeast, oomycetes, and even viruses—that are found on and in the above- and belowground parts of lettuce plants. Included in the lettuce microbiota (or "microbiome") are the pathogens that are featured in this compendium, as well as microorganisms for which the pathogenic potential has not been demonstrated and that are classified as "commensals" (i.e., living off the plant but causing no harm) or that confer a known or unknown benefit to the plant (often in exchange for some service by the plant). DNA-based technologies that do not require culturing of the microorganisms have lowered the threshold for exploring the identities of these microorganisms, how they interact with each other and their lettuce host, and how these interactions affect both the health of lettuce and the people who consume it.

This section will provide an overview of the types of microorganisms found on lettuce, their co-occurrence with each other, their functions (insofar as known), and the various factors that influence the structure of the microbiota, including the plant and the environment in which it grows. This overview is based on a small set of pioneering studies on the topic of lettuce microbiota, and many of the insights shared will require future scrutiny. Even so, several key principles have emerged and will be discussed at the end of this section.

Population Size, Structure, and Function of Lettuce Microbiota

There are many protocols for describing the size, structure, and function of microbial communities that associate with lettuce (and other plants). Most of these protocols begin with washing the leaf or root material in a suitable buffer to isolate microorganisms from the plant surface. These microorganisms are then transferred to nutrient broth or agar (culture-dependent

approaches), or microbial DNA, RNA, or protein is extracted from them (culture-independent approaches). Washing is sometimes replaced by surface swabbing (for leaves) or by maceration of the plant tissue to analyze endophytic microbial communities (i.e., those that reside inside the plant tissue).

Culture-dependent and -independent approaches can differ dramatically in how they represent the microbial community, both in terms of size and composition. For example, estimates of bacterial populations on leaf surfaces of field-grown lettuce were found to be from 10 to 1,000 times smaller based on agar plate counts than on DNA-based measurements of the number of copies of the 16S ribosomal RNA gene. There are several explanations for this difference. First, not all the bacteria retrievable from lettuce leaves are able to utilize the nutrients provided in the agar plates, and so not all the bacteria will grow, make a colony, and be included in the count. Second, some bacteria might be in a so-called viable but not culturable (VBNC) state, which precludes them from growing at all, regardless of the medium. A third possibility is that some of the single colonies on the agar plate represent outgrowth from more than one bacterial cell (e.g., a bacterial aggregate that was not properly broken up into individual cells after it was washed from the lettuce leaf). Together, these three explanations clearly warn of the limitations of culture-dependent approaches, which tend to underestimate microbial population size and diversity on plants. In contrast, the use of culture-independent approaches may result in overestimating the population and misrepresenting the community structure (e.g., because many bacteria carry more than one copy of the 16S ribosomal RNA gene on their genomes). These discrepancies suggest that a survey of lettuce microbiota should combine both culture-dependent and culture-independent approaches.

Much of the microbial data collected from lettuce suggests that different parts of the lettuce plant represent different habitats that feature significantly different microbial communities. While some microbial taxa can be found in both habitats (as contaminants or true inhabitants), most taxa appear to be unique to either the leaves or the roots. The next two subsections will discuss leaf and root communities, and later subsections will provide more detailed descriptions of the various factors that affect the size, structure, and function of microbial communities on lettuce.

Leaves

On lettuce leaves, the populations of culturable bacteria range between 10^3 and 10^8 colony-forming units (CFUs) per gram of plant tissue. Estimates vary greatly among field-grown, laboratory-grown, and store-bought samples and depend on whether the bacteria were washed from the leaf surface or extracted from inside the leaf tissue.

The most commonly found taxa among culturable bacteria from lettuce leaf surfaces are *Acinetobacter*, *Arthrobacter*, *Bacillus*, *Flavobacterium*, *Pantoea*, and *Pseudomonas*. Of these, the genus *Pantoea* is of particular interest. Members of this genus belong to the family Enterobacteriaceae and are typical leaf dwellers; they are commonly found on the foliage of many plant species in addition to lettuce, including trees. However, the genus *Pantoea* is also classified (together with its cousin *Erwinia*) as a "coliform": a term that is often (and unfortunately) misinterpreted. The best-known coliforms are the fecal ones, such as *Escherichia coli* (*E. coli*), which resides in the gastrointestinal tracts of humans and animals and is therefore a good indicator organism for fecal contamination of drinking water, raw meat, and leafy greens and other produce. Fecal coliforms, however, are only a subset of all coliforms; the others, including *Pantoea*, are nonfecal or environmental coliforms. They are ubiquitous in soil, on plants, and in other natural habitats.

Obviously, the distinction between environmental and fecal coliforms is important (and regrettably not always made, especially in the popular press). A positive outcome of a so-called total coliform test, which does not distinguish between fecal and environmental, does not necessarily signify a fecal contamination event and will require further testing. Contamination of lettuce with human pathogens such as *E. coli* is a food safety issue and will be discussed in greater detail in the final section of this "Introduction."

Many of the culturable bacteria found on lettuce leaves (i.e., the lettuce phyllosphere) are also found in culture-independent analyses. Using this method, the bacterial taxa *Pseudomonas* and members of the Enterobacteriaceae such as *Pantoea* are among the most abundantly and consistently identified. Other commonly identified taxa include *Arthrobacter, Bacillus, Leuconostoc, Massilia,* and *Sphingomonas*. The genus *Leuconostoc* belongs to a group of so-called lactic acid bacteria (LAB), some of which have been shown to confer health benefits to humans (e.g., as probiotics). Finding *Leuconostoc* species on lettuce leaves has therefore led some researchers to speculate about the contribution of leaf-associated microbiota to the health benefits of raw lettuce consumption.

It is not uncommon for DNA-based profiles of leaf microbiota from field-grown and store-bought lettuce to show the presence of bacterial genera (i.e., *Pectobacterium, Pseudomonas,* and *Xanthomonas*) that include known foliar pathogens. However, most DNA-based methods are not of sufficient resolution to unambiguously confirm (without additional tests) whether the pathogens are nonpathogenic representatives of these genera or representatives with true pathogenic potential toward lettuce, such as *Pseudomonas marginalis* pv. *marginalis* (marginal leaf blight), *Pseudomonas cichorii* (varnish spot), *Xanthomonas campestris* pv. *vitians* (bacterial leaf spot), and *Pectobacterium carotovorum* subsp. *carotovorum* (bacterial soft rot).

Roots

Estimates of the sizes of microbial populations on lettuce roots differ greatly and depend on multiple factors, including the soil type and the method of analysis (i.e., culture-dependent or culture-independent methods). Population size may vary along the length of a single root and is typically larger in the rhizosphere than in bulk soil. This phenomenon is called the "rhizosphere effect" and is linked to the exudation of plant compounds into the soil surrounding the roots. A meta-analysis of literature on the bacterial biota of lettuce roots has revealed a consistent association with *Pseudomonas* species, although many other genera have been identified, as well. Compared with bulk soil, the soil surrounding the roots is enriched with genera that efficiently utilize root exudates. Root-endophytic communities (i.e., those inside the root tissue) are much less diverse than those associated with the root surface, suggesting that only a fraction of microorganisms in the rhizosphere are able to colonize plant root tissue.

Few studies have been dedicated to the functional (rather than the structural) diversity of the microbial communities of the lettuce rhizosphere. Most noteworthy is an analysis that involved the DNA sequencing of the entire genome (metagenome) of root-associated microbiota. Studies such as these provide the first insights into the adaptations that allow bacteria and fungi to survive and thrive in the lettuce rhizosphere, including adaptations such as ammonia assimilation, stress resistance, amino acid metabolism, and production of antimicrobial compounds. More approaches targeted toward functional diversity have revealed differences between the rhizosphere and bulk soil in the abundance of genes coding for proteases and alkaline phosphatases and a higher ratio of copiotrophic (i.e., growing in high-carbon environments) to oligotrophic (i.e., growing in low-carbon environments) bacteria at the root tip than at the root base. The latter is consistent with the exudation of carbon compounds by the lettuce root tips.

Plant Species, Cultivar, Age, and Growth

Studies that have compared the microbial community structures of lettuce with those of other plants grown under similar conditions suggest that there are lettuce-specific microbiota. The rhizosphere bacterial communities of lettuce are clearly different from those of other plants (e.g., zucchini, wheat, pumpkin, sweet pepper, tomato) grown under identical conditions. In addition, the bacterial communities on store-bought lettuce look very different from those retrieved from other types of produce (e.g., sprouts, tomato, pepper, strawberry, apple, peach, grape, mushroom), including another leafy green, *Spinacia oleracea* (spinach). Differences between the phyllosphere communities of field-grown lettuce and yet another leafy green, *Diplotaxis tenuifolia* (perennial wallrocket), have also been reported. Even the wild ancestor of lettuce, *Lactuca serriola,* has different microbial profiles on its leaves and roots compared with modern *L. sativa* cultivars.

Furthermore, leaf bacterial diversity from different lettuce accessions grown under similar conditions vary based on the cultivar. These differences correlate strongly with leaf characteristics such as morphology, levels of soluble carbohydrates, and phenolic compounds. This is interesting because many of these characteristics are genetically determined and could be used by breeders to indirectly target the structure and function of lettuce microbiota.

A key point about the plant genotype as a driver of microbial diversity is that while its effect can be demonstrated in carefully designed experiments, it is readily overruled by other factors, including the environment. Another point is that the plant genotype is not a static driver. In the course of a single growing season, as a lettuce plant grows and matures and different genes are expressed, the microbial community structures on the above- and belowground parts of the plant may change considerably. On the roots, bacterial diversity tends to increase over time, possibly because of the rich repertoire of rhizosphere exudates. On the leaves, bacterial diversity generally decreases between planting and harvest, which may be explained by domination of a few phyllosphere-competent bacterial taxa.

Location, Climate, and Season

Factors such as location, climate, and time of year all affect the microbial communities associated with lettuce plants. To experimentally determine the impact of each factor, different locations, climates, and times of year would need to be studied. Thus, the observed effects of season (summer versus autumn) or year (e.g., the same field sampled in subsequent years) on microbial community composition are difficult to interpret. Another consideration is that location, climate, and time of year can affect leaves and roots differently in terms of (a) inoculum (e.g., soil or air serving as the source of microorganisms to colonize the plant), (b) inoculation (e.g., weather phenomena that deliver airborne microbes to the foliage), and (c) incubation (e.g., temperature or moisture content of the air and soil, which impacts the growth of microorganisms on the plant surface). These points should be kept in mind when interpreting data on lettuce microbiota and the impact of location, climate, and season.

There are clear differences in the rhizosphere microbiota from plants grown in different types of soil, whether in the field or in the greenhouse. Differences in community composition are also apparent among bulk soil samples from fields in different locations, suggesting that lettuce roots are colonized by microorganisms that are only a subset of whatever microbiota exists in soil. This soil-dependent location effect evokes the idea of a "microbial terroir": a local, indigenous microbial soil community with a unique composition (and possibly function) that affects plant health, yield, and quality, preferably in a positive way.

A "location effect" has also been demonstrated for lettuce leaves, even when plants belong to the same lettuce cultivar. This suggests a rather strong impact of location, which is further evidenced by the finding that lettuce plants grown in the laboratory carry remarkably smaller and less diverse bacterial communities on their leaves than plants grown in the field. This phyllosphere location effect may have different underlying causes, one of which is that different environments (e.g., the lab versus the field) represent different sources of airborne bacteria that serve as inoculum for what is found on the leaves. A good illustration of the atmosphere as a source of foliar microorganisms is the dramatic change in bacterial community composition that occurs when a dust storm hits a lettuce field. Other weather phenomena have been shown to differentially affect members of the lettuce leaf microbiota. For example, temperature was found to affect members of both *Pseudomonas* and coliforms such as *Pantoea*. Radiation, rainfall, and wind had greater effects on members of *Pseudomonas* than members of *Pantoea*, whereas relative humidity had a greater effect on members of *Pantoea* than members of *Pseudomonas*. Experimentally controlled exposure to ultraviolet (UV) radiation decreased bacterial populations on lettuce leaves, confirming that UV radiation can greatly impact leaf microbiota. These examples also show that leaf microbiota are amenable to practical manipulation.

Impact of Pathogens and Management Practices

There is considerable interest in the question of whether a relationship exists between the composition of the microbial community and the presence or activity of plant (lettuce) pathogens. If such a relationship can be established, it might be practically useful. For example, depending on the direction and timing of the relationship, microbiota-based metrics might be used for the early detection or even prediction of pathogen outbreaks or for developing management strategies that aim to supplement the microbiota with microorganisms that minimize pathogen establishment.

Several studies have confirmed the impact of a soil pathogen—the fungus *Rhizoctonia solani*—on the microbial community structures of lettuce roots and lettuce leaves. In another study, the foliar presence of *X. campestris* pv. *vitians,* causal agent of bacterial leaf spot of lettuce, correlated positively with the relative abundance of bacteria from the genus *Alkanindiges* but negatively with bacteria from the genera *Bacillus, Erwinia,* and *Pantoea*. The cause-and-effect of this relationship remains unclear and untested (as of early 2017). Perhaps the presence and/or activity of *X. campestris* pv. *vitians* changes the leaf surface community. A similar observation was made after artificial inoculation of field-grown lettuce heads with *E. coli,* which for reasons unknown led to a significant shift in the microbial community on the leaves. Another explanation for the observed relationship between *X. campestris* pv. *vitians* and other bacterial taxa is that lettuce leaves are somehow more susceptible to establishment of the pathogen if they carry *Alkanindiges* species and less susceptible if they carry *Bacillus, Erwinia,* or *Pantoea* species. In this scenario, one might hypothesize that lettuce-derived isolates of *Bacillus, Erwinia,* and *Pantoea* make good candidates as biocontrol agents of *X. campestris* pv. *vitians* and bacterial leaf spot of lettuce.

Several studies have looked at the effect of biocontrol agents, rather than pathogens, on microbial community composition.

In most cases, the effect was deemed negligible or minimal (i.e., when two biocontrol agents were applied as a mixture). Relatively few studies have addressed the impact of disease-reducing or growth-promoting practices on the microbial community composition of lettuce. In a laboratory setting, soil fumigation with methyl bromide and methyl iodide surprisingly had no impact on root or leaf microbiology. In contrast, irrigation type and crop rotation had clear effects. The latter findings tie in nicely with the notion that the plant genotype is a driver of microbiota composition (see previous section "Plant Species, Cultivar, Age, and Growth").

Several studies have reported differences in leaf microbiota between conventionally and organically grown lettuce, although the underlying causes remain unknown. For example, the application of organic matter (i.e., manure, rice bran, fish meal) increased protease and alkaline phosphatase activity in the rhizosphere soil more than the application of chemical fertilizer. It was suggested but not actually measured that this increase in enzymatic activity helped the plant better absorb soil nitrogen and phosphate. Only one study has actually linked lettuce growth to the lettuce microbiota; in it, plant weight correlated negatively with fungal diversity richness in the soil and positively with the size of the *Pseudomonas fluorescens* population.

Conclusions and Outlook

From the studies published on the structure and function of the lettuce microbiota, several principles and questions have emerged. It is evident that lettuce harbors a microbial community that is unique compared with the microbial communities of other plants. It is also evident that the lettuce microbiota vary significantly along the shoot-to-root axis of a single lettuce plant and with plant age. A new and interesting insight is that the lettuce microbiota are manageable in the same way that lettuce pathogens are. By choosing different cultivars, applying different irrigation methods, and incorporating different soil amendments, alterations can be made to the microbial communities on leaves and roots.

Several key questions remain, however: What, if any, impact do such alterations have? Are some community structures better than others in providing plants with otherwise inaccessible soil nutrients or protecting them from pathogens and other stresses? Should researchers move on from studying only the structure and look into the functional traits of these microorganisms to establish a more mechanistic understanding of how different microbiota might impact plant growth and health? Very few studies have systematically addressed these questions, for which answers will be needed if the lettuce microbiota are to be exploited as a management tool for improving lettuce production.

Another knowledge gap has resulted from bacterial communities receiving disproportionally more attention than the communities of fungi, oomycetes, and viruses. How can it be determined if and how lettuce bacteria interact with or affect lettuce fungi/oomycetes, for example—including those that have the potential to cause disease—unless profiles are available for both types of communities? A more balanced approach is needed to make sense of pathogen abundance and activity as a function of the lettuce microbiota.

Perhaps less relevant to the purpose of this compendium but exciting nevertheless is the link between the lettuce leaf microbiota and consumer health. Much of the discussion of this link focuses on the contamination of lettuce and other leafy greens with microorganisms that can make humans sick, such as *E. coli, Salmonella* spp., and *Listeria* spp. (discussed in greater detail elsewhere in this book). Researchers are also exploring the idea of edible plant microbiota: microorganisms associated with food that is consumed raw, such as leafy greens, and that might serve as sources of bacteria with beneficial properties, such as probiotic activity and immune stimulation. Humans are exposed to different types of bacteria depending on the types of produce they consume and how that produce was grown (i.e., conventionally versus organically).

Selected References

Adesina, M. F., Grosch, R., Lembke, A., Vatchev, T. D., and Smalla, K. 2009. In vitro antagonists of *Rhizoctonia solani* tested on lettuce: Rhizosphere competence, biocontrol efficiency and rhizosphere microbial community response. Fems Microbiol. Ecol. 69:62-74.

Berg, G., Erlacher, A., Smalla, K., and Krause, R. 2014. Vegetable microbiomes: Is there a connection among opportunistic infections, human health and our 'gut feeling'? Microbial Biotechnol. 7:487-495.

Bonanomi, G., Chiurazzi, M., Caporaso, S., Del Sorbo, G., Moschetti, G., and Felice, S. 2008. Soil solarization with biodegradable materials and its impact on soil microbial communities. Soil. Biol. Biochem. 40:1989-1998.

Cardinale, M., Grube, M., Erlacher, A., Quehenberger, J., and Berg, G. 2015. Bacterial networks and co-occurrence relationships in the lettuce root microbiota. Environ. Microbiol. 17:239-252.

Chowdhury, S. P., Dietel, K., Randler, M., Schmid, M., Junge, H., Borriss, R., Hartmann, A., and Grosch, R. 2013. Effects of *Bacillus amyloliquefaciens* FZB42 on lettuce growth and health under pathogen pressure and its impact on the rhizosphere bacterial community. PLoS One 8(7):e68818. doi:10.1371/journal.pone.006881

Dees, M. W., Lysoe, E., Nordskog, B., and Brurberg, M. B. 2015. Bacterial communities associated with surfaces of leafy greens: Shift in composition and decrease in richness over time. Appl. Environ. Microbiol. 81:1530-1539.

Erlacher, A., Cardinale, M., Grosch, R., Grube, M., and Berg, G. 2014. The impact of the pathogen *Rhizoctonia solani* and its beneficial counterpart *Bacillus amyloliquefaciens* on the indigenous lettuce microbiome. Front. Microbiol. 5:175.

Grosch, R., Dealtry, S., Schreiter, S., Berg, G., Mendonca-Hagler, L., and Smalla, K. 2012. Biocontrol of *Rhizoctonia solani*: Complex interaction of biocontrol strains, pathogen and indigenous microbial community in the rhizosphere of lettuce shown by molecular methods. Plant Soil 361:343-357.

Hunter, P. J., Hand, P., Pink, D., Whipps, J. M., and Bending, G. D. 2010. Both leaf properties and microbe-microbe interactions influence within-species variation in bacterial population diversity and structure in the lettuce (*Lactuca* species) phyllosphere. Appl. Environ. Microbiol. 76:8117-8125.

Ibekwe, A. M., and Grieve, C. M. 2004. Changes in developing plant microbial community structure as affected by contaminated water. Fems Microbiol. Ecol. 48:239-248.

Ibekwe, A. M., Papiernik, S. K., and Yang, C. H. 2010. Influence of soil fumigation by methyl bromide and methyl iodide on rhizosphere and phyllosphere microbial community structure. J. Environ. Sci. Health Part B 45:427-436.

Jackson, C. R., Randolph, K. C., Osborn, S. L., and Tyler, H. L. 2013. Culture dependent and independent analysis of bacterial communities associated with commercial salad leaf vegetables. BMC Microbiol. 13:274.

Khalil, S., Baath, E., Alsanius, B., Englund, J. E., Sundin, P., Gertsson, U. E., and Jensen, P. 2001. A comparison of sole carbon source utilization patterns and phospholipid fatty acid profiles to detect changes in the root microflora of hydroponically grown crops. Can. J. Microbiol. 47:302-308.

Kohler, J., Knapp, B. A., Waldhuber, S., Caravaca, F., Roldan, A., and Insam, H. 2010. Effects of elevated CO_2, water stress, and inoculation with *Glomus intraradices* or *Pseudomonas mendocina* on lettuce dry matter and rhizosphere microbial and functional diversity under growth chamber conditions. J. Soils Sediments 10:1585-1597.

Krober, M., Wibberg, D., Grosch, R., Eikmeyer, F., Verwaaijen, B., Chowdhury, S. P., Hartmann, A., Puhler, A., and Schluter, A. 2014. Effect of the strain *Bacillus amyloliquefaciens* FZB42 on the microbial community in the rhizosphere of lettuce under field conditions analyzed by whole metagenome sequencing. Front. Microbiol. 5:252.

Leff, J. W., and Fierer, N. 2013. Bacterial communities associated with the surfaces of fresh fruits and vegetables. PLoS One 8:e59310.

Maloney, P. E., van Bruggen, A. H. C., and Hu, S. 1997. Bacterial community structure in relation to the carbon environments in lettuce and tomato rhizospheres and in bulk soil. Microb. Ecol. 34:109-117.

Medina-Martinez, M. S., Allende, A., Barbera, G. G., and Gil, M. I. 2015. Climatic variations influence the dynamic of epiphyte bacteria of baby lettuce. Food Res. Int. 68:54-61.

Paul, N. D., Moore, J. P., McPherson, M., Lambourne, C., Croft, P., Heaton, J. C., and Wargent, J. J. 2012. Ecological responses to UV radiation: Interactions between the biological effects of UV on plants and on associated organisms. Physiol. Plant. 145:565-581.

Pritchina, O., Ely, C., and Smets, B. F. 2011. Effects of PAH-contaminated soil on rhizosphere microbial communities. Water Air Soil Pollut. 222:17-25.

Rastogi, G., Tech, J. J., Coaker, G. L., and Leveau, J. H. 2010. A PCR-based toolbox for the culture-independent quantification of total bacterial abundances in plant environments. J. Microbiol. Methods 83:127-132.

Rastogi, G., Sbodio, A., Tech, J. J., Suslow, T. V., Coaker, G. L., and Leveau, J. H. 2012. Leaf microbiota in an agroecosystem: Spatio-temporal variation in bacterial community composition on field-grown lettuce. ISME J. 6:1812-1822.

Sakurai, M., Suzuki, K., Onodera, M., Shinano, T., and Osaki, M. 2007. Analysis of bacterial communities in soil by PCR-DGGE targeting protease genes. Soil Biol. Biochem. 39:2777-2784.

Sakurai, M., Wasaki, J., Tomizawa, Y., Shinano, T., and Osaki, M. 2008. Analysis of bacterial communities on alkaline phosphatase genes in soil supplied with organic matter. Soil Sci. Plant Nutr. 54:62-71.

Scherwinski, K., Grosch, R., and Berg, G. 2008. Effect of bacterial antagonists on lettuce: Active biocontrol of *Rhizoctonia solani* and negligible, short-term effects on nontarget microorganisms. FEMS Microbiol. Ecol. 64:106-116.

Schreiter, S., Ding, G. C., Grosch, R., Kropf, S., Antweiler, K., and Smalla, K. 2014. Soil type-dependent effects of a potential biocontrol inoculant on indigenous bacterial communities in the rhizosphere of field-grown lettuce. FEMS Microbiol. Ecol. 90:718-730.

Schreiter, S., Ding, G. C., Heuer, H., Neumann, G., Sandmann, M., Grosch, R., Kropf, S., and Smalla, K. 2014. Effect of the soil type on the microbiome in the rhizosphere of field-grown lettuce. Front. Microbiol. 5:144.

Suzuki, C., Takenaka, M., Oka, N., Nagaoka, K., and Karasawa, T. 2012. A DGGE analysis shows that crop rotation systems influence the bacterial and fungal communities in soils. Soil Sci. Plant Nutr. 58:288-296.

Williams, T. R., and Marco, M. L. 2014. Phyllosphere microbiota composition and microbial community transplantation on lettuce plants grown indoors. mBio 5:e01564-14.

Williams, T. R., Moyne, A.-L., Harris, L. J., and Marco, M. L. 2013. Season, irrigation, leaf age, and *Escherichia coli* inoculation influence the bacterial diversity in the lettuce phyllosphere. PLoS One 8:e68642.

Zwielehner, J., Handschur, M., Michaelsen, A., Irez, S., Demel, M., Denner, E. B. M., and Hasiberger, A. G. 2008. DGGE and real-time PCR analysis of lactic acid bacteria in bacterial communities of the phyllosphere of lettuce. Mol. Nutr. Food Res. 52:614-623.

(Prepared by J. H. J. Leveau)

Food Safety

Plant-Associated Foodborne Pathogens

Food safety represents a serious challenge in food production and public health. More than 9 million cases of foodborne illness are caused each year in the United States by the consumption of contaminated foods, and many of these cases are attributed to contaminated leafy vegetables, including lettuce. According to the Centers for Disease Control and Prevention, from 1998 to 2008, more foodborne illnesses were associated with the consumption of leafy vegetables than dairy and poultry.

Although foodborne pathogens have been traditionally associated with animal products, it is now well recognized that these pathogens can colonize and persist within plants. However, unlike plant pathogens, human pathogens lack the necessary mechanisms to degrade plant tissue and/or cause disease on plants; for this reason, they are characterized as "plant-associated pathogens." Human bacterial pathogens such as *Salmonella enterica* and *Escherichia coli* O157:H7 commonly cause foodborne illness from fresh produce contamination, whereas *Listeria monocytogenes* and *Shigella* spp. are rare. Nonetheless, all of these bacteria are currently recognized as plant-associated foodborne pathogens.

Routes and Sources of Contamination

Plant contamination is thought to occur primarily in the field before harvest via contaminated water, soil, compost, seeds, and/or animals and via pathogen dispersal. The water used for crop irrigation or foliar applications of chemicals may be contaminated and place human bacterial pathogens in contact with plants above or below the ground. Surface water near animal operations has a high risk of contamination. This risk, coupled with the ability of pathogens such as *E. coli* and *S. enterica* to survive in water sediment, increases the risk of crop contamination following rainfall or flooding in a watershed area in which animal operations are conducted.

Harvesting equipment can serve as a source of inoculum. Coring tools can become contaminated through direct contact with contaminated soil, water, or plants and subsequently transfer bacterial pathogens to processed lettuce.

Domestic and wild animals also represent major reservoirs of human bacterial pathogens. These animals carry the bacteria in their intestines and can release them in the field through excreting contaminated waste. Additionally, several pests that occupy human and livestock habitats (e.g., filth flies, cockroaches, dung beetles) are vectors of bacterial foodborne pathogens. Although these insects mainly feed and reproduce on garbage, manure, and carrion, they can change habitat and move from an urban setting or animal production facility to a crop production field, thereby introducing the human bacterial pathogens they harbor. Plant-eating insects and free-living nematodes are capable of ingesting *E. coli* and/or *S. enterica* and can potentially serve as vectors of these pathogens. Thus, human bacterial pathogens can be introduced into agricultural fields by natural means and not necessarily by the negligence of field workers.

Environmental Survival

Human bacterial pathogens are capable of long-term survival under various conditions. High temperatures, high levels of soil moisture and clay content, and close proximity to water sources all increase the survival of human bacterial pathogens in agricultural fields.

S. enterica and *E. coli* O157:H7 can persist for several months in the edible parts of lettuce and in soil after the application of contaminated compost or irrigation water. These pathogens are also able to survive for extended periods under dry and low-humidity storage conditions. This survival ability is evidenced by the fact that viable *E. coli* O157:H7 and *S. enterica* have been recovered from stored butterhead lettuce seeds 2 years after being contaminated and caused the contamination of corresponding seedlings.

Both the environmental occurrence and the long-term persistence of human bacterial pathogens increase the risk of fresh produce contamination during production and harvest. It follows that there is a corresponding increase in the potential for plants to transmit these pathogens to human hosts.

Factors Contributing to Pathogen Survival and Growth on Leaf Surfaces

Plant-associated foodborne pathogens grow poorly on the surfaces of healthy plants and cannot draw nutrients from plants, as plant pathogens do. Nevertheless, these pathogens can grow on leaves damaged by insects and/or plant pathogens.

Insect feeding sites may represent a preferential niche that allows bacteria to multiply because of access to nutrients released from damaged plant tissues or to nutrient-rich substances excreted during or after feeding by insects. Infestation with the aster leafhopper (*Macrosteles quadrilineatus*) and feeding by the western flower thrips (*Frankliniella occidentalis*) and the cabbage looper (*Trichoplusia ni*) have been shown to enhance the persistence of human pathogens on lettuce leaves. *S. enterica* and *E. coli* O157:H7 grow on leafy greens in the regurgitation spots of house flies (*Musca domestica*) and honeydew (i.e., sugar-rich liquid waste) produced by aster leafhoppers and green peach aphids (*Myzus persicae*).

Physiological damage, such as tipburn, can also promote the growth of pathogens on and in lettuce leaves. Downy mildew disease (caused by the oomycete *Bremia lactucae*) and the presence of the bacterial soft rot pathogen (*Pectobacterium carotovorum* subsp. *carotovorum*) enhance the colonization and growth of both *S. enterica* and *E. coli* on lettuce leaves. Consequently, higher survival rates of these foodborne pathogens are often observed on plant tissues damaged by plant pathogens. Not all combinations of plant disease and plant-associated foodborne pathogens have been investigated, but research suggests that plant disease may be a risk factor for food safety.

Internalization

Both *S. enterica* and *E. coli* can enter plant tissues through natural apertures (e.g., stomata), lateral junctions of roots and flowers, and wounds and cracks. Contaminated water can also facilitate pathogen internalization into leaves when it is applied to the surfaces of plants. Internalization and survival of plant-associated foodborne pathogens on and within plants are strongly influenced by factors such as irrigation method, plant cultivar, leaf age, and nitrogen content. Lower *S. enterica* internalization has been observed in lettuce plants infected with certain plant pathogens under water stress. Thus, plant contamination can be sporadic in and among plants and depends on specific plant health and environmental conditions.

Decontamination

Reducing or eliminating plant-associated foodborne pathogens that have been internalized or attached to plant tissues is a major challenge, because conventional washing does not remove these pathogens. Ionizing radiation is recognized as an effective method of decontamination for reducing foodborne pathogens internalized in plant tissues. Acidified sodium chloride can reduce populations of *S. enterica*, *E. coli* O157:H7, and *L. monocytogenes* on leafy greens more effectively than chlorinated water. Similarly, adding food-grade detergents (but not conventional detergents) to traditional chlorine-based sanitizer solutions enhances the efficacy of wash treatments in reducing *E. coli* O157:H7 on lettuce. However, rewashing lettuce previously contaminated during a fresh-cut wash has proven ineffective for *E. coli* O157:H7. This finding reinforces the importance of maintaining an appropriate chlorine concentration in the wash solution to prevent pathogen cross-contamination. Avoiding the contamination of fresh produce may be more effective in guaranteeing food safety than applying postcontamination treatments to remove or eliminate plant-associated foodborne pathogens.

Improving Food Safety

Suggestions for mitigating the risk of lettuce contamination and foodborne illness are as follows:

- Preventing microbial contamination at all stages—from "the field to the fork"—is recommended over applying treatments to eliminate contamination after it has occurred.
- Prevent potential fecal contamination from humans and both domestic and wild animals in the field.
- Maintain healthy plants and minimize physical damage, especially around crop harvest.
- Discard plant tissues damaged by plant pathogens and insects, in which foodborne pathogens may accumulate.

Selected References

Barak, J. D., and Schroeder, B. 2012. Interrelationships of food safety and plant pathology: The life cycle of human pathogens. Annu. Rev. Phytopathol. 50:241-266.

Islam, M., Doyle, M. P., Phatak, S. C., Millner, P., and Jiang, X. 2004. Persistence of enterohemorrhagic *Escherichia coli* O157:H7 in soil and on leaf lettuce and parsley grown in fields treated with contaminated manure composts or irrigation water. J. Food Prot. 67:1365-1370.

Islam M., Morgan, J., Doyle, M. P., Phatak, S. C., Millner, P., and Jiang, X. 2004. Persistence of *Salmonella enterica* serovar *typhimurium* on lettuce and parsley and in soils on which they were grown in fields treated with contaminated manure composts or irrigation water. Foodborne Pathog. Dis. 1(1):27-35.

Simko, I., Zhou, Y., and Brandl, M. T. 2015. Downy mildew disease promotes the colonization of romaine lettuce by *Escherichia coli* O157:H7 and *Salmonella enterica*. BMC Microbiol. 15:19.

Soto-Arias, J. P., Groves, R., and Barak, J. D. 2013. Interaction of phytophagous insects with *Salmonella enterica* on plants and enhanced persistence of the pathogen with *Macrosteles quadrilineatus* infestation or *Frankliniella occidentalis* feeding. PLoS One 8(10):e79404.

Soto-Arias, J. P., Groves, R. L., and Barak, J. D. 2014. Transmission and retention of *Salmonella enterica* by phytophagous Hemipteran insects. Appl. Environ. Microbiol. 80:5447-5456.

(Prepared by J. P. Dundore-Arias and J. D. Barak)

Part I. Infectious Diseases

Diseases Caused by Fungi and Oomycetes

The plant-pathogenic fungi and oomycetes discussed in this section are also listed in the appendix. Readers will note that in both the appendix and the text, alternative names of fungi are identified exclusively as "synonyms," rather than as specific life cycle stages (e.g., "anamorph," "teleomorph"). This practice reflects the policy for naming fungi issued in 2011 by the International Botanical Congress: namely, that the use of multiple names for the same fungus be abandoned. (Readers interested in learning more about this policy are referred to the 2011 article by Hawksworth [see Selected Reference].) Going forward, accommodating this new policy may mean that the most familiar names of some fungi will change. Changes to the names of fungi, as well as other updates to taxonomy and nomenclature, will be made in the Common Names of Plant Diseases list for lettuce, which is available on the website of The American Phytopathological Society.

Selected Reference

Hawksworth, D. L. 2011. A new dawn for the naming of fungi: Impacts of decisions made in Melbourne in July 2011 on the future publication and regulation of fungal names. IMA Fungus 2:155-162.

Anthracnose

Anthracnose (also referred to as "shot hole," "ring spot," and "rust") occurs on lettuce worldwide. Losses from anthracnose are considerable in some areas, especially during periods of cool and moist conditions. In Australia, entire fields have been lost to this disease. Anthracnose affects most commercial varieties of lettuce, as well as wild lettuce, endive, and escarole.

Symptoms

The first symptom of anthracnose is the appearance of small, tan, water-soaked spots on the outermost foliage. These lesions may later expand to 2–3 mm in diameter and become straw colored and circular, unless constricted by veins (Fig. 9). As lesions mature, their necrotic centers fall out, giving the disease its characteristic shot-hole appearance. Infection is usually most prevalent along the midrib on the lower leaf surface. Lesions directly on the midrib become elongated (2.0–2.5 × 4–5 mm) along the leaf axis and are dark brown and sunken, but the tissue does not fall through (Fig. 10).

A severe infection may result in poor head formation and require excessive trimming at harvest. Damaged tissue is invaded by secondary organisms—particularly soft rot bacteria, which can rapidly decay an entire head.

Causal Organism

The causal agent of lettuce anthracnose is *Microdochium panattonianum* (syn. *Marssonina panattoniana*). The sexual stage has not been identified. Mycelia are composed of slender, hyaline, septate hyphae that grow inter- and intracellularly within the host tissue. Mycelia give rise to acervuli that consist of densely packed, upright conidiophores 20–60 μm tall. Conidia are typically two celled, slightly curved, and hyaline and may contain one or two large oil droplets. Conidia are usually constricted at the septa and measure 4 × 17 μm. Immature conidia may lack septa. Microsclerotia, which are 60–100 μm in diameter, may form within infected tissue and serve as a primary source of inoculum.

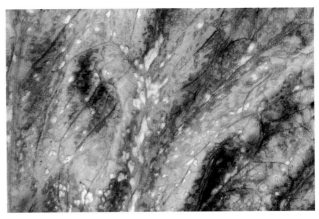

Fig. 9. Small, tan, water-soaked lesions on the outer foliage of crisphead lettuce, symptomatic of anthracnose (*Microdochium panattonianum*). (Courtesy S. T. Koike—© APS)

Fig. 10. Symptoms of anthracnose (*Microdochium panattonianum*) on midribs of crisphead lettuce. (Courtesy S. T. Koike—© APS)

Disease Cycle and Epidemiology

In the absence of lettuce, the pathogen survives in infested debris and as microsclerotia in the soil. Upon germination, microsclerotia produce hyphae and/or conidiophores capable of spore production. Free moisture from dew, rain, or overhead irrigation is required for conidia production, germination, and infection. The fungus may penetrate directly through the leaf epidermis or enter through stomatal openings.

Under favorable temperatures, periods of leaf wetness as short as 4 h may be suitable for infection, although longer durations are much more conducive. Splashing water is the most important method of dissemination, but conidia may also be spread by mechanical means when the foliage is wet. Anthracnose is favored by cool, wet conditions because of its water requirement. Maximum disease development occurs at 20°C.

The host range for the pathogen is confined largely to species of the genus *Lactuca*, although endive has also been reported as a host. The possibility of infected seed serving as an inoculum source for lettuce anthracnose has generally been discounted. Host plant resistance has been reported, along with at least five pathogenic variants of the pathogen.

Management

Methods for managing anthracnose include crop rotation, plowing to bury debris and microsclerotia, and controlling collateral hosts, such as wild lettuce. These measures serve to reduce the level of primary inoculum in the field. Cultural practices should be designed to minimize leaf wetness and to avoid physical contact with the plant when the canopy is wet.

Where conditions are frequently favorable and disease pressure is severe, fungicide applications may be economically justified. Strobilurin fungicides and phosphorous acid compounds were shown to be most efficacious in an Australian trial.

Breeding for anthracnose resistance has not generally been a priority. However, genetic resistance has been identified among commercially available cultivars and may offer management potential.

Selected References

Brandes, E. W. 1918. Anthracnose of lettuce caused by *Marssonina panattoniana*. J. Agric. Res. 13:261-280.

Couch, H. B., and Grogan, R. G. 1955. Etiology of lettuce anthracnose and host range of the pathogen. Phytopathology 45:375-380.

Galea, V. J., and Price, T. V. 1988. Survival of the lettuce anthracnose fungus (*Microdochium panattonianum*) in Victoria. Plant Pathol. 37:54-63.

Galea, V. J., Price, T. V., and Sutton, B. C. 1986. Taxonomy and biology of the lettuce anthracnose fungus. Trans. Br. Mycol. Soc. 86:619-628.

Ochoa, O., Delp, B., and Michelmore, R. W. 1987. Resistance in *Lactucae* spp. to *Microdochium panattonianum* (lettuce anthracnose). Euphytica 36:609-614.

Patterson, C. L., and Grogan, R. G. 1991. Role of microsclerotia as primary inoculum of *Microdochium panattonianum*, incitant of lettuce anthracnose. Plant Dis. 75:134-138.

Patterson, C. L., Grogan, R. G., and Campbell, R. N. 1986. Economically important diseases of lettuce. Plant Dis. 70:982-987.

Rogers, G., and Kimpton, T. 2012. Developing a Strategy to Control Anthracnose in Lettuce. Rep. no. VG10123. Horticulture Australia Limited, Sydney, New South Wales.

Wicks, T. J., Hall, B., and Pezzaniti, P. 1994. Fungicidal control of anthracnose (*Microdochium panattonianum*) on lettuce. Aust. J. Exp. Agric. 34:277-283.

(Prepared by R. N. Raid)

Black Root Rot

Black root rot of lettuce has been reported in Australia and the United States (California) but otherwise is not widely distributed on lettuce. When it occurs, plants can be significantly stunted because of extensive damage to small feeder roots.

Symptoms

Affected lettuce seedlings can be stunted and delayed in development but otherwise appear healthy. If black root rot is severe early in the crop cycle, infected lettuce plants will remain small, the field will appear uneven (Fig. 11), and plants will not reach marketable size (Fig. 12). Stunting is usually most evident from the rosette stage through plant maturity. In advanced cases, the lower leaves of the plant may turn yellow or even brown.

Root symptoms of black root rot include the formation of numerous small (4–8 mm long), dark-brown to black bands and lesions on small feeder and larger secondary roots (Fig. 13). As the disease progresses, the lesions coalesce and cause significant damage to the root system. The lesions do not penetrate into the root vascular tissue.

Black root rot affects both crisphead and leaf/romaine cultivars.

Causal Organism

Black root rot is caused by the soilborne fungus *Thielaviopsis basicola* (syn. *Chalara elegans*). This pathogen is widespread throughout the world and has a broad host range.

On most agar media, colonies of *T. basicola* are gray with a velvety texture. Endoconidia are hyaline, thin walled, single celled, and cylindrical, and they measure 3–6 × 7–17 µm. Conidia form within slender phialides and are then pushed out from the tips of the conidiophores in fragile chains that readily break apart. Because these spores are catenulate, the ends of the endoconidia are truncated. *T. basicola* also forms aleurioconidia that are dark brown, thick walled, single celled, and subrectangular. Aleurioconidia are 5–8 × 10–16 µm and form in stacks or chains of five to eight or more spores; these stacks tend to remain intact until the spores reach maturity, at which point they break apart.

Differences in isolates of *T. basicola* may exist. When lettuce isolates were inoculated onto lettuce and various other crops known to be hosts, *T. basicola* was very aggressive and caused significant damage to lettuce and bean; however, inoculation did not result in disease on cotton or other crops. Thus, *T. basicola* isolates from lettuce may have a host preference for lettuce and a few other plants.

Disease Cycle and Epidemiology

Aleurioconidia enable *T. basicola* to survive in dry soil for extended periods (more than 1 year). Under moist conditions, however, survival is reduced to 7 months or less. Optimum temperatures for infection and disease development range

Fig. 11. Uneven growth of romaine lettuce plants, caused by black root rot (*Thielaviopsis basicola*). (Courtesy S. T. Koike—© APS)

from 15 to 20°C. Inoculum is spread by the movement of soil via tillage operations and flooding. Repeated cropping of lettuce and other susceptible crops likely increases inoculum levels in the soil.

T. basicola has been recovered from peat-based rooting media, indicating that it may be a source of primary inoculum if lettuce transplants are used. Shore fly (*Scatella stagnalis*) adults and larvae can be internally contaminated with *T. basicola* aleurioconidia and thereby serve as possible vectors of the pathogen among transplants in a greenhouse.

Management

Black root rot of lettuce is a minor problem, and management in the field is not warranted. For other crops, black root rot is managed through a combination of resistant cultivars, crop rotation to nonhosts, sanitation practices (to prevent spreading contaminated soil/mud to uninfested fields), and application of fungicides to seedlings. Lettuce cultivars vary in susceptibility to *T. basicola*.

Fig. 12. Reduced size of romaine lettuce plants infected with *Thielaviopsis basicola*, causal agent of black root rot. (Courtesy S. T. Koike—© APS)

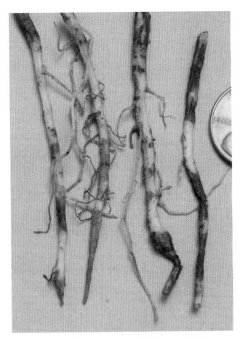

Fig. 13. Banded roots and reduced-sized secondary roots caused by black root rot (*Thielaviopsis basicola*). (Courtesy S. T. Koike—© APS)

Selected References

Ellis, M. B., and Subramanian, C. V. 1968. *Thielaviopsis basicola.* Descriptions of Pathogenic Fungi and Bacteria, no. 170. Commonwealth Mycological Institute, Kew, Surrey, UK.

Graham, J. H., and Timmer, N. H. 1991. Peat-based media as a source of *Thielaviopsis basicola* causing black root rot on citrus seedlings. Plant Dis. 75:1246-1249.

Koike, S. T. 2008. Black root rot caused by *Thielaviopsis basicola* on lettuce in California. Plant Dis. 92:1368.

O'Brien, R. G., and Davis, R. D. 1994. Lettuce black root rot—A disease caused by *Chalara elegans*. Australas. Plant Path. 23:106-111.

Stanghellini, M. E., Rasmussen, S. L., and Kim, D. H. 1999. Aerial transmission of *Thielaviopsis basicola*, a pathogen of corn-salad, by adult shore flies. Phytopathology 89:476-479.

Tabachnik, M., DeVay, J. E., Garber, R. H., and Wakeman, R. J. 1979. Influence of soil inoculum concentrations on host range and disease reactions caused by isolates of *Thielaviopsis basicola* and comparison of soil assay methods. Phytopathology 69:974-977.

(Prepared by S. T. Koike and R. F. Smith)

Black Rot

The only report of black rot on hydroponically grown lettuce came from Brazil in 2006. Since then, reports from Brazil and other lettuce-producing countries have been unavailable; thus, the impact of black rot on lettuce production is uncertain.

The symptoms of black rot are fairly nondescript; they include severe stunting of plants and the entire root system turning black and becoming shriveled and rotten. White mycelium and partially sunken perithecia appear in symptomatic hypocotyl and roots.

The pathogen, *Ceratocystis fimbriata*, produces dark-brown perithecia that have globose bases of 140–210 μm and are ornamented with hyphal hairs. The neck of a perithecium is erect, 650–890 μm long, and ornamented with divergent ostiolar hyphae. At the base of the neck, the width is 23–33 μm, and at the apex, 15–18 μm. Acospores are hyaline and hat shaped, measure $2.6–4.7 \times 7.3–7.8$ μm, and are surrounded by a gelatinous matrix.

Selected Reference

Halfeld-Vieira, B. A., and Nechet, K. L. 2006. Black rot in lettuce: A new disease caused by *Ceratocystis fimbriata* in hydroponic culture in Brazil. Plant Pathol. 55:300.

(Prepared by K. V. Subbarao)

Bottom Rot

Lettuce bottom rot was first described in Massachusetts (United States) glasshouses in 1900, and the first field occurrence was reported in Florida (United States) in 1905. The disease is now found wherever lettuce is grown. Although the fungal pathogen can cause damping-off of seedlings, bottom rot is most commonly associated with plants at or near maturity. Favored by warm, wet conditions, the disease can cause crop losses as high as 70% (Fig. 14). Under severe disease pressure, entire lettuce heads are unmarketable, but even under less favorable conditions, the extra trimming required to remove affected leaves reduces head weight and size, strongly influencing packaging and marketability.

Bottom rot occurs on all types of lettuce, as well as on escarole and endive. Other lettuce diseases often confused with bottom rot are gray mold and lettuce drop.

Symptoms

Lesions typically appear first on lower leaves in direct contact with the soil. Symptoms of initial infection include small, rust-colored to chocolate-brown spots primarily on the undersides of leaf midribs (Fig. 15). While these symptoms may be evident as early as 4 weeks after direct seeding, advanced symptoms of the disease are usually not apparent until heading (Fig. 16).

Under favorable temperature and moisture conditions, bottom rot lesions are capable of rapid expansion, quickly rotting the midribs and leaf blades (Fig. 17). Amber-colored droplets sometimes ooze from the lesions on infected midribs. The stem, which is somewhat more resistant to colonization by the patho-gen, is the last part of the head to decay. Wilting of the outer wrapper leaves is one of the first symptoms observed when infected plants are viewed from above. Decaying heads are at first slimy and brown but become almost black as they collapse and dry. A tan to brown, weblike mycelium of the causal fungus is frequently observed without magnification within infected head tissue and on the soil immediately beneath the head (Fig. 18). Irregularly shaped, cinnamon-brown to dark-brown sclerotia are produced during later stages of the disease (Fig. 19).

The damage caused by infection also provides entry points for secondary rot organisms, particularly soft rot bacteria. These organisms may be responsible for the rapid decay observed in later stages of bottom rot.

Causal Organism

Bottom rot is caused by the soilborne fungus *Rhizoctonia solani* (syn. *Thanatephorus cucumeris*). *R. solani* hyphae are white to brown and septate. A hypha typically branches at a near-right angle, and a crosswall develops just after branching. Branches are conspicuously constricted (Fig. 20). Asexual fruit-

Fig. 14. Near-mature crisphead lettuce plants with bottom rot, caused by *Rhizoctonia solani*. (Courtesy S. Glucksman—© APS)

Fig. 15. Early symptoms of bottom rot (*Rhizoctonia solani*) include rust-colored lesions along lettuce midribs. (Courtesy R. N. Raid—© APS)

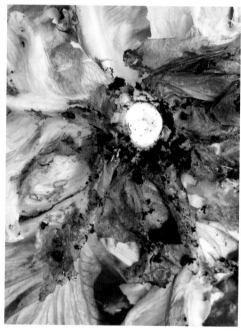

Fig. 16. Later symptoms of bottom rot (*Rhizoctonia solani*) include sunken lesions on lettuce midribs. (Courtesy S. Glucksman—© APS)

Fig. 17. Rotted midribs and leaf blades are advanced symptoms of bottom rot, caused by *Rhizoctonia solani*. (Courtesy R. N. Raid—© APS)

Fig. 18. Advanced stage of bottom rot on lettuce, indicated by a light-brown mycelial web of the causal agent, *Rhizoctonia solani.* (Courtesy R. N. Raid—© APS)

Fig. 19. Sclerotia of *Rhizoctonia solani,* the fungus that causes bottom rot, beginning to form on infected lettuce tissue. (Courtesy R. N. Raid—© APS)

Fig. 20. Hyphae of *Rhizoctonia solani.* Note constriction of the hyphae and septation near branching. (Courtesy R. N. Raid—© APS)

ing structures and spores are lacking. Small, tan to dark-brown sclerotia form among connecting mycelial threads. Basidia of the perfect state measure 8–11 × 18–23 μm. Basidiospores are hyaline and single celled (4–7 × 7–13 μm).

R. solani exhibits extensive biological specialization. Field isolates capable of hyphal fusion (anastomosis) are assigned to the same anastomosis group (AG). Anastomosis occurs between isolates in the same group but not between isolates in different groups. *R. solani* AG 1-1B was most frequently isolated from infected lettuce in Germany, along with AG 1-1C and AG 2-1. AG 1-1B isolates also caused strong symptom development on spinach, broccoli, radish, kohlrabi (*Brassica oleracea* var. *gongylodes*), and millet (*Pennisetum glaucum*) but little symptom development on maize, tomato, and onion.

Disease Cycle and Epidemiology

R. solani is a common soil inhabitant. As a capable soil saprophyte, the fungus survives between crops as sclerotia and mycelium associated with infected crop debris. It is disseminated and carried long distances (especially as sclerotia) in any manner that moves soil. Basidiospores, which are disseminated via wind and water, are also capable of long-distance spread. Under favorable moisture and temperature conditions, sclerotia germinate and produce mycelial growth capable of extending 7–10 cm to reach a food source.

The pathogen is capable of direct penetration, entering the plant through healthy or wounded tissue or through stomata. Colonization is both inter- and intracellular.

Warm, moist conditions are most conducive to the development of brown rot. Optimal mycelial growth occurs between 20 and 30°C (optimum 25°C) and over a broad range of pH (from 5 to 8). The interval from infection to initial symptom development may be as short as 36–48 h. Minimum and maximum temperatures for mycelial growth are 5 and 36°C, respectively. The incubation period lengthens considerably as the temperature varies from the optimal range.

R. solani isolates vary significantly in pathogenicity, virulence, and survival, and it is difficult to make generalized statements. However, the occurrence of bottom rot is heavily influenced by the previous crop, the length of time between crops, the virulence of the particular isolates present, and the ability of those isolates to survive in the soil.

Management

Optimum management of bottom rot is achieved by using various cultural practices in combination with fungicide applications. Plowing instead of disking before planting effectively buries sclerotia, and the viability of these survival structures appears to lessen as the depth of incorporation increases. Crop rotation also reduces inoculum potential. Growing lettuce on high beds improves aeration and minimizes foliar contact with the ground—the point at which infection typically occurs.

Avoiding irrigation close to harvest and planting lettuce cultivars with erect plant architecture may reduce losses. Good drainage and weed control are also important.

Several fungicides registered in the early 2000s for use on lettuce have greatly improved the prospects for managing bottom rot. Placement and timing are extremely important. Biological controls have shown promise, but season-long, commercially acceptable levels of control have not been achieved in the field.

Selected References

Clark, W. S., and McPherson, G. M. 1981. The use of iprodione for control of Rhizoctonia bottom rot of lettuce. Proc. Brighton Crop Prot. Conf. 2:475-479.

Grosch, R., and Kofoet, A. 2003. Influence of temperature, pH, and inoculum density on bottom rot of lettuce caused by *Rhizoctonia solani.* J. Plant Dis. Prot. 110:366-378.

Grosch, R., Schneider, J. H. M., and Kofoet, A. 2003. Characterization of *Rhizoctonia solani* anastomosis groups causing bottom rot in field-grown lettuce in Germany. Eur. J. Plant Path. 110:53-62.

Grosch, R., Koch, T., and Kofoet, A. 2004. Control of bottom rot on lettuce caused by *Rhizoctonia solani* with commercial biocontrol agents and a novel fungicide. J. Plant Dis. Prot. 111:572-582.

Heo, K. R., Lee, K. Y., Lee, S. H., Jung, S. J., Lee, S. W., and Moon, B. J. 2008. Control of crisphead lettuce damping-off and bottom rot by seed coating with alginate and *Pseudomonas aeruginosa* LY-11. Plant Pathol. J. 24:67-73.

Herr, L. J. 1992. Characteristics of *Rhizoctonia* isolates associated with bottom rot of lettuce in organic soils in Ohio. Phytopathology 82:1046-1050.

Herr, L. J. 1993. Host sources, virulence and overwinter survival of *Rhizoctonia solani* anastomosis groups isolated from field lettuce with bottom rot symptoms. Crop Prot. 12:521-526.

Koike, S., and Martin, F. 2005. Evaluation of fungicides for controlling bottom rot of iceberg lettuce. Fung. Nemat. Tests 60:V150.

Mahr, S. E. R., Stevenson, W. R., and Sequeira, L. 1986. Control of bottom rot of head lettuce with iprodione. Plant Dis. 70:506-509.

Pieczarka, D. J., and Lorbeer, J. W. 1974. Control of bottom rot of lettuce by ridging and fungicide application. Plant Dis. Rep. 58:837-840.

Pieczarka, D. J., and Lorbeer, J. W. 1975. Microorganisms associated with bottom rot of lettuce grown on organic soil in New York State. Phytopathology 65:16-21.

Stone, G. E., and Smith, R. E. 1900. The rotting of greenhouse lettuce. Mass. Agric. Exp. Stn. Bull. 69.

Townsend, G. R. 1934. Bottom rot of lettuce. N.Y. (Cornell) Agric. Exp. Stn. Mem. 158.

Weber, G. F., and Foster, A. C. 1928. Diseases of lettuce, romaine, escarole, and endive. Fla. Agric. Exp. Stn. Bull. 195.

(Prepared by R. N. Raid)

Cercospora Leaf Spot

Cercospora leaf spot of lettuce is found in many parts of the world but is rarely destructive in the field. First reported in 1929, it is most common in the tropics and subtropics. Reports of its economic significance are varied. For example, it is not considered an important disease in China, but it is responsible for major crop losses in the Ivory Coast. In the United States, Cercospora leaf spot has been reported in Florida, Illinois, Indiana, Texas, Virginia, and Wisconsin. It can affect both cultivated and wild lettuce, and since 2000, it has been reported as a major pathogen in glasshouse lettuce production, where warm temperatures and high humidity levels favor spore production and infection by the pathogen.

Symptoms

Infection normally appears first on older, lower leaves. Lesions begin as minute, brown spots surrounded by chlorotic tissue and enlarge to become irregular or angular spots that vary in color from tan to brown (Fig. 21) and frequently have white spots in their centers (Fig. 22). Fully developed lesions are slightly sunken and necrotic.

Cercospora leaf spot spreads progressively upward. Extensive areas of tissue may be killed when infections are numerous.

Causal Organisms

A number of *Cercospora* spp. have been reported to cause Cercospora leaf spot. In Asia and the United States, Cercospora leaf spot is caused by *C. lactucae-sativae* (syn. *C. longissima*), and in Australia, it is caused by *C. apii*. Like other *Cercospora* spp., lettuce isolates may exhibit narrow host specificity.

Young hyphae of *C. lactucae-sativae* are septate, slender, and 1.5–3.5 µm wide; they appear granular. More mature hyphae are thicker (3–6 µm) and more closely septate; they frequently contain conspicuous oil globules. Hyphae are initially hyaline but quickly acquire pigmentation. In culture, mature mycelium generally ranges from dark green to dark brown in color.

Conidiophores are amphigenous, fasciculate, olivaceous brown, unbranched, and septate; they bear conidia on newly developed tips. Conidial scars at the points of conidial attachment are large and conspicuous. Conidia are hyaline and cylindrical to obclavate, with an obconically truncate base and a tapering, obtuse apex. They range from 11 to 170 µm in length and have basal and apical widths that average 7.5 and 3.8 µm, respectively. A conidium generally has from one to 18 septa but can have as many as 28. Although germ tubes may rise from any or all cells, the basal cell usually germinates first, followed by the apical cell. No sexual stage has been reported.

Disease Cycle and Epidemiology

Spread of Cercospora leaf spot in the field appears to occur entirely by means of conidia and is heavily dependent on relatively long periods of leaf wetness. The pathogen survives between cropping seasons on plant material in the field and in association with wild lettuce and closely related hosts.

Conidial germination occurs only in the presence of free moisture or under nearly saturated atmospheric conditions.

Fig. 21. Chlorotic and necrotic lesions on lettuce caused by *Cercospora lactucae-sativae,* the causal agent of Cercospora leaf spot. (Courtesy S. Glucksman—© APS)

Fig. 22. White-centered lesions on lettuce, symptomatic of Cercospora leaf spot (*Cercospora lactucae-sativae*). (Courtesy R. N. Raid—© APS)

Reportedly, durations of leaf wetness in excess of 24 h are required for germ tube development and successful penetration of the leaf through the stomata. Appressoria are not necessary for penetration. Following initial penetration, germ tubes branch repeatedly, facilitating intercellular colonization of host tissues. At the optimal temperature of 25°C, susceptible tissues are rapidly colonized by the advancing hyphae, and symptoms may become apparent within 3 days after inoculation. At the suboptimal temperatures of 15, 20, and 30°C, incubation periods of 7, 5, and 5 days, respectively, have been reported. Subsequently, sporulation may begin in as few as 5 days at 25°C. Conidia are borne singly on conidiophores produced in fascicles on the leaf surface and become airborne during periods of low humidity when exposed to even the slightest turbulence. In addition to atmospheric transport, spores are scattered by rain and by irrigation splash.

In culture, Czapek-Dox V-8 juice agar supports maximum radial growth and sporulation. The average optimum temperature for growth, sporulation, and production of the longest conidia on this particular medium is 25°C.

Management

Cultural practices for the management of Cercospora leaf spot include crop rotation, good drainage, and destruction of wild lettuce and other closely related hosts near the lettuce crop. In certain areas, the application of foliar fungicides may be justified for disease control.

Selected References

Liberato, J. R., and Stephens, P. M. 2006. *Cercospora apii* s. lat. on lettuce in Australia. Australas. Plant Path. 35:379-381.

Raid, R. N., and Nagata, R. T. 2002. Evaluation of assorted foliar applications for control of Cercospora leaf spot on lettuce. Fung. Nemat. Tests 58:V120.

Raid, R. N., and Nagata, R. T. 2002. Evaluation of fungicides for control of Cercospora leaf spot and downy mildew on lettuce. Fung. Nemat. Tests 58:V119.

Savery, S. 1983. Epidemiology of Cercospora leaf spot of lettuce in Republic of Ivory Coast. Argon. Sci. Prod. Veg. Environ. 3:903-909.

Suwan, N., Nuandee, N., Akimitsu, K., and Sarunya, N. 2012. Analysis of β-tubulin gene from carbendazim resistant isolates of *Cercospora lactucae-sativae* on lettuce in Thailand. J. Agric. Tech. 8:711-723.

Szeto, M., and Bau, Y. S. 1975. Some notes on leaf spot (*Cercospora longissima*) disease of lettuce. Agric. Hong Kong 1:278-285.

Toro, R. A. 1929. Plant disease notes from the Central Andes II. Phytopathology 19:969-974.

(Prepared by R. N. Raid)

Damping-Off

Damping-off of lettuce seedlings occurs wherever the crop is grown. The disease is expressed as seed decay, pre- or postemergence damping-off, and infection of roots or stems of young plants. Damping-off is favored by excessive soil moisture, compacted and poorly drained soils, and temperatures unfavorable for germination and lettuce growth.

Symptoms

Lettuce may be attacked by damping-off pathogens and destroyed before seed germination, during emergence of the radicle, or before the hypocotyl has reached the soil surface. After seedling emergence, the hypocotyl may be penetrated near the soil surface, leading to plant collapse and death (Fig. 23). As the seedling grows, the damping-off pathogens can destroy only the outer layer of cells around the stem. This type of injury is identified by a discolored, constricted area near the soil surface (Fig. 24). The magnitude of the dark discoloration is dependent on the age of the seedling and the duration of environmental conditions favorable for disease development. As the lettuce seedling continues to grow, root-tip necrosis may continue to develop, but the risk of plant death from postemergence damping-off rapidly decreases.

Partially girdled plants, as well as those subject to continued root-tip necrosis, may be stunted to varying degrees, resulting in lettuce plantings with uneven growth and development.

Causal Organisms

Pythium irregulare, P. myriotylum, P. sylvaticum, and *P. ultimum* can cause pre- and postemergence damping-off of lettuce, whereas *P. dissotocum, P. uncinulatum,* and *P. violae* incite root-tip necrosis and inhibition of lateral root formation.

Rhizoctonia solani may also cause pre-emergence death of seedlings but usually causes necrosis of the stem at or near the soil surface, which is marked by a distinct margin between infected and healthy tissue.

Fig. 23. Damping-off of lettuce seedlings caused by *Pythium ultimum.* (Courtesy F. N. Martin and K. V. Subbarao—© APS)

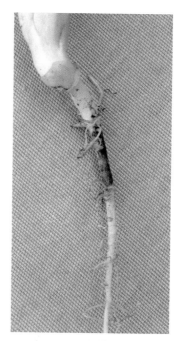

Fig. 24. Discolored, constricted root of a lettuce seedling infected by *Rhizoctonia solani,* a causal agent of damping-off. (Courtesy S. T. Koike—© APS)

Disease Cycle and Epidemiology

Pythium spp. survive in soil as thick-walled oospores and as sporangia in some species. These spores are stimulated to germinate by nutrients such as those in seed and root exudates. After the primary infection, secondary infections may occur from zoospores released from sporangia. Zoospores are motile and swim short distances in films of water in soil or move greater distances in surface water.

Pythium spp. have a broad host range and can also colonize fresh organic matter in soil. Damping-off caused by *Pythium* spp. usually occurs in fields with high organic matter and/or poor drainage—conditions that favor the growth and asexual reproduction of these pathogens.

R. solani survives between crops as sclerotia or mycelium in soil and infested plant debris. It infects host cells directly by infection pegs produced from infection cushions or by individual hyphae that colonize the plant through natural openings and wounds.

Damping-off incited by a *Pythium* or *Rhizoctonia* pathogen is favored by suboptimal growth of lettuce seedlings caused by factors such as unfavorable temperatures, excessive moisture, low light, and overfertilization.

Management

Cultural and chemical measures can be effective means of managing damping-off. Planting high-quality seed under environmental conditions that favor rapid germination and seedling growth reduces the chance of infection. Excessive irrigation and compacted and poorly drained soils should be avoided. Seed and soil treatments with appropriate fungicides may prevent infection and protect seedlings when they are most susceptible to damping-off.

Selected References

Hine, R., Matheron, M., and Byrne, D. 1991. Diseases of lettuce in Arizona. Univ. Ariz. Coll. Agric. Publ. 191050.

Sherf, A. F., and MacNab, A. A. 1986. Vegetable Diseases and Their Control. 2nd ed. John Wiley & Sons, New York.

Stanghellini, M. E., and Kronland, W. C. 1986. Yield loss in hydroponically grown lettuce attributed to subclinical infection of feeder rootlets by *Pythium dissotocum*. Plant Dis. 70:1053-1056.

Stanghellini, M. E., Kim, D. H., Rakocy, J., Gloger, K., and Klinton, H. 1998. First report of root rot of hydroponically grown lettuce caused by *Pythium myriotylum* in a commercial production facility. Plant Dis. 82:831.

(Prepared by M. E. Matheron)

Downy Mildew

Downy mildew is a major disease of lettuce in field and greenhouse production systems worldwide. Relatively cool temperatures and humid climatic conditions favor infection and spread of downy mildew. A downy mildew epidemic can be devastating during a cool and/or wet season. In a semiarid climate, such as in California (United States) and Australia, disease intensity and crop loss vary dramatically among seasons and weather conditions. Because lettuce is most commonly consumed fresh, a relatively low level of infection can downgrade the crop, cause significant trimming losses at harvest, and escalate postharvest decay during transit and storage. A high level of disease can render an entire planting unmarketable.

Symptoms

The typical symptom of downy mildew is the development of local lesions on leaves, appearing first on lower leaves. These lesions are at first light green or slightly chlorotic, and they turn yellow or necrotic after the onset of sporulation (Fig. 25). Le-

sions are angular, variable in size, and often limited by large veins. Under optimal environmental conditions, a downy, white mat of asexual sporangiophores and sporangia forms 1–2 weeks after infection, primarily on the lower sides of leaves (Fig. 26). Older lesions often become necrotic or transparent because of the presence of secondary pathogens. Necrotic lesions with few or no sporangiophores also develop when oospores are produced as part of the sexual cycle.

Lettuce is susceptible to downy mildew at all growth stages. Adult plants are rarely killed by the pathogen, but young seedlings are particularly susceptible; their cotyledons and primary leaves may be completely covered by sporangiophores, and they may die of severe infection. An early infection rarely leads to a systemic infection. Systemic symptoms on leaves include elongated discolored regions, which turn dark green to brown; sporulation is often not present until late in disease development. The central core of the stem and roots of a systemically infected plant is streaked dark brown to black (Fig. 27).

Sporulation of the pathogen can be induced after incubating the infected tissue in a moist chamber in darkness.

Causal Organisms

The primary causal agent of lettuce downy mildew is *Bremia lactucae,* an obligate parasite. The hyphae of the pathogen are coenocytic, filamentous, branched, and hyaline. The mycelium grows intercellularly and forms spherical or claviform haustoria in host cells. One to three sporangiophores arise from stomata. The sporangiophores are septate and colorless; they are inflated at the base, and the upper part branches several times. Branching of sporangiophores is acute and dichotomous (or rarely trichotomous). The tip of each branch expands into a disc or spherical shape, and three to six sterigmata are formed, each with one sporangium at the tip. Sporangia are colorless, spherical or oval, 12–31 µm long, and 11.0–27.5 µm wide.

Two mating types, B_1 and B_2, are needed for sexual reproduction of *B. lactucae,* although homothallic isolates have also been found. Both mating types have been frequently isolated in Europe and in New York State (United States). Isolates from

Fig. 25. Advanced symptoms of downy mildew (*Bremia lactucae*) on **(A)** crisphead lettuce and **(B)** stem lettuce. (Courtesy A. H. C. van Bruggen and K. V. Subbarao—© APS)

cultivated lettuce in California are predominately the B₂ mating type, whereas isolates carrying the B₁ mating type are rare. Oospores have rarely been observed in nature but are abundantly produced in cotyledons or leaves artificially inoculated with the two mating types. When hyphae of opposite mating types meet, asexual sporulation is suppressed and gametangia (oogonium and antheridium) are produced at the point of contact. Meioses occur synchronously in the oogonium and antheridium, and haploid gametes are transferred from the antheridium to the oogonium for fertilization. Oospores are yellow brown, spherical (27–30 μm in diameter), and surrounded by a thick wall (Fig. 28). Germination of oospores has only occasionally been observed under controlled conditions, and the conditions required for oospore germination remain unclear.

In addition to the mating types, pathotypes can also be distinguished by their virulence on lettuce genotypes with differential resistance genes (*Dm*). Studies have revealed multiple dominant genes for resistance (*Dm* genes) in lettuce plants matched by avirulence genes (*Avr*) in *B. lactucae*. High diversity of virulence phenotypes has been observed in Europe, California, and New York State. Prevalent races and pathotypes occur in Europe (BL1 to 32) and in California (CAI to VIII), respectively, that are widely distributed and persist from year to year.

Another pathogen, *Plasmopara lactucae-radicis,* causes downy mildew exclusively on the roots of hydroponically grown lettuce. This pathogen has not been observed on field-grown lettuce.

Disease Cycle and Epidemiology

Potential sources of initial inoculum of *B. lactucae* include lettuce seed, plant debris, wild *Lactuca* spp., and nearby lettuce fields. Lettuce seed may be an important source, based on findings from an early study that six out of 23,000 seeds were contaminated with the pathogen. However, the risk of infection from contaminated seed has not been determined.

Both mating types are observed in many parts of the world, and oospores in lettuce debris may serve as primary inoculum (although oospores of the pathogen are apparently absent and have not been reported in California). However, *B. lactucae* has been found to change virulence phenotypes in response to the deployment of new *Dm* genes, and it is unclear how the pathogen survives crop-free periods in California. *B. lactucae* has been reported to infect plants in several genera in the Asteraceae. However, isolates of *B. lactucae* are host specific, and the wild lettuce species *L. serriola* (prickly lettuce) seldom supports growth of the pathogen. Although sporangia from nearby lettuce fields can be another source of inoculum, their long-distance dispersal is questionable, because they survive for less than 15 h after release because of damage produced by ultraviolet radiation and high temperatures in sunlight.

Secondary spread of *B. lactucae* occurs via airborne sporangia. Sporulation is affected significantly by temperature, relative humidity, and wind speed. Sporangia of *B. lactucae* are produced at night after a few hours of near-saturation humidity and low wind speed. Spore production is suppressed by light, and suppression increases with temperature. The most suppressive wavelength is from 400 to 450 nm. At 15°C, sporulation of *B. lactucae* follows a clear diurnal pattern independent of lightness or darkness at the onset of sporulation. Although spore production is optimal at 15°C, sporulation occurs over a wide temperature range (5–25°C). Spore production is abundant at relative humidity greater than or equal to 90% in still air, and spores are not formed at wind speeds greater than 0.5 ms⁻¹. Sporangia are released in the morning; release is triggered by light initiation and a reduction in relative humidity. The density of *B. lactucae* sporangia in the air usually starts to increase at sunrise and peaks between 10:00 A.M. and noon. The longevity of sporangia is mainly affected by solar radiation (particularly in the ultraviolet B spectrum), ambient humidity, and temperature. Relatively short periods of exposure to sunlight or hot conditions can inactivate sporangia of the pathogen in arid climates. In more humid climates, sporangia can survive during the day and infect the next night.

Germination of sporangia and penetration of plants by the pathogen requires a relatively low temperature and free water or relative humidity near saturation, and this process can take as little as 2–3 h under optimum temperatures (approximately 15°C). High temperatures within a few hours immediately after penetration (as measured in California) can significantly reduce successful infection. After that, the temperature mainly affects

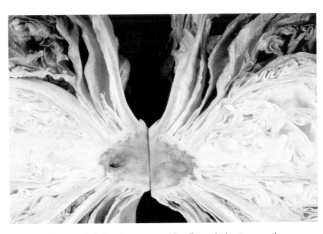

Fig. 27. Systemic infection caused by *Bremia lactucae,* the oomycete that causes downy mildew on lettuce. (Courtesy A. H. C. van Bruggen—© APS)

Fig. 26. Sporulating downy mildew lesions (*Bremia lactucae*) on crisphead lettuce. (Courtesy A. H. C. van Bruggen—© APS)

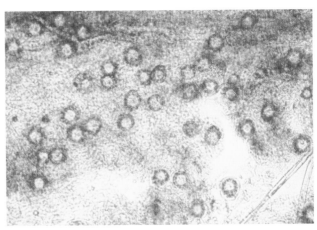

Fig. 28. Oospores of *Bremia lactucae.* (Courtesy A. H. C. van Bruggen—© APS)

the length of the latent period. Under constant or slightly varying temperatures, downy mildew has a short latent period (4–7 days) at 20–22°C and a long latent period (24–34 days) at 6°C. However, under oscillating temperatures, the mean daily temperature has a relatively small effect on the latent period compared with constant temperatures with the same mean. Field studies in California have found that infection of lettuce by *B. lactucae* occurs primarily on days during which leaf wetness ends late in the morning. Thus, sporangia released around sunrise may infect that same morning if leaf wetness continues 3 h or longer.

In commercial production, irrigation practices also have significant effects on epidemics of lettuce downy mildew. Usually, disease is more severe under sprinkler irrigation than under furrow irrigation, because longer leaf wetness duration, increased canopy air humidity, and/or enhanced dispersal of inoculum by splashing are usually associated with sprinkler irrigation. To some extent, these effects are also dependent on the time that irrigation is applied. Downy mildew is further reduced in surface and subsurface drip-irrigated fields compared with furrow-irrigated fields, probably because of the longer daily wet period and higher daytime humidity associated with furrow-irrigated fields. Additionally, growing five or more rows of lettuce on a wide (2-m) bed may create microclimatic conditions conducive to lettuce downy mildew because of the high canopy density and poor drainage associated with the wide bed configuration. However, in coastal California, mesoclimate effects on downy mildew development seem to outweigh microclimate effects as a result of differences in irrigation.

Management

The easiest and cheapest way to manage downy mildew is to select and grow resistant cultivars with either pathotype-specific resistance genes (single dominant genes) or moderate levels of field resistance (probably multiple genes). Single-gene resistance has provided high levels of control for specific races, but the use of resistant cultivars often results in genetic changes in pathogen populations and the rise of strains of *B. lactucae* that overcome this resistance. Although considerable effort has been made to develop resistant cultivars, these cultivars have provided only transient control, because *B. lactucae* has overcome many of the downy mildew resistance genes employed. Interactions between cultivars of lettuce and isolates of *B. lactucae* are defined by numerous gene-for-gene relationships. Specificity is determined by dominant resistance genes (*Dm*) or resistance factors in the plants matched by dominant factors for avirulence (avr factors) in the pathogen. At least 27 major *Dm* genes or resistance (*R*) factors are known that provide resistance against specific isolates of *B. lactucae* in a gene-for-gene manner. Older cultivars often have moderate levels of quantitative resistance, which is presumably conferred by multiple resistance genes with minor effects. Classical plant breeding, combined with the identification of quantitative trait loci (QTLs), has been revived to produce modern cultivars with durable resistance.

Several protective fungicides (e.g., mancozeb, maneb, azadirachtin, fenamidone, ametoctradin–dimethomorph mixture) and systemic fungicides (e.g., fosetyl-aluminum, mandipropamid, metalaxyl, oxathiapiprolin, propamocarb hydrochloride) are available for downy mildew control. Systemic fungicides can provide good control with fewer sprays per lettuce crop in most climates. The use of systemic fungicides is expensive for growers, however, and often induces the development of insensitive isolates of *B. lactucae*. *B. lactucae* is genetically highly variable, particularly when sexual recombination occurs. Isolates with insensitivity to the fungicide metalaxyl had become widespread by the 1990s. As a result, metalaxyl became ineffective, and it has rarely been applied since that time. Fosetyl-aluminum and maneb have been used since the failure of metalaxyl to control downy mildew. Subsequently, the majority of isolates of *B. lactucae* collected in California between 1997

and 2000 were found to have reduced sensitivity to fosetyl-aluminum. In humid climates, fungicides must be applied regularly to prevent or curb the development of epidemics.

Research has demonstrated that some phosphites (i.e., potassium phosphite) have also proven to be somewhat effective in controlling downy mildew. While using these products exclusively is not recommended, using them as part of a comprehensive management program may increase efficacy and help avoid the development of fungicide resistance.

In some climates, disease-warning systems can be used to minimize the number of fungicide applications and to optimize the timing of applications relative to infection periods. Several warning systems for lettuce downy mildew have been developed based primarily on the end of morning leaf wetness duration and temperature, and some systems also consider the night conditions for sporulation of *B. lactucae*. Applying fungicides based on the recommendations of these models, instead of a calendar-based schedule, can reduce the number of fungicide applications and achieve similar disease control.

When lettuce is produced under irrigation, practices can be adjusted to reduce the risk of downy mildew development. Surface and subsurface drip irrigation produce a less conducive environment for downy mildew than furrow and sprinkler irrigation. If sprinkler irrigation is used, sprinklers should be operated in the afternoon to prevent extending the natural leaf wetness period that occurs in the morning.

Other cultural practices focused on field hygiene may also help to control downy mildew—for example, maintaining a lettuce-free period, rotating crops, removing debris and sporulating plants, and destroying possible weed hosts.

Selected References

Brown, S., Koike, S. T., Ochoa, O. E., Laemmlen, F., and Michelmore, R. W. 2004. Insensitivity to the fungicide fosetyl-aluminum in California isolates of the lettuce downy mildew pathogen, *Bremia lactucae*. Plant Dis. 88:502-508.

Cohen, Y., Rubin, E., and Gottlieb, D. 2008. Activity of carboxylic acid amide (CAA) fungicides against *Bremia lactucae*. Eur. J. Plant Pathol. 122:169-183.

Crute, I. R. 1992. The role of resistance breeding in the integrated control of downy mildew (*Bremia lactucae*) in protected lettuce. Euphytica 63:95-102.

Crute, I. R., and Johnson, A. G. 1976. The genetic relationship between races of *Bremia lactucae* and cultivars of *Lactuca sativa*. Ann. Appl. Biol. 83:125-137.

Fall, M. L., van der Heyden, H., Beaulieu, C., and Carisse, O. 2015. *Bremia lactucae* infection efficiency in lettuce is modulated by temperature and leaf wetness duration under Quebec field conditions. Plant Dis. 99:1010-1019.

Hovius, M. H. Y., Carisse, O., Philion, V., and McDonald, M. R. 2007. Field evaluation of weather-based spray programs for the control of downy mildew of lettuce (*Lactuca sativa*), caused by *Bremia lactucae*, in Quebec and Ontario. Can. J. Plant Pathol. 29:9-17.

Ilott, T. W., Hulbert, S. H., and Michelmore, R. W. 1989. Genetic analysis of the gene-for-gene interaction between lettuce (*Lactuca sativa*) and *Bremia lactucae*. Phytopathology 79:888-897.

Judelson, H. S., and Michelmore, R. W. 1992. Temperature and genotype interactions in the expression of host resistance in lettuce downy mildew. Physiol. Molec. Plant Pathol. 40:233-245.

Kushalappa, A. C. 2001. BREMCAST: Development of a system to forecast risk levels of downy mildew on lettuce (*Bremia lactucae*). Int. J. Pest Manag. 47:1-5.

Lebeda, A., Petrzelová, I., and Maryška, Z.. 2008. Structure and variation in the wild-plant pathosystem: *Lactuca serriola–Bremia lactucae*. Eur. J. Plant Pathol. 122:127-146.

Michelmore, R. W., and Wong, J. 2008. Classical and molecular genetics of *Bremia lactucae*, cause of lettuce downy mildew. Eur. J. Plant Pathol. 122:19. doi:10.1007/s10658-008-9305-2

Michelmore, R. W., Ochoa, O, and Wong, J. 2009. *Bremia lactucae* and lettuce downy mildew. Pages 241-262 in: Oomycete Genetics and Genomics: Diversity, Plant and Animal Interactions, and Toolbox. K. Lamour and S. Kamoun, eds. Wiley-Blackwell, New York.

Nordskog, B., Gadoury, D. M., Seem, R. C., and Hermansen, A. 2007. Impact of diurnal periodicity, temperature, and light on sporulation of *Bremia lactucae*. Phytopathology 97:979-986.

Scherm, H., and van Bruggen, A. H. C. 1994. Effects of fluctuating temperatures on the latent period of lettuce downy mildew (*Bremia lactucae*). Phytopathology 84:853-859.

Scherm, H., and van Bruggen, A. H. C. 1995. Comparative study of microclimate and downy mildew development in subsurface drip- and furrow-irrigated lettuce fields in California. Plant Dis. 79:620-625.

Scherm, H., and van Bruggen, A. H. C. 1995. Concurrent spore release and infection of lettuce by *Bremia lactucae* during mornings with prolonged leaf wetness. Phytopathology 85:552-555.

Schettini, T. M., Legg, E. J., and Michelmore, R. W. 1991. Insensitivity to metalaxyl in California populations of *Bremia lactucae* and resistance of California lettuce cultivars to downy mildew. Phytopathology 81:64-70.

Simko, I., Atallah, A. J., Ochoa, E. O., Antonise, R., Galeano, C. H., Truco, M. J., and Michelmore, R. W. 2013. Identification of QTLs conferring resistance to downy mildew in legacy cultivars of lettuce. Sci. Rep. 3:2875.

Stanghellini, M. E., Adaskaveg, J. E., and Rasmussen, S. L. 1990. Pathogenesis of *Plasmopara lactucae-radicis,* a systemic root pathogen of cultivated lettuce. Plant Dis. 74:173-178.

Su, H., van Bruggen, A. H. C., and Subbarao, K. V. 2000. Spore release of *Bremia lactucae* on lettuce is affected by timing of light initiation and decrease in relative humidity. Phytopathology 90:67-71.

Su, H., van Bruggen, A. H. C., Subbarao, K. V., and Scherm, H. 2004. Sporulation of *Bremia lactucae* affected by temperature, relative humidity, and wind in controlled conditions. Phytopathology 94:396-401.

Subbarao, K. V., Hubbard, J. C., and Schulbach, K. F. 1997. Comparison of lettuce diseases and yield under subsurface drip and furrow irrigation. Phytopathology 87:877-883.

Wu, B. M., Subbarao, K. V., and van Bruggen, A. H. C. 2000. Factors affecting the survival of *Bremia lactucae* sporangia deposited on lettuce leaves. Phytopathology 90:827-833.

Wu, B. M., van Bruggen, A. H. C., Subbarao, K. V., and Scherm, H. 2002. Incorporation of temperature and solar radiation thresholds to modify a lettuce downy mildew warning system. Phytopathology 92:631-636.

Wu, B. M., Subbarao, K. V., and van Bruggen, A. H. C. 2005. Analyses of the relationships between lettuce downy mildew and weather variables using geographic information system techniques. Plant Dis. 89:90-96.

(Prepared by B. M. Wu, A. H. C. van Bruggen, and K. V. Subbarao)

Drop

Lettuce drop (also known as "Sclerotinia rot") was first described in 1890 on greenhouse-grown lettuce in Massachusetts (United States). The disease has since been reported from greenhouse and field lettuce production systems worldwide, including from Australia, Canada, China, the Netherlands, New Zealand, Spain, the United Kingdom, the United States, Venezuela, and other parts of the world. In the United States, lettuce drop occurs in all major lettuce-producing states, including Arizona, California, Florida, New Jersey, and New York.

Once introduced, the sclerotia of the pathogen persist in the field for several years. Depending on the season, disease incidence may range from a few isolated plants to more than 70% in some fields. The disease may cause devastating loses in extensive production systems under conditions of cool weather and high soil moisture.

Symptoms

Lettuce drop infection can be initiated either by soilborne sclerotia at any growth stage of the plant or by airborne ascospores starting approximately 30–40 days after the canopy closes. The former type of infection usually starts from the roots, the crown, or senescent leaves in contact with the soil. The initial aboveground symptom is wilting of the outermost layer of leaves, giving the plant a stressed appearance (Fig. 29). As infection progresses rapidly inward to the other leaf layers, the entire plant wilts, including the head. The entire plant may collapse in less than 2 days—hence the name "drop," which best describes the typical symptom on lettuce (Figs. 30 and 31). Layers of collapsed leaves lie flat on the soil surface even

Fig. 29. Field of different types of lettuce infected by *Sclerotinia minor,* one of the pathogens that causes lettuce drop. (Courtesy K. D. Puri—© APS)

Fig. 30. Romaine lettuce infected by *Sclerotinia minor,* a lettuce drop pathogen. (Courtesy K. D. Puri—© APS)

Fig. 31. Crisphead lettuce infected by *Sclerotinia minor,* a lettuce drop pathogen. (Courtesy K. D. Puri—© APS)

though the inner leaves remain green (Fig. 32). A soft, watery decay follows on both the above- and belowground plant parts (Fig. 33). When airborne ascospores initiate infection, the symptoms are similar to those described previously, except that they originate on exposed plant parts, where ascospores settle and infect (Figs. 34, 35, and 36).

In both cases, the fungus produces a snowy-white mycelium under moist conditions. Black sclerotia are produced on the infected plant parts (Figs. 33, 35, and 37). They can be as small as a mustard seed or as large as a bean, depending on the pathogen species and environmental conditions. Usually, small sclerotia are produced on the lower surfaces of leaves touching the soil, around the crown, and throughout the subterranean taproot, whereas large sclerotia are produced mainly on plant parts above the ground, around the crown, and occasionally in the taproot near the soil surface.

Causal Organisms

Lettuce drop is caused by two species of *Sclerotinia*: *S. minor* and *S. sclerotiorum*. One or the other may predominate in a certain area, but both species can occur in the same field.

In culture, sclerotia of *S. sclerotiorum* are produced at the margins of the colony after the mycelium reaches the edge of the petri dish, forming concentric rings, radial lines, and other patterns. Sclerotia are generally black on the outside and white on the inside, but very old sclerotia are black throughout. Scle-

Fig. 32. Layers of collapsed romaine leaves with inner green leaves, symptomatic of lettuce drop (*Sclerotinia* sp.). (Courtesy K. D. Puri—© APS)

Fig. 33. Decay of crisphead lettuce caused by lettuce drop; mycelium and sclerotia (*Sclerotinia* sp.) are visible on the cut end. (Courtesy K. D. Puri—© APS)

Fig. 34. Lettuce drop caused by infection from airborne ascospores of *Sclerotinia sclerotiorum* in a crisphead lettuce field. (Courtesy K. V. Subbarao—© APS)

Fig. 35. Lettuce drop of crisphead lettuce caused by infection from airborne ascospores of *Sclerotinia sclerotiorum;* large sclerotia are visible beneath. (Courtesy K. V. Subbarao—© APS)

Fig. 36. Ascospore release by apothecia produced by *Sclerotinia sclerotiorum,* a pathogen of lettuce drop. (Photo by J. K. Clark; Reproduced by permission of University of California Statewide IPM Project)

rotia typically measure 2–20 × 3–7 mm. The sclerotial rind is composed of a layer of dark-walled, globose cells two to six cells thick. In the field, sclerotia are usually produced on infected plant parts above the ground, around the crown, and in the root core near the crown. Sclerotia of *S. sclerotiorum* can germinate carpogenically (Fig. 38) to produce airborne ascospores (Fig. 36) or eruptively to form mycelium, although the regulation of germination pathways remains unknown. Each sclerotium may germinate carpogenically to produce one to more than 10 apothecia, depending on the size of sclerotium and the conditions. Apothecia are usually cup shaped but are sometimes flat and have a central dimple. They are usually white, yellow, or a shade of brown. Asci are cylindrical–clavate and measure up to 10 × 130 μm; each has eight ascospores of the same size. The ascospores are nonseptate, uniseriate, hyaline, and elliptical and measure 4–5 × 9–13 μm. Cylindrical,

Fig. 37. Black sclerotia produced on roots infected by *Sclerotinia minor,* a lettuce drop pathogen. (Courtesy K. V. Subbarao—© APS)

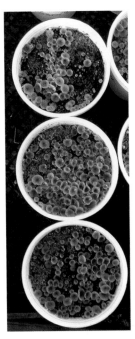

Fig. 38. Apothecia produced by carpogenic germination of *Sclerotinia sclerotiorum* sclerotia. (Courtesy K. V. Subbarao—© APS)

hyaline paraphyses are present on the hymenium. At maturation, ascospores are forcefully ejected into the air from time to time, with a major peak occurring in the late morning. Sclerotia of *S. sclerotiorum* can also germinate eruptively and, although less important in an epidemic, can infect lettuce directly.

On infected lettuce, sclerotia from *S. minor* are mostly spherical and uniform in diameter, but sometimes, multiple sclerotia cluster into large clumps. In culture, sclerotia are initiated around the edge of the petri dish, but abundant sclerotia (0.5–2.0 mm in diameter) are also scattered throughout the colony. Sclerotia of *S. minor* are relatively small and uniform compared with those of *S. sclerotiorum,* which are large and irregularly shaped. Carpogenic germination and production of apothecia are rare in *S. minor;* instead, sclerotia of *S. minor* primarily germinate eruptively.

Disease Cycle and Epidemiology

Both species survive in the soil as sclerotia, which are mainly affected by interactions of soil temperature, soil moisture, and oxygen level. Generally, sclerotia of *S. sclerotiorum* survive longer than those of *S. minor;* therefore, *S. sclerotiorum* has a very wide geographical distribution, whereas *S. minor* prevails mostly in cool regions. Occasionally, both pathogens may survive as active mycelium in living or dead plants.

The two species differ in their strategies for infection and reproduction. *S. minor* produces many small sclerotia, which require very restrictive conditions for carpogenic germination and therefore infect lettuce primarily by eruptive germination. In contrast, *S. sclerotiorum* produces many fewer large sclerotia, which produce millions of ascospores via carpogenic germination once conditions are favorable (i.e., topsoil remains near saturation for approximately 40 days at 15–20°C). Because of the specific requirements for apothecia production and ascospore release, lettuce drop caused by *S. sclerotiorum* is sporadic and unpredictable. In contrast, *S. minor* sclerotia rarely produce apothecia; thus, all infections are caused by eruptive germination of sclerotia. Drop caused by *S. minor* occurs consistently in infested fields and is determined mainly by the density of soilborne sclerotia.

Infection via eruptive germination by either species can occur at any stage of crop growth, but infection via airborne ascospores usually occurs close to crop maturity. Sclerotia of both species in the topsoil profile (less than 2 cm for *S. minor* and up to 4–5 cm for *S. sclerotiorum*) can germinate carpogenically when the soil moisture is maintained at near saturation for a time (i.e., more than 4 weeks for *S. sclerotiorum* and slightly longer for *S. minor*). Temperatures around 15°C are particularly favorable for the formation of apothecial initials, and low-temperature chilling (i.e., 4–10°C with moisture) can promote carpogenic germination of sclerotia, particularly for sclerotia produced at temperatures higher than 25°C. The optimal temperature range for carpogenic germination of sclerotia is wider for *S. sclerotiorum* than for *S. minor.* After the initials are exposed to sunlight, they expand into small, tan, cup-shaped apothecia, each of which produces millions of ascospores that are forcefully ejected into the air and dispersed by wind throughout the field and to adjacent fields. Ascospores are released over a period of 2–3 weeks. In the presence of free water, they germinate and infect senescent or dead lettuce leaves within 48 h.

In the field, mycelial infection from eruptively germinating sclerotia is rare for *S. sclerotiorum* but common for *S. minor.* Under optimum soil moisture conditions, sclerotia of *S. minor* within 2 cm of the taproot and 8 cm of the soil surface germinate eruptively, producing masses of hyphae that infect lettuce roots, stems, and senescent leaves. Plant-to-plant spread occurs occasionally by mycelial contact. Studies have suggested that the survival of sclerotia is affected primarily by soil moisture, soil temperature, and oxygen level (which are in turn affected by burial depth and soil structure). When combined, high temperature, high soil moisture, and low oxygen can cause a loss of viability of sclerotia of both species within a couple of weeks. Under field conditions during the summer in central California, sclerotia of *S. sclerotiorum* can survive longer than sclerotia of *S. minor*. Germination of sclerotia is also affected by the moisture status. Those produced on host tissue germinate poorly soon after they are formed because of their high moisture content. Most sclerotia must dry to a certain extent before they can germinate.

Management

Application of fungicides immediately after thinning and cultivation (at the four to six true-leaf stage) significantly reduces the incidence of lettuce drop caused by *S. minor*. However, repeated application of dicarboximide fungicides may result in the selection of microbes that rapidly degrade these fungicides, resulting in less than satisfactory control in some fields. Lettuce drop caused by *S. sclerotiorum* generally cannot be reduced by applying fungicides after thinning, but disease can be reduced significantly by applying fungicides during the rosette stage (approximately 30–40 days before harvest). Split applications of fungicides result in even better control.

Biocontrol agents—including *Trichoderma* spp., *Sporidesmium sclerotivorum*, and *Coniothyrium minitans*—have been tested against *Sclerotinia* spp. in various cropping systems. Evaluation of these treatments against lettuce drop caused by *S. sclerotiorum* and *S. minor* revealed that *C. minitans* (Contans) was highly effective against *S. sclerotiorum* on lettuce, but none of the three treatments was effective against *S. minor* when applications were made similar to the label recommendations for *S. sclerotiorum*. However, Contans was subsequently developed into an effective treatment against *S. minor* by altering the application time to match the most vulnerable stage of the pathogen, which is the mycelial stage. It follows that Contans applications should be made just after lettuce harvest, when diseased, unharvested plants have not formed sclerotia. Doing so not only reduces the level of inoculum returned to the soil after crop disking but also lowers the incidence of disease in subsequent lettuce crops.

Using irrigation methods such as subsurface drip also provides as much or better control than applying fungicides. Keeping the top 5–8 cm of soil on planting beds dry is critical for the control of drop. A modified technique, surface drip, has been widely adopted in California and can also reduce the incidence of drop significantly. In contrast, since the early 2000s, growers have adopted lettuce cultivation on 2-m-wide beds with five or more rows of lettuce. Adopting this practice has increased lettuce drop caused by both species and particularly the risk of infection by airborne ascospores of *S. sclerotiorum*.

Deep plowing may provide adequate control in soil with a low sclerotium density, and soil fumigation can significantly reduce the density of soilborne sclerotia but is not generally economical. Removing infected lettuce plants and weeds can effectively reduce the inoculum level in the field, although doing so is costly and time consuming. Leaving fields fallow and rotating with nonhosts (e.g., small grains, broccoli) should be practiced when possible. In Florida, growers flood fallow their lettuce fields for 4–6 weeks during the off-season (summer), and this results in near total control of *S. sclerotiorum*—the lettuce drop pathogen most prevalent in their muck soils.

Efforts to develop lettuce cultivars resistant to drop are ongoing.

Selected References

Abawi, G. S., and Grogan, R. G. 1979. Epidemiology of diseases caused by *Sclerotinia* species. Phytopathology 69:899-904.

Abawi, G. S., Grogan, R. G., and Duniway, J. M. 1985. Effect of water potential on survival of sclerotia of *Sclerotinia minor* in two California soils. Phytopathology 75:217-221.

Adams, P. B. 1975. Factors affecting survival of *Sclerotinia sclerotiorum* in soil. Plant Dis. Rep. 59:599-603.

Chitrampalam, P., Turini, T. A., Matheron, M. E., and Pryor, B. M. 2010. Effect of sclerotium density and irrigation on disease incidence and on efficacy of *Coniothyrium minitans* in suppressing lettuce drop caused by *Sclerotinia sclerotiorum*. Plant Dis. 94:1118-1124.

Chitrampalam, P., Wu, B. M., Koike, S. T., and Subbarao, K. V. 2011. Interactions between *Coniothyrium minitans* and *Sclerotinia minor* affect biocontrol efficacy of *C. minitans*. Phytopathology 101:358-366.

Hao, J. J., Subbarao, K. V., and Koike, S. T. 2003. Effects of broccoli rotation on lettuce drop caused by *Sclerotinia minor* and on the population density of sclerotia in soil. Plant Dis. 87:159-166.

Hayes, R. J., Wu, B. M., Pryor, B. M., Chitrampalam, P., and Subbarao, K. V. 2010. Assessment of resistance in lettuce (*Lactuca sativa* L.) to mycelial and ascospore infection by *Sclerotinia minor* Jagger and *S. sclerotiorum* (Lib.) de Bary. HortScience 45:333-341.

Hayes, R. J., Wu, B. M., and Subbarao, K. V. 2011. A single recessive gene conferring short leaves in romaine × Latin type lettuce (*Lactuca sativa* L.) crosses, and its effect on plant morphology and resistance to lettuce drop caused by *Sclerotinia minor* Jagger. Plant Breed. 130:388-393.

Imolehin, E. D., and Grogan, R. G. 1980. Factors affecting survival of sclerotia, and effects of inoculum density, relative position, and distance of sclerotia from the host on infection of lettuce by *Sclerotinia minor*. Phytopathology 70:1162-1167.

Klose, S., Wu, B. M., Ajwa, H. A., Koike, S. T., and Subbarao, K. V. 2010. Reduced efficacy of Rovral and Botran to control *Sclerotinia minor* in lettuce production in the Salinas Valley may be related to accelerated fungicide degradation in soil. Crop Prot. 29:751-756.

Kohn, L. M. 1979. Delimitation of the economically important plant pathogenic *Sclerotinia* species. Phytopathology 69:881-886.

Subbarao, K. V. 1998. Progress toward integrated management of lettuce drop. Plant Dis. 82:1068-1078.

Subbarao, K. V., Koike, S. T., and Hubbard, J. C. 1996. Effects of deep plowing on the distribution and density of *Sclerotinia minor* sclerotia and lettuce drop incidence. Plant Dis. 80:28-33.

Wu, B. M., and Subbarao, K. V. 2003. Effects of irrigation and tillage on temporal and spatial dynamics of *Sclerotinia minor* sclerotia and lettuce drop incidence. Phytopathology 93:1572-1580.

Wu, B. M., and Subbarao, K. V. 2008. Effects of soil temperature, moisture, and burial depths on carpogenic germination of *Sclerotinia sclerotiorum* and *S. minor*. Phytopathology 98:1144-1152.

Wu, B. M., Subbarao, K. V., and Liu, Y.-B. 2008. Comparative survival of sclerotia of *Sclerotinia minor* and *S. sclerotiorum*. Phytopathology 98:659-665.

Wu, B. M., Koike S. T., and Subbarao, K. V. 2011. Impact of consumer-driven changes to crop production practices on lettuce drop caused by *Sclerotinia sclerotiorum* and *S. minor*. Phytopathology 101:340-348.

(Prepared by B. M. Wu and K. V. Subbarao)

Fusarium Wilt

Fusarium wilt (also referred to as "Fusarium root rot") was first recognized as a disease of lettuce in Japan, where it was reported in 1967. Fusarium wilt was discovered in the San Joaquin Valley of California (United States) in 1990 and subsequently became widespread in both California and Arizona, where together 99% of lettuce is grown in the United States. Fusarium wilt of lettuce has also been reported in Argentina, Brazil, Iran, Italy, Portugal, and Taiwan.

Symptoms

Stunting is a common symptom of Fusarium wilt and may be severe (Fig. 39). Older leaves become chlorotic and/or necrotic, and plants may die before the crop reaches maturity. Even plants with only six to eight true leaves can show foliar symptoms of Fusarium wilt.

The roots do not typically display external symptoms, but a reddish-brown internal discoloration is common (Fig. 40). Rotting at the core of the root can be extensive (Fig. 41) and is often apparent in plants in advance of any visible damage aboveground.

Causal Organism

Fusarium oxysporum f. sp. *lactucae* was described as the cause of root rot of lettuce in Japan in 1967. The fungus has morphological features that are diagnostic of *F. oxysporum,* including three or four septate macroconidia, microconidia borne in false heads on short monophialides, and chlamydospores formed singly or in clumps.

In controlled conditions in Japan and the United States, *F. oxysporum* f. sp. *lactucae* was incapable of causing disease on all the tested crops other than lettuce. Thus, the available evidence indicates that the pathogen is host specific. In Japan, where major gene resistance has been deployed, three pathogenic races of *F. oxysporum* f. sp. *lactucae* have been identified based on the reactions of different cultivars. Race 3 has been reported to occur in Taiwan, but otherwise, only race 1 has been found outside Japan.

Pathogenic races of *F. oxysporum* f. sp. *lactucae* are not closely related, which suggests that each race arose independently and not as a mutant derivative of a pre-existing pathotype. Race 1 isolates found in Italy, Japan, Taiwan, and the United States have all been shown to be somatically compatible, suggesting a common origin of a globally distributed race 1 strain. In a survey of race 1 isolates in California, *F. oxysporum* f. sp. *lactucae* had a distinctive colony morphology on Komada's medium, which served to distinguish the pathogen from nonpathogenic strains of *F. oxysporum.* Both somatic compatibility and molecular markers based on polymerase chain reaction (PCR) can be used to identify race 1 of *F. oxysporum* f. sp. *lactucae.*

Disease Cycle and Epidemiology

The disease cycle of Fusarium wilt of lettuce is similar to that of the Fusarium wilts that affect other crops. The dissemination of *F. oxysporum* f. sp. *lactucae* occurs primarily by movement of infested soil and plant debris. The pathogen can also be seedborne, which may help to explain its movement between continents. *F. oxysporum* f. sp. *lactucae* can survive in soil and is reported to have a half-life of approximately 6 months following incorporation of infested crop residue. The decline in viability may be offset by colonization of crops grown in rotation with lettuce. The pathogen is reported to infect the roots of cauliflower and broccoli but develops only to a limited extent. *F. oxysporum* f. sp. *lactucae* colonizes spinach more extensively and can be recovered from the vascular stele, making this a less desirable crop to be grown in rotation with lettuce.

The first step in the development of Fusarium wilt in lettuce is an infection of the root cortex. This infection occurs to the same extent in both resistant and susceptible cultivars and does not initially result in visible damage to the root in either case. Colo-

nization can extend into the vascular stele, even in a resistant cultivar; some cultivars sustain extensive damage to the taproot without showing aboveground symptoms of disease. In susceptible cultivars, damage to the root system eventually results in foliar symptoms. How soon these symptoms become evident depends on the inoculum density in the soil and the temperature to which the crop is exposed during the growing season.

A significant effect of temperature on disease development has been reported in Italy, Japan, and the United States (Arizona and California), with higher temperatures resulting in more severe disease. Under controlled conditions, plants maintained under a day/night temperature regime of 33/23°C sustained significantly more damage from Fusarium wilt than plants maintained at 23/18°C.

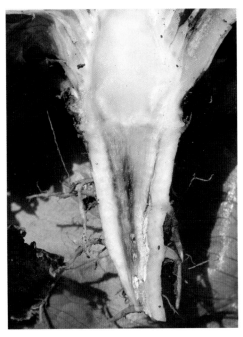

Fig. 40. Vertical section of lettuce taproot showing reddish-brown internal discoloration, characteristic of Fusarium wilt (*Fusarium oxysporum* f. sp. *lactucae*). (Courtesy T. R. Gordon—© APS)

Fig. 41. Vertical sections of lettuce taproots showing extensive rotting, symptomatic of Fusarium wilt (*Fusarium oxysporum* f. sp. *lactucae*). (Courtesy T. R. Gordon—© APS)

Fig. 39. Healthy crisphead lettuce plant (left) versus plant with stunted growth (right) caused by Fusarium wilt (*Fusarium oxysporum* f. sp. *lactucae*). (Courtesy T. R. Gordon—© APS)

This effect of temperature explains the significant effect of planting date on disease severity. Cultivars of intermediate susceptibility were observed to be more severely diseased when planted in June than in July or August. Mean daily high/low soil temperatures for the June, July, and August plantings were 30/20°C, 25/19°C, and 24/18°C, respectively. Planting date may have a significant effect on disease severity even when plantings are separated by only 1 week.

Management

An essential element in the management of Fusarium wilt is to minimize dissemination of the pathogen to areas in which it is not already established. Long-distance movement is most readily accomplished with contaminated seed. Therefore, it is important to recognize how seed becomes contaminated and to adopt practices that will minimize production of infested seed lots. To this end, producers should avoid growing seed crops in fields in which the pathogen is present. Chemical seed treatments are available, and carbendazim and prochloraz (among other fungicides) have been shown to reduce the incidence of *F. oxysporum* f. sp. *lactucae* on seed.

Diagnostic tests for the presence of the pathogen based on quantitative PCR have been developed and may provide more efficient means of detection than isolations on a selective medium. However, based on the detection thresholds that have been reported, low levels of the pathogen (e.g., <0.1%) may still escape detection.

To minimize the risk of local dissemination of *F. oxysporum* f. sp. *lactucae,* it is highly advisable to remove soil from farming equipment as completely as possible before equipment is moved between fields. This is a good practice even when there is no history of Fusarium wilt, because the pathogen may be resident in the soil for many years before it increases to a level that can cause disease. Consequently, the pathogen may be present even in fields with no history of Fusarium wilt.

Any practice that lowers the soil inoculum density can reduce the risk of disease. In field studies conducted in Arizona, solarization reduced the incidence of Fusarium wilt on lettuce sown in naturally infested soil by up to 91% compared with nonsolarized plots. Flooding soil to achieve anaerobic conditions has been shown to reduce populations of soilborne pathogens, but limited tests of this procedure did not demonstrate a beneficial effect on control of Fusarium wilt of lettuce. Soil fumigation can be effective, but its cost is generally prohibitive.

The inoculum level of *F. oxysporum* f. sp. *lactucae* should decline in a field cropped to a nonsusceptible host, and hence, crop rotation can be beneficial. As noted previously, cauliflower and broccoli appear not to support significant development of *F. oxysporum* f. sp. *lactucae* and so represent suitable rotation crops when Fusarium wilt of lettuce is a concern. Spinach is less desirable, as it is prone to more extensive colonization by the pathogen. An even greater contribution to the soil population of *F. oxysporum* f. sp. *lactucae* can result from growing lettuce cultivars that are resistant to Fusarium wilt—some of which sustain extensive colonization of the root vascular stele. Thus, although some lettuce cultivars do not suffer economic damage from Fusarium wilt, they may allow the inoculum level to increase to the point that disease will have a significant impact on subsequent plantings of susceptible cultivars.

As noted previously, the planting date can have a significant influence on the development of Fusarium wilt. In areas in which lettuce can be grown throughout the year, such as California, knowing how temperature influences disease severity can guide growers in selecting appropriate cultivars for each planting window; the most susceptible cultivars should be grown only during the cooler parts of the year.

Significant differences in susceptibility to Fusarium wilt among lettuce cultivars are well documented, and genetically resistant cultivars have been deployed in Japan. Based on studies conducted in Italy and the United States, it appears that although crisphead lettuce cultivars differ in susceptibility to Fusarium wilt, none is truly resistant. However, high levels of resistance are apparent in some leaf and romaine cultivars. Both controlled environment and field studies have confirmed that the leaf cultivar Lolla Rossa and the romaine cultivars Caesar and King Henry remain free of disease symptoms even under optimal conditions for disease development. Experimental work in Japan has suggested that resistance to race 2 may be determined primarily by a single dominant locus, with lesser contributions from minor loci. In California, progeny of a cross between the crisphead cultivar Salinas (which has moderate resistance) and Valmaine (a highly resistant romaine cultivar) revealed three quantitative trait loci (QTLs) associated with resistance to race 1—each on a different linkage group. At two of these loci, the alleles conferring resistance were derived from Valmaine, whereas at the third locus, the Salinas allele was responsible for resistance. Combining these positive alleles from both parents should provide a higher level of resistance than is conferred by either parent alone. Overall, the genetic resources that have been identified should contribute to more effective control of Fusarium wilt in the future.

Selected References

Garibaldi, A., Gilardi, G., and Gullino, M. L. 2004. Seed transmission of *Fusarium oxysporum* f. sp. *lactucae.* Phytoparasitica 32:61-65.
Garibaldi, A., Gilardi, G., and Gullino, M. L. 2004. Varietal resistance of lettuce to *Fusarium oxysporum* f. sp. *lactucae.* Crop Prot. 23:845-851.
Gordon, T. R., and Koike, S. T. 2015. Management of Fusarium wilt of lettuce. Crop Prot. 73:45-49. doi:org/10.1016/j.cropro.2015.01.011
Matheron, M. E., and Porchas, M. 2010. Evaluation of soil solarization and flooding as management tools for Fusarium wilt of lettuce. Plant Dis. 94:1323-1328.
Matheron, M. E., McCreight, J. D., Tickes, B. R., and Porchas, M. 2005. Effect of planting date, cultivar, and stage of plant development on incidence of Fusarium wilt of lettuce in desert production fields. Plant Dis. 89:565-570.
Scott, J. C., Gordon, T. R., Shaw, D. V., and Koike, S. T. 2010. Effect of temperature on severity of Fusarium wilt of lettuce caused by *Fusarium oxysporum* f. sp. *lactucae.* Plant Dis. 94:13-17.
Scott, J. C., Kirkpatrick, S. C., and Gordon, T. R. 2010. Variation in susceptibility of lettuce cultivars to Fusarium wilt caused by *Fusarium oxysporum* f. sp. *lactucae.* Plant Pathol. 59:139-146.
Scott, J. C., Gordon, T. R., Kirkpatrick, S. C., Koike, S. T., Matheron, M. E., Ochoa, O. E., Truco, M. J., and Michelmore, R. W. 2012. Crop rotation and genetic resistance reduce risk of damage from Fusarium wilt in lettuce. Calif. Agric. 66:20-24.

(Prepared by T. R. Gordon and S. T. Koike)

Gray Mold

Gray mold is usually a minor disease of lettuce, but it can cause significant damage if field conditions are favorable for the pathogen or if lettuce is grown in a greenhouse. The disease occurs wherever lettuce is grown.

Symptoms

Symptoms of gray mold include a water-soaked, brown-gray to brown-orange, soft, mushy rot that occurs most commonly on the oldest leaves, which are in contact with the soil. These leaves are often damaged or senescent and therefore particularly susceptible. From this food base, the pathogen progresses into the healthy parts of the lettuce plant and causes a decay of the crown and attached leaves. A characteristic fuzzy, gray to brown growth (i.e., conidiophores and conidia of the fungus) covers diseased areas, especially the basal leaf and crown tissues, which are shaded and protected from drying by overlying foliage (Fig. 42). Black sclerotia may form on infected tissues.

In advanced stages of gray mold, lettuce crowns can become completely rotted, and entire plants will wilt and collapse (Fig. 43). The wilting and collapsing symptoms may closely resemble those caused by *Sclerotinia minor* and *Boeremia exigua* (syn. *Phoma exigua*); therefore, to obtain an accurate diagnosis, the crown tissue must be carefully examined and tested.

Seedlings (especially transplanted lettuce) can become infected when the stem is in contact with soil (Fig. 44); such an infection can cause the plant to have delayed development or to collapse. Gray mold can therefore result in significant stand reduction.

Gray mold can develop on the upper foliage of lettuce if tissue is damaged or compromised. For example, leaves with tipburn may be colonized and rotted (Fig. 45).

Causal Organism

Gray mold is caused by the necrotrophic pathogen *Botrytis cinerea*. (The perfect stage, *Botryotinia fuckeliana*, has not been observed on lettuce.) Conidiophores of *B. cinerea* are long (1–2 mm), gray-brown at maturity, and somewhat paler at the apex. The irregularly branched conidiophores bear grapelike clusters of conidia at the tip of each branch. The ellipsoid to obovoid conidia (4–11 μm wide × 6–18 μm long) are colorless to pale brown and have a prominent hilum. Some isolates sporulate poorly in culture unless incubated under light (12 h light/12 h dark). Sclerotia, if present, vary greatly in size but are generally round to oval to oblong in shape.

Disease Cycle and Epidemiology

B. cinerea survives in and around fields as a saprophyte on crop debris, as a pathogen on numerous crops and weed plants, and as sclerotia in soil. Conidia develop from these sources and become windborne. Conidia that land on senescent or damaged lettuce tissue germinate in the presence of free moisture and rapidly colonize the tissue. Once established, the pathogen grows into adjacent healthy leaves and stems. Tissue colonized by gray mold also can be invaded by other decay organisms, which further contributes to the rapid breakdown of the tissue.

Cool temperatures and high humidity favor the development of gray mold. In some areas, seasonal fluctuations in disease incidence occur, presumably as a result of changes in the environment and inoculum levels.

Lettuce tissues are predisposed to infection by damage caused by abiotic factors such as frost and heat, physiological disorders such as tipburn, and the activity of other pathogens, such as *Bremia lactucae* on the leaves and *B. exigua* (syn. *P. exigua*), *Rhizoctonia solani*, and *Sclerotinia* spp. on the crowns and basal leaves. Diagnosis of gray mold as a primary pathogen is made difficult because of the ability of *B. cinerea* to grow as

Fig. 44. Lettuce transplant infected with *Botrytis cinerea*, which causes gray mold. (Courtesy S. T. Koike—© APS)

Fig. 42. Fuzzy, gray to brown growth of mycelia produced by *Botrytis cinerea*, the gray mold pathogen. (Courtesy S. T. Koike—© APS)

Fig. 43. Collapse of a romaine lettuce plant caused by gray mold (*Botrytis cinerea*). (Courtesy S. T. Koike—© APS)

Fig. 45. Romaine lettuce with tipburn caused by *Botrytis cinerea*, the gray mold pathogen. (Courtesy S. T. Koike—© APS)

a secondary decay organism following infection caused by one of these pathogens.

B. cinerea inoculum can be windborne, and gray mold epidemiology may also involve seed. The pathogen may be present in or on lettuce seed, successfully infect the germinated lettuce seedling, and grow systemically in lettuce as an endophyte. Endophytic *B. cinerea* mycelium may colonize lettuce roots, stems, and leaves without causing any symptoms.

Management

Because *B. cinerea* colonizes injured tissue, damage caused by farming practices, environmental extremes, and other pathogens and pests should be minimized. Reducing the duration of leaf wetness by avoiding sprinkler irrigation may help lower the severity of gray mold. Similarly, scheduling crop incorporation and soil preparation to minimize excessive plant residues at planting may also reduce the disease. Greenhouses should be adequately ventilated or heated to reduce humidity.

Growers should use lettuce transplants that are not overgrown; old transplants are subject to additional leaf breakage and damage during planting and hence are more susceptible to gray mold infection. Romaine transplants are especially prone to gray mold disease, so this lettuce type should be direct-seeded when possible.

Fungicides may be useful in protecting plants from gray mold. However, *B. cinerea* isolates resistant to anilinopyrimidine, dicarboximide, hydroxyanilide, methyl benzimidazole carbamate, phenylpyrrole, quinone outside inhibitors (QoIs), and succinate dehydrogenase inhibitor (SDHI) fungicides are widespread in some lettuce-growing areas. Lettuce isolates of *Botrytis* with multiple resistances are not uncommon. Growers should therefore use chemical products with different modes of action to reduce the risk of fungicide insensitivity.

If seedborne *B. cinerea* is found to be important in gray mold disease, seed treatments to surface-sterilize seed may be appropriate.

Selected References

Chatzidimopoulos, M., Papaevaggelou, D., and Pappas, A. C. 2013. Detection and characterization of fungicide resistant phenotypes of *Botrytis cinerea* in lettuce crops in Greece. Eur. J. Plant Pathol. 137:363-376.

Cornford, C. A., Pitt, D., and Wakley, G. 1985. Comparative ultrastructure of lettuce cotyledons infected with *Botrytis cinerea* and *Bremia lactucae* and the histochemical localization of acid phosphatase. Trans. Br. Mycol. Soc. 84:669-678.

Delon, R., Kiffer, E., and Mangenot, F. 1977. Ultrastructural study of host-parasite interactions: II. Decay of lettuce caused by *Botrytis cinerea* and phyllosphere bacteria. Can. J. Bot. 55:2463-2470.

Ogiso, H., and Fujinaga, M. 2008. Occurrence of fungicide resistance in *Botrytis cinerea* and *Sclerotinia sclerotiorum* isolates from commercial lettuce field in Nagano Prefecture. Annu. Rep. Kanto-Tosan Plant Prot. Soc. 55:175-178.

Powell, M., Cowan, J., Miles, C., and Inglis, D. A. 2013. Effect of a High-Tunnel, Organic Cropping System on Lettuce Diseases in Western Washington. Online. Plant Health Progress. doi:10.1094/PHP-2013-0922-01-RS

Sowley, E. N. K., Dewey, F. M., and Shaw, M. W. 2010. Persistent, symptomless, systemic, and seed-borne infection of lettuce by *Botrytis cinerea*. Eur. J. Plant Path. 126:61-71.

Wareing, P. W., Wang, Z.-N., Coley-Smith, J. R., and Jeeves, T. M. 1986. Fungal pathogens in rotted basal leaves of lettuce in Humberside and Lancashire with particular reference to *Rhizoctonia solani*. Plant Pathol. 35:390-395.

Weber, R. W. S., and Wichura, A. 2013. Fungicide resistance of *Botrytis cinerea* on lettuce in Northern Germany. J. Plant Dis. Prot. 120:115-121.

(Prepared by S. T. Koike)

Phoma Leaf Spot and Basal Rot

A disease caused by *Phoma exigua* (current name *Boeremia exigua*) was first reported as a leaf spot and basal rot in greenhouse butterhead lettuce production in the United Kingdom in the early 1990s. Beginning in 2000, this pathogen caused significant damage to the crowns of field-grown romaine in California (United States). In 2012, a different species, *P. tropica*, was reported to cause leaf spots on lettuce grown under plastic tunnels in Italy.

Symptoms

In greenhouse-grown and occasionally in field-grown lettuce in the United Kingdom, *B. exigua* causes the formation of circular to oblong, dark-gray to black leaf spots that can expand up to 3 cm in diameter (Fig. 46). With time, the inner leaf spot tissue can become dry, crack, and fall out, resulting in a shot-hole effect. The fruiting bodies of the pathogen can be observed in leaf spot tissues. This leaf spot phase has not been found on lettuce in the United States.

Symptoms of the basal rot phase include the formation of dark-brown to black, sunken cavities with distinct margins on the crown and the upper taproot tissues (Fig. 47). These cavities are notably dry and firm. Infected internal tissues are black and can extend deep into the crowns and taproots, weakening the plant structure; such a plant can easily be broken off at ground level (Fig. 48). The initial aboveground symptom is stunting.

Fig. 46. Black leaf spot on lettuce caused by *Phoma exigua*, the pathogen that causes Phoma leaf spot and basal rot. (Courtesy T. M. O'Neill—© APS)

Fig. 47. Dark-brown, sunken cavity on a lettuce root, a symptom of the basal rot phase of Phoma leaf spot and basal rot (*Phoma exigua*). (Courtesy S. T. Koike—© APS)

Affected plants later display chlorosis of the lower leaves, wilting of foliage, one-sided growth, and eventual collapse.

The foliar wilting and collapsing symptoms may closely resemble those caused by *Sclerotinia* spp. and *Botrytis cinerea*. These three crown rot pathogens can be differentiated, however, by the texture of the crown rot (i.e., soft and mushy for *B. cinerea* and *Sclerotinia* spp. but very firm and hard for *B. exigua*) and the presence or absence of signs of the pathogen (i.e., fuzzy, gray growth for *B. cinerea*; white mycelium and black sclerotia for *Sclerotinia* spp.; and occasional pycnidia for *B. exigua*).

In Italy, Phoma leaf spot caused by *P. tropica* produces irregularly shaped, dark-brown, necrotic spots that have chlorotic borders. Spots initially range in size from 0.5 to 3.0 mm. In advanced stages of the disease, the spots coalesce, producing large (2–3 cm) lesions and causing the leaves to wither. *P. tropica* has not been found to infect lettuce crowns.

Causal Organisms

In the United Kingdom and the United States, Phoma leaf spot and basal rot is caused by *B. exigua*, a soilborne fungus. The fungus produces dark, ostiolate pycnidia that bear hyaline, straight or slightly curved, ellipsoid or cylindrical conidia that measure 2–4×5–10 µm. Conidia are mostly single celled but can become uniseptate. Pycnidia can be found in leaf spots and sometimes in crown lesions. Most lettuce types are at least somewhat susceptible to this disease, but romaine cultivars appear to be most susceptible.

As noted earlier, in Italy, Phoma leaf spot is caused by *P. tropica*. The disease caused by *P. tropica* is not economically significant (as of early 2017), but continued cultivation of susceptible lettuce cultivars could make it an important disease in the future.

Disease Cycle and Epidemiology

The epidemiology of Phoma leaf spot and basal rot has not been documented. Both pathogens are soilborne, and repeated planting of lettuce into infested soil results in increased disease incidence. For greenhouse-grown lettuce in the United Kingdom, the disease can be more common during the winter months.

Management

Soil should not be kept overly wet, since in the United Kingdom, the disease is associated with wet conditions. Susceptible cultivars, especially romaine types, should not be planted in infested fields. Several fungicides are effective at protecting lettuce crowns from infection.

Fig. 48. *Phoma*-infected lettuce head separated from the root, characteristic of Phoma leaf spot and basal rot. (Courtesy S. T. Koike—© APS)

Selected References

Garibaldi, A., Gilardi, G., Ortu, G., and Gullino, M. L. 2012. First report of leaf spot of lettuce (*Lactuca sativa* L.) caused by *Phoma tropica* in Italy. Plant Dis. 96:1380.

Koike, S. T., Subbarao, K. V., Verkley, G. J. M., Fogle, D., and O'Neill, T. M. 2006. Phoma basal rot of romaine lettuce in California caused by *Phoma exigua*: Occurrence, characterization, and control. Plant Dis. 90:1268-1275.

O'Neill, T. M., and Stokes, D. 2001. Disease Control in Protected Lettuce. HDC Factsheet 07/01. Horticultural Development Council, East Malling, Kent, UK.

O'Neill, T. M., Gladders P., and Ann, D. M. 1997. Prospects for integrated control of lettuce diseases. Pages 485-490 in: Crop Protection and Food Quality—Meeting Customers' Needs. British Crop Protection Council, Farnham, UK.

O'Neill, T. M., Bennison, J., and Gaze, R. H. 2000. Pests and diseases of protected vegetables and mushrooms. Pages 317-373 in: Pest and Disease Management Handbook. D. V. Alford, ed. Blackwell Science, Oxford, UK.

(Prepared by S. T. Koike, K. V. Subbarao, and T. M. O'Neill)

Phytophthora Stem and Root Rot

Several *Phytophthora* spp. have been reported to cause a stem and root rot of lettuce. *P. porri* was initially reported to cause stem rot of lettuce in Greece and Australia, but a subsequent taxonomic analysis of the isolates from Greece placed them in a new species: *P. lactucae*. (Isolates from Australia were not analyzed in the same study, so their taxonomic status is uncertain.)

Symptoms

P. lactucae causes root and stem rot of lettuce. This pathogen eventually causes complete wilting of lettuce heads during the winter growing season.

Causal Organisms

P. lactucae is phylogenetically placed in clade 8b along with other cool-weather pathogens, such as *P. porri* and *P. brassicae*. *P. lactucae* is morphologically similar to other homothallic species within the group. It can be distinguished from *P. brassicae* by antheridial type (i.e., *P. brassicae* has predominantly amphigynous instead of paragynous antheridia), from *P. dauci* by the lower maximum temperature for growth, and from *P. primulae* by the higher growth rate and maximum temperature for growth in culture. *P. lactucae* is host specific and can also be distinguished from other group members based on internal transcribed spacer (ITS), *ypt1*, *nad1*, and *cox*1 sequences.

In Japan, *P. pseudolactucae* has been described as the causal agent of root rot. This pathogen differs from *P. lactucae* primarily by having the sporangia germinate directly and by having a different *cox1* sequence.

P. cryptogea causes a root rot in hydroponically grown lettuce in Arizona (United States), and *P. drechsleri* causes a root rot in Australia, Korea, and Mexico. Identification of isolates as *P. cryptogea* using morphological features can be challenging. Historically, lack of growth at 35°C was one approach used to differentiate *P. cryptogea* from the morphologically similar *P. drechsleri* (although this is not a reliable characteristic). Several mitochondrial and nuclear loci can better differentiate these two species based on DNA sequence.

Disease Cycle and Epidemiology

In general, *P. lactucae* is slow growing in culture medium and can be overgrown by other fungal colonizers when field samples are plated.

43

In Arizona, root and stem necrosis caused by *P. cryptogea* was observed at 18°C and at 28°C; plant death occurred at both temperatures 5–7 days following inoculation. In contrast, in Australia, temperatures below 20°C were found to reduce the incidence of disease caused by *P. drechsleri*.

Management

Control of Phytophthora stem and root rot in hydroponic systems has been reported with the addition of potassium phosphonate (KH_2PO_3 or K_2HPO_3) into the nutrient solution at a rate of 100 ppm. While not experimentally verified, the application of phosphonates or other oomycete-active fungicides (e.g., mefenoxam) might provide control in field production systems.

As with most diseases caused by *Phytophthora* spp., managing water to prevent flooding may also reduce disease incidence. Resistant cultivars have not been identified.

Selected References

Alhussaen, K. 2006. *Pythium* and *Phytophthora* associated with root disease of hydroponic lettuce. Ph.D. diss., University of Technology, Sydney, New South Wales, Australia.

Bertier, L., Brouwer, H., de Cock, A. W. A. M., Cooke, D. E. L., Olsson, C. H. B., and Höfte, M. 2013. The expansion of *Phytophthora* clade 8b: Three new species associated with winter grown vegetable crops. Persoonia 31:63-76.

Elena, K., Grigoriou, A., and Antonopoulos, F. D. 2006. *Phytophthora porri* causing stem rot of lettuce in Greece: First report in Europe. Ann. Benaki Phytopathol. Inst. 20:88-100.

Jee, H.-J., Cho, W.-D., and Kim, C.-H. 2002. Effect of potassium phosphonate on the control of Phytophthora root rot of lettuce in hydroponics. Plant Pathol. J. 18:142-146.

Linde, A. R., Stanghellini, M. E., and Matheron, M. E. 1990. Root rot of hydroponically grown lettuce caused by *Phytophthora cryptogea*. Plant Dis. 74:1037.

Martin, F. N., Blair, J. E., and Coffey, M. D. 2014. A combined mitochondrial and nuclear multilocus phylogeny of the genus *Phytophthora*. Fungal Genet. Biol. 66:19-32.

Rahman, M. Z., Uematsu, S., Kimishima, E., Kanto, T., Kusunoki, M., Motohashi, K., Ishiguro, Y., Suga, H., and Kageyama, K. 2015. Two plant pathogenic species of *Phytophthora* associated with stem blight of Easter lily and crown rot of lettuce. Mycoscience 56:419-433.

Rodriguez-Alvarado, G., Perez-Caliz, M. I., Caudillo-Ruiz, K. B., and Garay-Serrano, E. 2009. Root rot of hydroponically grown lettuce caused by *Phytophthora drechsleri* in Mexico. Plant Dis. 93:1077.

Sitepu, D., and Bumbieris, M. 1981. Stem rot of lettuce caused by a low temperature *Phytophthora porri* in South Australia. Australas. Plant Pathol. 10:59-60.

Sitepu, D., and Wallace, H. R. 1984. Crop Disease Studies. Lettuce Diseases. Biennial Report of the Waite Agricultural Research Institute, 1982-1983. University of Adelaide, South Australia.

(Prepared by F. N. Martin)

Powdery Mildew

Powdery mildew is generally considered a minor problem of lettuce. However, in some regions, under certain conditions, and on some cultivars, the disease can significantly reduce crop quality and cause economic loss. The first authenticated report of lettuce powdery mildew was made in 1941 from California's Salinas Valley (United States). Since then, the disease has been reported from throughout North America, Europe, the Mediterranean area, and Asia.

Symptoms

The initial signs of powdery mildew are tiny, white, mycelial patches that usually develop first on the older, lower leaves of the lettuce plant. Colonies develop on both abaxial and adaxial leaf surfaces. As the disease progresses, the number of

colonies increases and the colonies coalesce and merge, often resulting in the complete blanketing of the leaf with a dusty, white mycelial and conidial layer (Fig. 49). The older leaves are affected most severely. Infected leaves may become chlorotic and display some twisting and buckling. In advanced stages of the disease, leaves may take on a brown, scorched appearance and senesce.

The pathogen can form small, round, dark-brown fruiting bodies (chasmothecia) on leaves (Fig. 50). However, in some regions, such chasmothecia are quite rare.

Fig. 49. Powdery mildew on crisphead lettuce, caused by *Golovinomyces cichoracearum*. (Courtesy S. T. Koike—© APS)

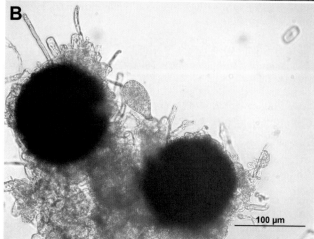

Fig. 50. A, Chasmothecia of *Golovinomyces cichoracearum* on infected lettuce. **B,** Photomicrograph of chasmothecia of *G. cichoracearum* from lettuce (Courtesy A. Lebeda—© APS)

If plants are infected early in the crop cycle, they may be small and of poor quality. With the exception of some resistant butterhead cultivars, most types of lettuce are susceptible.

Causal Organisms

Powdery mildew of lettuce is caused by the ascomycete *Golovinomyces cichoracearum* (syn. *Erysiphe cichoracearum*). The pathogen produces ectophytic mycelium that grows superficially on leaf surfaces and supports the conidiophores. Hyphal appressoria are nipple shaped. Conidia are produced in long chains (euoidium type); are hyaline, single celled, and ellipsoid to ovoid; and lack fibrosin bodies. Conidia measure 14–25 × 25–45 µm and have a length-to-width ratio of approximately 2. Germ tubes from conidia develop mostly from the end walls and terminate in club-shaped appressoria.

G. cichoracearum is heterothallic, so if + and – mating types are present, the chasmothecium sexual stage may be formed. Globose chasmothecia are dark brown; have numerous external myceloid, septate appendages; measure between 85 and 160 µm in diameter; and contain 5–25 asci. Each mature ascus contains two single-celled ascospores, which are ovoid to ellipsoid.

G. cichoracearum is identified in the literature as infecting more than 300 plant species from numerous families. However, host range studies and morphological analyses indicate that *G. cichoracearum* is a complex of morphologically similar but host-specific forms. *G. cichoracearum* from lettuce appears to be specific to *Lactuca* spp. and other genera in the Asteraceae. Cross-inoculation studies have not yet clearly defined this complicated host–pathogen relationship. For example, in one laboratory study, a lettuce isolate of *G. cichoracearum* was able to infect species of *Calendula, Dahlia, Senecio, Helianthus,* and *Zinnia* plus a species of wild lettuce, *L. serriola* (prickly lettuce). In a different study, however, isolates from *Calendula, Picris,* and *Zinnia* failed to infect lettuce. In yet another study, *G. cichoracearum* from wild lettuce did not infect lettuce. More comprehensive studies using standardized methods and materials are needed to clarify the host ranges of *G. cichoracearum* isolates from lettuce and the extent to which lettuce is susceptible to isolates from other Asteraceae hosts. For the *Lactuca*–powdery mildew system, a differential set for determining races has been developed for showing virulence variations of *G. cichoracearum* and race-specific interactions on lettuce and wild lettuce, including *L. saligna*.

Some diversity exists among powdery mildew diseases on lettuce and closely related *Lactuca* spp. In South Korea, powdery mildew caused by *Podosphaera fusca* (syn. *Sphaerotheca fusca*) has been reported on lettuce. In parts of North America, Europe, and Asia, *P. xanthii* has been reported on wild *Lactuca* spp. but apparently not on cultivated lettuce. In France, a pseudoidium type of powdery mildew likely caused by a pathogen in the genus *Erysiphe* was found on pliant lettuce (*L. viminea* subsp. *chondrilliflora*).

Disease Cycle and Epidemiology

G. cichoracearum can apparently overwinter and survive between lettuce crops in either the asexual conidial or sexual chasmothecial stage. Initial inoculum therefore has been associated with either conidia or ascospores from volunteer lettuce, weedy *Lactuca* spp., lettuce crop residue (for ascospores), and perhaps other hosts in the Asteraceae. Both spore types can be readily dispersed long distances by wind. Conidia can germinate at temperatures between 5 and 33°C; the optimum temperature for germination and mycelial growth is 18°C. While conidia can germinate under dry conditions (50–75% relative humidity), maximum spore germination occurs at 96–98% relative humidity; free moisture will inhibit germination. Secondary spread and the development of a powdery mildew epidemic takes place via windborne conidia.

In most regions, powdery mildew occurs on lettuce during the summer through the autumn seasons. Chasmothecia tend to form mostly on leaves that are senescing.

Management

Cultivars that are resistant or tolerant to powdery mildew should be used, although such lines are not generally available for most lettuce types. Some butterhead lettuce cultivars are resistant, and researchers report some differences in susceptibility among other cultivars.

Sulfur-based and other fungicides are useful in protecting plants from powdery mildew if applications are made prior to infection. The use of fungicides with different modes of action will likely reduce the risk of developing fungicide insensitivity.

Crop rotation is less relevant for an airborne disease, such as powdery mildew. Even so, avoiding back-to-back lettuce crops will allow lettuce residues infested with chasmothecia and conidia to decompose before planting another lettuce crop.

Selected References

Deslandes, J. A. 1954. Studies and observations on lettuce powdery mildew. Plant Dis. Rep. 38:560-562.

Koike, S. T., and Saenz, G. S. 1996. Occurrence of powdery mildew, caused by *Erysiphe cichoracearum,* on endive and radicchio in California. Plant Dis. 80:1080.

Lebeda, A., and Mieslerova, B. 2011. Taxonomy, distribution and biology of lettuce powdery mildew (*Golovinomyces cichoracearum sensu stricto*). Plant Pathol. 60:400-415.

Lebeda, A., Mieslerova, B., Dolezalova, I., and Kristkova, E. 2002. Occurrence of powdery mildew on *Lactuca viminea* subsp. *chondrilliflora* in south France. Mycotaxon 84:83-87.

Lebeda, A., Mieslerova, B., Petrzelova, I., Korbelova, P., and Cesnekova, E. 2012. Patterns of virulence variation in the interaction between *Lactuca* spp. and lettuce powdery mildew (*Golovinomyces cichoracearum*). Fungal Ecol. 5:670-682.

Lebeda, A., Mieslerova, B., Petrzelova, I., and Korbelova, P. 2013. Host specificity and virulence variation in populations of lettuce powdery mildew pathogen (*Golovinomyces cichoracearum s. str.*) from prickly lettuce (*Lactuca serriola*). Mycol. Prog. 12:533-545.

Pryor, D. E. 1941. A unique case of powdery mildew on lettuce in the field. Plant Dis. Rep. 25:74.

Schnathorst, W. C. 1959. Heterothallism in the lettuce strain of *Erysiphe cichoracearum.* Mycologia 51:708-711.

Schnathorst, W. C. 1959. Spread and life cycle of the lettuce powdery mildew fungus. Phytopathology 49:464-468.

Schnathorst, W. C. 1960. Effects of temperature and moisture stress on the lettuce powdery mildew fungus. Phytopathology 50:304-308.

Schnathorst, W. C., Grogan, R. G., and Bardin, R. 1958. Distribution, host range, and origin of lettuce powdery mildew. Phytopathology 48:538-543.

Shin, H. D., Jee, H. J., and Shim, C. K. 2006. First report of powdery mildew caused by *Podosphaera fusca* on *Lactuca sativa* in Korea. Plant Pathol. 55:814.

Simko, I., Rauscher, G., Sideman, R. G., McCreight, J. D., and Hayes, R. J. 2014. Evaluation and QTL mapping of resistance to powdery mildew in lettuce. Plant Pathol. 63:344-353.

Turini, T. A., and Koike, S. T. 2002. Comparison of fungicides for control of powdery mildew on iceberg lettuce, 2001. Fung. Nemat. Rep. 57:V042.

(Prepared by S. T. Koike)

Pythium Wilt, Leaf Blight, and Root Rot

In addition to the species of *Pythium* that cause damping-off of lettuce seedlings, several other *Pythium* spp. are associated with wilt, leaf blight, and root rot of lettuce. *P. uncinulatum* causes both damping-off and a root and crown rot of mature plants. In a field in California (United States), the pathogen was associated with yield reductions of about 30%. In winter fields in Japan, *P. uncinulatum* caused wilt and a root rot of plants at the heading stage.

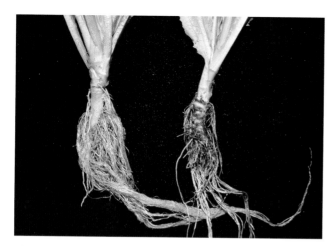

Fig. 51. Romaine lettuce roots infected by a *Pythium* sp. (Courtesy R. M. Davis—© APS)

Symptoms

Symptoms caused by *P. uncinulatum* include general stunting of plants, yellowing of the outer leaves, and dark-yellow to brown discoloration of the taproots of maturing lettuce. The root systems are reduced, and the root tips are necrotic (Fig. 51).

Causal Organisms

As noted earlier, several other *Pythium* spp. have been reported on the roots and lower leaves of lettuce, including *P. aphanidermatum, P. megalacanthum, P. polymastum, P. spinosum, P. tracheiphilum,* and *P. ultimum. P. tracheiphilum* also causes a wilt of lettuce. Overall, the damage to lettuce caused by these fungi has been minor.

Disease Cycle and Epidemiology

Spiny oogonia of *P. uncinulatum* encase aplerotic oospores, which probably serve as overwintering structures in the soil. Motile zoospores are produced from globose sporangia. Based on greenhouse pathogenicity tests, *P. uncinulatum* is primarily a pathogen of composites. Isolates from Japan failed to cause symptoms on spinach, melon, tomato, pepper, onion, carrot, radish, cabbage, broccoli, and other crucifers. In the Netherlands, at least one of three isolates of *P. uncinulatum* was weakly pathogenic on seedlings of cauliflower, tomato, cucumber, pea, and flax (*Linum usitatissimum*). No symptoms developed on carrot, radish, leek (*Allium porrum*), or wheat. All three isolates were highly virulent on lettuce.

Management

Specific control measures are generally not warranted for Pythium wilt, leaf blight, and root rot. Even so, it is prudent to prevent infection by minimizing periods of excessive moisture. Methods such as providing good drainage, planting on raised beds, and maintaining dry bed tops typically reduce the diseases caused by *Pythium* spp.

Selected References

Blok, I., and Van der Plaats-Niterink, A. J. 1978. *Pythium uncinulatum* sp. nov. and *P. tracheiphilum* pathogenic to lettuce. Neth. J. Plant Pathol. 84:135-147.

Davis, R. M., Winterbottom, C. Q., and Aquiar, J. L. 1995. First report of *Pythium uncinulatum* on romaine lettuce in California. Plant Dis. 79:642.

Matsuura, K., Kanto, T., Tojo, M., Uzuhashi, S., and Kakishima, M. 2010. Pythium wilt of lettuce caused by *Pythium uncinulatum* in Japan. J. Gen. Plant Pathol. 76:320–323.

Tortolero, O., and Sequeira, L. 1978. A vascular wilt and leaf blight disease of lettuce in Wisconsin caused by a new strain of *Pythium tracheiphilum*. Plant Dis. Rep. 62:616-620.

Van Beneden, S., Pannecoucque, J., Debode, J., De Backer, G., and Höfte, M. 2008. Characterisation of fungal pathogens causing basal rot of lettuce in Belgian greenhouses. Eur. J. Plant Pathol. 124:9-19.

Van der Plaats-Niterink, A. J. 1981. Monograph of the Genus *Pythium*. Studies in Mycology, no. 21. Centraalbureau voor Schimmelcultures, Baarn, the Netherlands.

(Prepared by R. M. Davis)

Septoria Leaf Spot

Septoria leaf spot of lettuce is distributed widely and has been reported in North and South America, Europe, Asia, Africa, and the South Pacific region. The disease was first identified in Italy in 1878. Although it is now found in many countries, the disease generally occurs sporadically and becomes economically important only under conditions of prolonged high humidity and leaf wetness.

Symptoms

Leaf spots first appear on the oldest foliage of the lettuce plant and later spread to the younger leaves. Initial symptoms consist of small (<5 mm), chlorotic leaf spots that are irregular and somewhat vein delimited. As the disease progresses, the spots enlarge, turn brown, and desiccate (Fig. 52). The tissue in dried spots may tear and fall out, creating holes in the leaves. Leaf spots vary in shape from irregular to circular, depending on the lettuce cultivar infected. Chlorotic halos may surround the spots. On severely infected leaves, the lesions may coalesce, resulting in extensive necrosis and drying. Numerous dark-brown to black pycnidia develop in the leaf spots (Fig. 53).

On lettuce plants grown for seed, the pathogen can produce spots on leaves, flower stalks, flower bracts, and flowers. Pycnidia may be observed on the external surfaces of lettuce seed.

Causal Organisms

More than six *Septoria* spp. have been reported on lettuce, but Septoria leaf spot is caused primarily by *S. lactucae* and *S. birgitae*. A comprehensive comparison of the various *Septoria* spp. on lettuce has not been completed, however, and relationships between the species are unclear.

The morphological characters of *S. lactucae* and *S. birgitae* overlap somewhat. Both species produce numerous subglobose, immersed pycnidia that later become erumpent and release conidia through ostioles. The filiform conidia are hyaline, vary greatly in length and measure $14 - 25 – 40 - 50 \times 1$–$2$ µm, and have from zero to three septa. *Septoria* spp. are seedborne in lettuce, and pycnidia form in the seed coat.

Fig. 52. Brown spots on romaine lettuce leaves, characteristic of Septoria leaf spot (*Septoria* spp.). (Courtesy S. T. Koike—© APS)

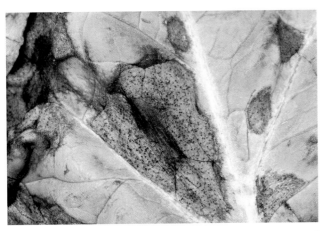

Fig. 53. Pycnidia produced by a *Septoria* sp., symptomatic of Septoria leaf spot. (Courtesy S. T. Koike—© APS)

The host range of these pathogens is narrow and includes only cultivated lettuce and weedy *Lactuca* spp., such as the wild lettuce species *L. serriola* (prickly lettuce) and *L. virosa*.

Disease Cycle and Epidemiology

The pathogens survive in lettuce seed, and transport of infested seed enables the pathogens to travel long distances and move between countries and regions. Once infested seed is planted, the pathogens can develop on germinated seedlings and cause disease. Humid or wet weather stimulates the release of conidia in the form of spore tendrils, and splashing water spreads the tendrils and conidia to uninfected plants. Prolonged high humidity and leaf wetness are required for infection.

Between crops, the pathogens can survive in lettuce crop residue and on *Lactuca* weeds and volunteer lettuce plants. These *Septoria* spp. can survive only a maximum of 3 months in the soil, especially once the level of crop residue has dissipated.

Management

Planting pathogen-free and/or treated seed is the important first step in managing Septoria leaf spot. Seed crops should be grown in areas with limited rainfall or in which Septoria leaf spot is not common on either cultivated or wild lettuce. This practice has already reduced the transmission of *Septoria* pathogens on lettuce seed. Hot-water seed treatments (47–48°C for 30 min) can greatly decrease the level of seedborne inoculum; however, one study found a 16% reduction in germination for treated 1-year-old seed.

Cultivars that are resistant to *S. lactucae* are not available, but there are significant differences in susceptibility among some cultivars. Because infested lettuce debris may be a source of inoculum for subsequent lettuce crops, crop rotations and planting schedules should be implemented that allow sufficient time for decomposition of plant residue. Overhead sprinkler irrigation encourages infection, disease development, and spread of inoculum and should therefore be avoided.

Selected References

Bedlan, G. 1999. *Septoria birgitae,* a new pathogen causing leaf spots on *Lactuca sativa*. Mycotaxon 70:51-53.

Bertus, A. L. 1972. The eradication of seedborne *Septoria lactucae* from lettuce with aerated steam. J. Hort. Sci. 47:259-261.

Lohmeier, U., Farahani-Kofoet, R. D., Kofoet, A., and Grosch, R. 2013. Factors affecting incidence and severity of leaf spot disease on lettuce caused by *Septoria birgitae*. Ann. Appl. Biol. 162:221-230.

Moore, W. C. 1940. New and interesting plant diseases. Trans. Br. Mycol. Soc. 24:345-351.

Nao, M. 2008. Effects of inoculum density, leaf wetness duration and nitrate concentration on the occurrence of lettuce leaf spot. J. Gen. Plant Pathol. 74:208-212.

Punithalingam, E., and Holliday, P. 1972. *Septoria lactucae*. Descriptions of Pathogenic Fungi and Bacteria, no. 335. Commonwealth Mycological Institute, Kew, Surrey, UK.

Smith, P. R. 1961. Seedborne *Septoria* in lettuce: Eradication by hot water treatment. J. Dep. Agric. Victoria 59:555-556.

Sousa, C. S., Kerr, W. E., Santos, M. R., Arruda, A. S., Spini, V. B. M. G., Juliatti, F. C., and Takatsu, A. 2003. Lettuce Septoria leaf spot: Isolation, inoculation, cultivar evaluation in field and greenhouse conditions. Fitopatol. Bras. 28:555-558.

(Prepared by S. T. Koike)

Southern Blight

Southern blight has been reported from nearly every country between the northern and southern latitudes of 38°. Favored by warm temperatures, this disease is especially rampant in the subtropics and tropics. The name "southern blight" is derived from the prevalence of the disease in the southeastern United States. Other common names of southern blight are "southern stem rot" and "Sclerotium stem rot."

First reported on tomato in Florida in 1892, the pathogen has since been reported on hundreds of plant species, including monocots and dicots. Its host range includes many economically important ornamental, field, and vegetable crops, including lettuce. Fortunately, the low to moderate temperature requirements of the crop limit the impact of this pathogen on lettuce. The pathogen's prolific growth, persistence in soil, and extensive host range make southern blight extremely difficult to control.

Symptoms

Initially, water-soaked areas develop on the stem at or near the soil surface. Infections typically arise at canopy closure because of the increased humidity and foliar contact with the soil. From this point, the pathogen spreads down into the root system or up into the canopy. Leaf petioles are frequently rotted at the stem base, causing leaves to wilt. Infected basal stems eventually turn light to dark brown, and the entire plant may collapse (Fig. 54). White, stringlike mycelia, radiating out from the stem base, often develop on the soil surface beneath the collapsed heads (Fig. 55), followed soon by the development of small, almost spherical, light- to dark-brown sclerotia. The final symptoms on lettuce closely resemble those of lettuce drop, bottom rot, and soft rot (Fig. 56).

Fig. 54. Romaine lettuce head infected with *Athelia rolfsii*, the pathogen that causes southern blight. (Courtesy R. N. Raid—© APS)

Causal Organism

The causal agent of southern blight is *Athelia rolfsii* (syn. *Sclerotium rolfsii*). It is readily cultured on most general media, where basidial formation is influenced by the isolate, nutrient status, light intensity, and age of the culture. White mycelium is produced in abundance. The coarse hyphae consist of cells that measure 2–9 × 150–250 μm, and clamp connections are present. Sclerotia are initially white but become light tan to dark brown; they are spherical and 0.50–1.55 mm in diameter. The teleomorph produces an exposed hymenium with clavate basidia. Basidiospores are hyaline, pyriform, and 1.0–1.7 × 6–12 μm.

Disease Cycle and Epidemiology

A. rolfsii can survive for many years as sclerotia in the soil or host plant debris. Strongly saprophytic, the fungus is also capable of producing abundant growth on various host substrates. It produces oxalic acid, cellulolytic enzymes, and pectinolytic enzymes, facilitating direct hyphal penetration of nonwounded tissues. Volatile compounds produced by senescent plant tissues appear to stimulate sclerotial germination.

Fig. 55. White mycelial web on lettuce and surrounding soil produced by *Athelia rolfsii*, causal agent of southern blight. (Courtesy R. N. Raid—© APS)

Fig. 56. Final symptoms of southern blight (*Athelia rolfsii*) resemble those of lettuce drop, bottom rot, and soft rot, resulting in total collapse of infected lettuce heads. (Courtesy R. N. Raid—© APS)

Mycelial growth develops at temperatures ranging from 8 to 40°C, but growth is greatly inhibited at temperatures below 15°C. Mycelium is killed at freezing temperatures, but sclerotia can withstand temperatures as cold as –10°C. The prevalence of the fungus in warm climates is reflective of its relatively high optimum temperature range (27–30°C).

Moist soil conditions also favor disease development, and serious outbreaks are often associated with unusually wet conditions. Acidic soils seem to favor the disease, as well, while highly alkaline, calcareous soils appear to be inhibitory.

Southern blight is influenced by certain forms of fertilizer. Disease incidence may be reduced by the use of ammoniacal nitrogen sources and fertilizers that contain plant-available calcium.

As with many other soilborne diseases, southern blight is typically distributed in clusters in the field. The pathogen is disseminated by cultivation and tillage equipment, movement in irrigation and drainage water, and movement of infested soil or debris. The role of the sexual stage in the epidemiology of southern blight has not been firmly established.

Management

Because of the crop's relatively cool temperature requirements, southern blight of lettuce is usually not important enough to warrant control measures in most lettuce-growing regions. In subtropical areas, planting should be planned to take advantage of the cooler growing seasons.

Although crop rotation by itself is not an effective or practical method of management, rotating from lettuce to a crop unaffected by the pathogen (e.g., corn or a small grain) may result in less disease in subsequent years. Deep plowing that buries sclerotia and infected debris deep in the soil reduces their viability as sources of inoculum.

Many fungicides have been tried as soil amendments, but most are too expensive to use or cause injuries to the crop at the rates required for effective disease control. Whereas soil fumigation is generally cost prohibitive for lettuce, soil solarization has proven successful in reducing soil inoculum levels in some areas. Biological control and host plant resistance are two management measures under investigation.

Selected References

Aycock, R. 1966. Stem rot and other diseases caused by *Sclerotium rolfsii*. N.C. Agric. Exp. Stn. Tech. Bull. 174.

Baxter, L. W., Jr., Witcher, W., Fagan, S. G., and Owen, M. G. 1977. Control of southern stem blight of tomatoes by physical means. Plant Dis. Rep. 61:341-342.

Garren, K. H. 1961. Control of *Sclerotium rolfsii* through cultural practices. Phytopathology 51:120-124.

Jenkins, S. F., and Averre, C. W. 1986. Problems and progress in integrated control of southern blight of vegetables. Plant Dis. 70:614-619.

Mullen, J. 2001. Southern Blight, Southern Stem Blight, White Mold. The Plant Health Instructor. doi:10.1094/PHI-I-2001-0104-01

Punja, Z. K. 1985. The biology, ecology, and control of *Sclerotium rolfsii*. Annu. Rev. Phytopathol. 23:97-127.

(Prepared by R. N. Raid)

Stemphylium Leaf Spot

A leaf spot of lettuce linked to the genus *Stemphylium* was first reported in England in 1931. It has since been reported in many areas of the world, including other European countries, Israel, South Africa, the United States, and, most recently, China and Malaysia. While typically of limited significance in the field, Stemphylium leaf spot has the potential to be an important storage disease, particularly when a crop undergoes prolonged storage or shipping.

Symptoms

Leaf lesions initially appear as small, round, brown, often zonate spots, which are usually 2–3 mm in diameter (Fig. 57). The spots frequently appear to be sunken in the center, because the tissue has become necrotic. In larger lesions, the necrotic center occasionally falls out, leaving a small hole. Field infections on crisphead lettuce are typically confined to the mature outer leaves and may be associated with leafminer (*Liriomyza* spp.) damage and other predisposing factors. During periods of long storage, the lesions often enlarge, eventually covering large areas of leaves.

Depending on the conditions and length of time in storage, the fungus may penetrate adjoining tissues and continue to develop, resulting in significant decay of the product during shipment. In addition, *Stemphylium* infections frequently provide opportunities for secondary infections by soft rot bacteria.

Causal Organisms

In Malaysia and China, *Stemphylium solani* has been implicated as the causal agent, whereas in most other regions of the world, *S. botryosum* f. sp. *lactucum* (syn. *Pleospora tarda*) is generally acknowledged as the cause of this leaf spot. Although lettuce isolates do not differ morphologically from the *S. botryosum* isolates from other hosts, in various host range studies, they have demonstrated a strong (although not absolute) specialization for lettuce, cross-infecting only carrot. The fungus is easily cultured on potato dextrose agar.

Mycelium is branched, septate, and olivaceous green to brown. Conidiophores are short, rigid, olivaceous, and septate; they are seldom branched and have bulbous apical swellings. Conidia are dark, muriform, and oblong to rectangular; in culture, they are occasionally borne in very short chains (two to four spores long). The ascigerous form produces brown to black, uniloculate, ostiolate pseudothecia, which are scattered and immersed in host tissue. Asci are bitunicate and cylindrical–clavate; they have short stalks and six to eight spores. Ascospores are dictyosporous, ellipsoidal, oblong to clavate, and yellow to dark brown.

Fig. 57. Green oak leaf lettuce, grown for spring mix production, with small, brown lesions, characteristic of Stemphylium leaf spot (*Stemphylium botryosum* f. sp. *lactucum*). (Courtesy R. N. Raid—© APS)

Disease Cycle and Epidemiology

The organisms survive saprophytically on lettuce debris in the field. The pathogens may also survive and be distributed on infested seed. Mycelial growth occurs over the range of 13–37°C, with optimum growth at 27°C. While the optimum temperature range for sporulation is rather broad (17–30°C), germination is favored by the upper limits of this range (27–30°C).

High humidity or free moisture is particularly important during the early stages of infection; therefore, the disease is most prevalent in moist, humid climates and during wet seasons. Limited airflow through the thick canopy may produce highly favorable conditions for extended leaf wetness and hence, disease development.

Windborne spores germinate to produce germ tubes, which penetrate lettuce tissues through stomatal openings. Colonizing hyphae kill the host tissue in advance of mycelial growth, but this growth appears to be limited in healthy tissue. For this reason, field infections are frequently limited to the four outermost foliar layers. The fungi resume development when infected leaves fall to the ground or harvested heads are placed in storage.

The importance of the asexual stage in the epidemiology of the disease has been clearly established, but little is known about the importance of the ascigerous stage of *S. botryosum* f. sp. *lactucum* (*P. tarda*). In the case of spring mix production, in which lettuce is densely planted for "baby leaf" using large quantities of seed (>2 million/ha), seed infestation can be an important factor.

Management

Crop rotation and sanitation are generally recommended for reducing levels of primary inoculum in the field. Overhead irrigation should be avoided, if possible, to avoid extended periods of leaf wetness.

The application of foliar fungicides, when warranted, also reduces disease severity. Seed fungicide treatments may be beneficial, particularly when lettuce seed is intended for densely planted spring mix production.

The trimming of infected wrapper leaves at the time of harvest has been suggested as a method of limiting postharvest losses. Maintaining proper refrigeration and moisture conditions during transit is also important.

Efforts are ongoing to incorporate host plant resistance to Stemphylium leaf spot into commercially acceptable cultivars.

Selected References

Brophy, G., and Clancy, K. J. 1989. Evaluation of lettuce cultivar susceptibility to *Stemphylium botryosum* using whole plants and detached leaves. Tests Agrochem. Cultiv. 114 (Suppl.):142-143.

Clancy, K. J., and Brophy, G. 1989. Evaluation of six fungicides for control of Stemphylium leaf spot of lettuce. Tests Agrochem. Cultiv. 114 (Suppl.):46-47.

Nasehi, A., Kadir, J. B., Esfahani, M. N., Mahmodi, F., Ghadirian, H., Ashtiani, F. A., and Soleimani, N. 2013. Leaf spot on lettuce (*Lactuca sativa*) caused by *Stemphylium solani,* a new disease in Malaysia. Plant Dis. 97:689.

Netzer, D., Globerson, D., Weintal, C. H., and Elyassi, R. 1985. Sources and inheritance of resistance to Stemphylium leaf spot of lettuce. Euphytica 34:393-396.

Padhi, B., and Snyder, W. C. 1954. Stemphylium leaf spot of lettuce. Phytopathology 44:175-180.

Sivan, J., and Barkai-Golan, R. 1976. *Stemphylium botryosum* f. sp. *lactucae*—Its development *in vitro* and its pathogenicity to lettuce leaves. Ann. Appl. Biol. 82:425-432.

(Prepared by R. N. Raid)

Texas Root Rot

Texas root rot is considered a minor disease of lettuce. The causal organism, *Phymatotrichopsis omnivora* (syn. *Phymato-*

trichum omnivorum), is an important pathogen of cotton in the southeastern United States and attacks more than 2,000 species of dicotyledonous plants.

Symptoms of Texas root rot generally include yellowing or bronzing of young leaves, followed by sudden wilting and death of the plant. Brown, threadlike strands of hyphae encompass the roots and grow toward the soil surface. Near the surface, a cottony mycelial growth often appears.

P. omnivora grows best in alkaline, calcareous, clay soils with minimal organic matter. Methods of management are based on increasing the organic matter and microbial activity of the soil. Four-year cycles of crop rotation with monocots (especially those that return a large amount of crop residue to the soil) have been shown to improve crop yields.

Selected References

Lyda, S. D. 1978. Ecology of *Phymatotrichum omnivorum*. Annu. Rev. Phytopathol. 16:193-209.

Riggs, J. L. 2001. Phymatotrichum root rot. Pages 31-32 in: Compendium of Cotton Diseases. 2nd ed. T. L. Kirkpatrick and C. S. Rothrock, eds. American Phytopathological Society, St. Paul, MN.

Streets, R. B., and Bloss, H. E. 1973. Phymatotrichum Root Rot. Monogr. 8. American Phytopathological Society, St. Paul, MN.

(Prepared by H. J. Kendrick)

Verticillium Wilt

Verticillium wilt affects many vegetable, fiber, oil-seed, fruit, and nut crops, as well as herbaceous and woody ornamentals, forest trees, and various weeds. The causal pathogen is commonly found in agricultural soils in temperate regions around the world.

On lettuce, Verticillium wilt was first recorded in California (United States) in 1995, and it has also been reported from Greece and Italy. Concern over Verticillium wilt of lettuce is increasing in California. The disease is spreading, has caused heavy losses in all types of lettuce, and is difficult to control.

Symptoms

The first symptom of Verticillium wilt is brown discoloration of the vasculature in the tips of lateral roots. As the discoloration progresses into the taproot and the stem (Figs. 58 and 59), the first foliar symptoms appear as early as at the rosette stage. Leaf symptoms include angular, necrotic lesions starting from the leaf margins, along with chlorosis and wilting (Fig. 60). Following head formation, the outer leaves die but remain appressed to the head (Fig. 61). Microsclerotia (the survival structures of the pathogen) may be visible as black dots along the veins of the outer leaves and may also form on the roots (Fig. 62).

Following necrosis of the outer leaves and just before the crop reaches market maturity, the disease progresses quickly toward the center of the head, killing the plant (Fig. 63). Crisphead lettuce cultivars are most susceptible to Verticillium wilt, but the disease has been recorded on all types of lettuce grown in California.

Verticillium wilt can be confused with Fusarium wilt. In Fusarium wilt, the discoloration of the vasculature is reddish brown, whereas in Verticillium wilt, it is greenish brown. Also, in Fusarium wilt, the discoloration can extend into the leaves of the head and may be limited to only one side of the plant.

Causal Organisms

Verticillium wilt is caused primarily by the fungus *Verticillium dahliae,* which can be cultured from infested soil or plant tissues on a variety of growth media, including the semiselec-

Fig. 58. Vascular discoloration of lettuce taproots, stems, and leaves caused by Verticillium wilt (*Verticillium dahliae*). (Courtesy K. V. Subbarao—© APS)

Fig. 59. Brown discoloration in the vertical section of the lettuce taproot, caused by Verticillium wilt (*Verticillium dahliae*). (Courtesy K. V. Subbarao—© APS)

Fig. 60. Crisphead lettuce head with foliar symptoms of Verticillium wilt (*Verticillium dahliae*) (left) compared with a healthy lettuce head (right). (Courtesy K. V. Subbarao—© APS)

Fig. 61. A, Crisphead lettuce field severely affected by Verticillium wilt (*Verticillium dahliae*). **B,** The outer leaves have died but remain appressed to the head. (Courtesy K. V. Subbarao—© APS)

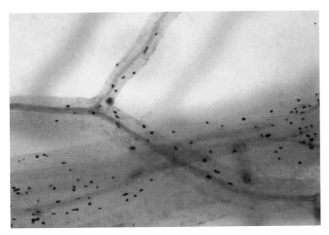

Fig. 62. Microsclerotia of *Verticillium dahliae* on infected lettuce roots. (Courtesy K. V. Subbarao—© APS)

Fig. 63. Mature crisphead lettuce plants killed by Verticillium wilt (*Verticillium dahliae*). (Courtesy K. V. Subbarao—© APS)

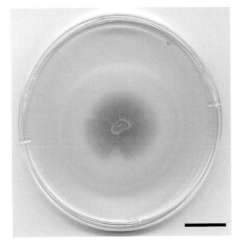

Fig. 64. *Verticillium dahliae* colony on potato dextrose agar. (Scale bar = 2 cm.) (Courtesy P. Inderbitzin—© APS)

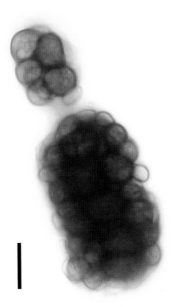

Fig. 65. Microsclerotia of the fungus *Verticillium dahliae* from culture. (Scale bar = 20 µm.) (Courtesy P. Inderbitzin—© APS)

tive NP-10 medium. Colonies on potato dextrose agar measure 2–3 cm across after 1 week of growth; they are white at the margins and dark brown to black in the centers (Fig. 64). The dark color is caused by the production of microsclerotia inside the agar medium. Microsclerotia are small, brown structures and round to elongate; they measure 25–100 µm across and are composed of thick-walled, melanized cells (Fig. 65). Spores (conidia) are colorless, one celled, and cylindrical to oval; they are 5–8 µm long and 2.5–3.5 µm wide (Fig. 66). Conidia accumulate at the tips of narrow, elongate, conidiogenous cells (phialides) and form small, sticky drops (Fig. 67).

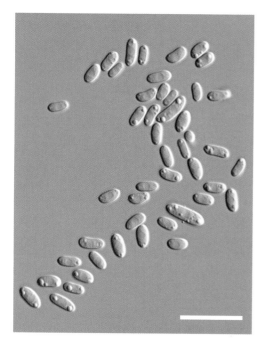

Fig. 66. Conidia of the fungus *Verticillium dahliae* from culture. (Scale bar = 20 μm.) (Courtesy P. Inderbitzin—© APS)

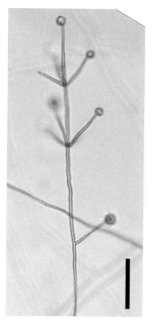

Fig. 67. Phialides on a conidiophore of *Verticillium dahliae* accumulating droplets of conidia. (Scale bar = 50 μm.) (Courtesy P. Inderbitzin—© APS)

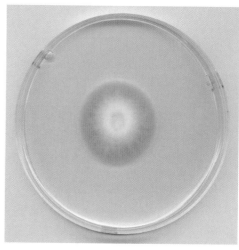

Fig. 68. Colony of *Verticillium isaacii* that has produced the characteristic yellow pigment. (Courtesy P. Inderbitzin—© APS)

Two races of *V. dahliae* have been described, race 1 and race 2, and they can be distinguished by a diagnostic polymerase chain reaction (PCR) assay. Both races are widespread in California. Resistance results from recognition of the *V. dahliae* effector protein, Ave1, by the lettuce immune receptor, Vr1. Race 2 lacks the *Ave1* gene and is thus not recognized by Vr1, resulting in disease.

V. dahliae is not host specific and infects many other crops, including mint (*Mentha* spp..), potato, spinach, and tomato, as well as common weeds. In greenhouse pathogenicity tests, *V. dahliae* isolates from lettuce were also found to be pathogenic on artichoke (*Cynara scolymus*), chili pepper (*Capsicum annuum*), cotton, eggplant, tomato, and watermelon, and *V. dahliae* isolates from bell pepper, chili pepper, cotton, eggplant, potato, strawberry, tomato, and watermelon also caused disease on lettuce.

Two additional *Verticillium* spp., *V. isaacii* and *V. klebahnii,* cause Verticillium wilt in lettuce. However, the symptoms they produce are generally less severe than those produced by *V. dahliae,* and these two pathogens are less important as agents of Verticillium wilt than *V. dahliae.* Lettuce cultivars resistant to *V. dahliae* race 1 are also resistant to *V. isaacii* and *V. klebahnii. V. isaacii* and *V. klebahnii* have a much narrower host range and geographic distribution than *V. dahliae.* The three species can be identified by PCR assay and by DNA sequencing. Also, colonies of *V. isaacii* and *V. klebahnii* produce yellow or orange pigments (Fig. 68), resting mycelium, and chlamydospores (Fig. 69)—all of which are absent in *V. dahliae. V. isaacii* and *V. klebahnii* are morphologically identical and can be differentiated only by PCR assay and by DNA sequencing.

Disease Cycle and Epidemiology

Verticillium spp. are soilborne and initiate infection at the beginning of the season. Hyphae penetrate near the root tips and grow into the xylem (the water-conductive part of the vasculature). Inside the xylem, the infection moves up into the stem and leaves. Six to eight weeks after the initial infection, the first symptoms appear inside the taproot, and over the next 2 weeks, the first foliar symptoms develop on the outer leaves. Near vegetative maturity of the plant, the foliar symptoms progress rap-

idly toward the center and the plant collapses. Floral tissues (including seeds) can also be infected (Fig. 70).

Microsclerotia form on symptomatic leaves and remain viable in the soil for at least 14 years. Conidia may form on dead tissue, but their role in survival and spread is limited. The fungi survive as microsclerotia and other resting structures in soil and seed, and the disease is spread through infested soil, plant debris, and seed. Infested seed, in particular, can transport *Verticillium* strains over long distances. This has been documented for *V. dahliae* from lettuce grown in California that was introduced repeatedly with spinach seed from Washington State and northern Europe. To minimize the risk of introducing new strains, some jurisdictions prohibit the importation of seed infested with *V. dahliae.*

Verticillium wilt is a monocyclic disease, and secondary inoculum is not produced. The threshold for infection of lettuce is 100 microsclerotia per gram of soil—much higher than for other hosts. (For example, strawberry has a threshold of 2–3 microsclerotia per gram of soil.) In the Salinas Valley of California, symptoms are more severe in the fall crop compared with the spring crop, possibly because of higher temperatures promoting fungal growth in the summer and fall.

Management

Verticillium wilt is difficult to eradicate once established. For this reason, it is crucial to prevent spread of the disease into new areas.

Using clean seed is essential, including the seed of a crop grown in rotation with lettuce, because *Verticillium* spp. can infest the seeds of different crops and are not host specific. Seed treatments to reduce *Verticillium* infestation are available for some crops.

To avoid pathogen movement between fields, soil should be removed from farm equipment before it is used in a new field. Soil should be removed even if symptoms of Verticillium wilt are absent, because the pathogens may be present in the soil in quantities below the threshold for causing a noticeable level of disease.

Crop rotation is ineffective because of the long-term viability of microsclerotia in the soil and the wide host range of *V. dahl-*

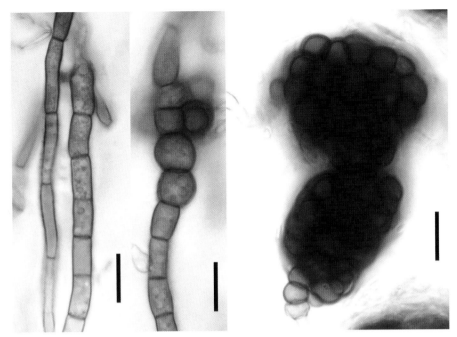

Fig. 69. Pigmented *Verticillium klebahnii* hyphae (left), chlamydospores (center), and microsclerotia (right). (Scale bars = 20 μm.) (Courtesy P. Inderbitzin—© APS)

Fig. 70. Lettuce seed covered in *Verticillium dahliae* mycelium expressing green fluorescent protein. (Courtesy G. E. Vallad and K. V. Subbarao—Reproduced, by permission, from Vallad and Subbarao, 2008)

iae. Some hosts, including broccoli, are resistant to Verticillium wilt and can serve as alternatives to lettuce. Planting time also impacts the severity of Verticillium wilt, which on lettuce is more severe during the warmer months.

Once Verticillium wilt has been established, management should focus on reducing the soil population of microsclerotia, which has traditionally been achieved by fumigation. No fumigation treatments are currently available that match the efficacy of methyl bromide, which was banned because of environmental concerns. Incorporation of broccoli residue into the soil can effectively reduce the number of microsclerotia, but this method has not been tested with the extremely high levels of microsclerotia that may be encountered in lettuce fields.

Host resistance is available only against *V. dahliae* race 1 and *V. isaacii* and *V. klebahnii* (but not *V. dahliae* race 2). Lettuce cultivars with resistance against race 1 include La Brillante, Little Gem, and others. No resistant cultivars are currently available against race 2.

Selected References

Atallah, Z. K., Maruthachalam, K., du Toit, L., Koike, S. T., Davis, R. M., Klosterman, S. J., Hayes, R. J., and Subbarao, K. V. 2010. Population analyses of the vascular plant pathogen *Verticillium dahliae* detect recombination and transcontinental gene flow. Fungal Genet. Biol. 47:416-422.

Atallah, Z. K., Maruthachalam, K., Vallad, G. E., Davis, R. M., Klosterman, S. J., and Subbarao, K. V. 2011. Analysis of *Verticillium dahliae* suggests a lack of correlation between genotypic diversity and virulence phenotypes. Plant Dis. 95:1224-1232.

de Jonge, R., van Esse, P. H., Maruthachalam, K., Bolton, M. D., Santhanam, P., Saber, M. K., Zhang, Z., Usami, T., Lievens, B., Subbarao, K. V., and Thomma, B. P. H. J. 2012. Tomato immune receptor Ve1 recognizes effector of multiple fungal pathogens uncovered by genome and RNA sequencing. Proc. Natl. Acad. Sci. U.S.A. 109:5110-5115.

du Toit, L. J., and Hernandez-Perez, P. 2005. Efficacy of hot water and chlorine for eradication of *Cladosporium variabile, Stemphylium botryosum*, and *Verticillium dahliae* from spinach seed. Plant Dis. 89:1305-1312.

Garibaldi, A., Gilardi, G., and Gullino, M. L. 2007. First report of verticillium wilt caused by *Verticillium dahliae* on lettuce in Italy. Plant Dis. 91:770.

Gurung, S., Short, D. P. G., Hu, X., Sandoya, G. V., Hayes, R. J., Koike, S. T., and Subbarao, K. V. 2015. Host range of *Verticillium isaacii* and *Verticillium klebahnii* from artichoke, spinach, and lettuce. Plant Dis. 99:933-938.

Hayes, R. J., Vallad, G. E., Qin, Q.-M., Grube, R. C., and Subbarao, K. V. 2007. Variation for resistance to Verticillium wilt in lettuce (*Lactuca sativa* L.). Plant Dis. 91:439-445.

Hayes, R. J., McHale, L., Vallad, G., Truco, M., Michelmore, R., Klosterman, S., Maruthachalam, K., and Subbarao, K. 2011. The inheritance of resistance to Verticillium wilt caused by race 1 isolates of *Verticillium dahliae* in the lettuce cultivar La Brillante. Theor. Appl. Gen. 123:509-517.

Inderbitzin, P., and Subbarao, K. V. 2014. *Verticillium* systematics and evolution: How confusion impedes Verticillium wilt management and how to resolve it. Phytopathology 104:564-574.

Inderbitzin, P., Bostock, R. M., Davis, R. M., Usami, T., Platt, H. W., and Subbarao, K. V. 2011. Phylogenetics and taxonomy of the fungal vascular wilt pathogen *Verticillium,* with the descriptions of five new species. PLoS ONE 6:e28341.

Inderbitzin, P., Davis, R. M., Bostock, R. M., and Subbarao, K. V. 2013. Identification and differentiation of *Verticillium* species and *V. longisporum* lineages by simplex and multiplex PCR assays. PLoS One 8:e65990.

Kabir, Z., Bhat, R. G., and Subbarao, K. V. 2004. Comparison of media for recovery of *Verticillium dahliae* from soil. Plant Dis. 88:49-55.

Ligoxigakis, E. K., Vakalounakis, D. J., and Thanassoulopoulos, C. C. 2002. Host range of *Verticillium dahliae* in cultivated species in Crete. Phytoparasitica 30:141-146.

Maruthachalam, K., Atallah, Z. K., Vallad, G. E., Klosterman, S. J., Hayes, R. J., Davis, R. M., and Subbarao, K. V. 2010. Molecular variation among isolates of *Verticillium dahliae* and polymerase chain reaction-based differentiation of races. Phytopathology 100:1222-1230.

Pegg, G. F., and Brady, B. L. 2002. Verticillium wilts. CABI, Wallingford, Oxon, UK.

Qin, Q.-M., Vallad, G. E., Wu, B. M., and Subbarao, K. V. 2006. Phylogenetic analyses of phytopathogenic isolates of *Verticillium* spp. Phytopathology 96:582-592.

Sorensen, L. H., Schneider, A. T., and Davis, J. R. 1991. Influence of sodium polygalacturonate sources and improved recovery of *Verticillium* spp. from soil. (Abstr.) Phytopathology 81:1347.

Subbarao, K. V. 2002. Introduction. Phytopathology 92:1334-1336.

Subbarao, K. V., Hubbard, J. C., and Koike, S. T. 1999. Evaluation of broccoli residue incorporation into field soil for Verticillium wilt control in cauliflower. Plant Dis. 83:124-129.

Vallad, G. E., and Subbarao, K. V. 2008. Colonization of resistant and susceptible lettuce cultivars by a green fluorescent protein-tagged isolate of *Verticillium dahliae.* Phytopathology 98:871-885.

Vallad, G. E., Bhat, R. G., Koike, S. T., Ryder, E. J., and Subbarao, K. V. 2005. Weedborne reservoirs and seed transmission of *Verticillium dahliae* in lettuce. Plant Dis. 89:317-324.

Vallad, G. E., Qin, Q.-M., Grube, R., Hayes, R. J., and Subbarao, K. V. 2006. Characterization of race-specific interactions among isolates of *Verticillium dahliae* pathogenic on lettuce. Phytopathology 96:1380-1387.

Wilhelm, S. 1955. Longevity of the Verticillium wilt fungus in the laboratory and field. Phytopathology 45:180-181.

(Prepared by P. Inderbitzin and K. V. Subbarao)

Diseases Caused by Bacteria

Bacterial Leaf Spot

Bacterial leaf spot (BLS) of lettuce was first described in the United States in 1918 and again in California in 1963. It was considered to be a minor disease with little economic impact. Since the early 2000s, however, BLS has emerged as a more important disease. It has been reported from most lettuce-growing regions of the world, and in many of these regions, it has caused economic losses. BLS has been reported from Asia (Japan, South Korea, and Taiwan), Australia, Canada, Europe (France, Germany, and Italy), New Zealand, Saudi Arabia, South Africa, South America (Venezuela), Trinidad and Tobago, Turkey, and the United States (California, Hawaii, New York, and Ohio). Since 2010, significant outbreaks of the disease have occurred in Asia, the Middle East, the Mediterranean Basin, Europe, and North America.

Symptoms

The initial symptom of BLS is the development of small (2–5 mm), water-soaked lesions, which typically form on the older, outer lettuce leaves—often, toward the margins. These lesions are typically delimited by veins, giving them an angular appearance, and they can be viewed on both the adaxial and abaxial leaf surfaces. Under favorable conditions (i.e., cool temperatures and high moisture levels), the lesions expand quickly and turn dark brown to black with a greasy appearance. The black, greasy lesions are a diagnostic symptom of the disease (Fig. 71). The lesions may have light-green to yellow borders and extend down the veins of infected leaves. An individual leaf may have a large number of lesions, which can coalesce and result in yellowing, collapse, and death (Fig. 72). Older lesions may become dry and papery in texture but remain dark brown to black.

If diseased lettuce heads are packed in cartons, secondary decay organisms (e.g., *Botrytis* spp.) can colonize the lesions and cause postharvest problems. Baby leaf lettuce that is clipped and harvested for bagged salad products is particularly susceptible to BLS, because it is planted at a very high density (7.4 million seeds/ha), allowing for rapid spread of the disease in planted beds. If lettuce is grown as transplants in the greenhouse, water-soaked lesions may develop on the cotyledons and provide inoculum that is spread via splashing water to emerging true leaves. On lettuce seed crops, black lesions may develop on stems and inflorescence (including seed bracts) (Fig. 73). A yellow-brown bacterial ooze may emerge from these lesions under humid and moist conditions.

BLS occurs on all types of lettuce (crisphead, romaine, leaf, butterhead) and can be particularly severe on butterhead and romaine cultivars. Because BLS lesions are dark, the disease is more difficult to observe on dark-red leaf lettuce cultivars.

Causal Organism

BLS is caused by *Xanthomonas campestris* pv. *vitians,* a typical leaf spot xanthomonad. The bacterium is a motile, aerobic, gram-negative rod that measures 0.7–1.0 × 2.0–2.7 µm and has a single polar flagellum. On general media such as nutrient agar (NA), sucrose peptone agar (SPA), and the general bacterial medium 523, colonies of the pathogen are relatively slow growing and round, convex, mucoid, and yellow (because of

Fig. 71. Lesions on crisphead lettuce caused by bacterial leaf spot (*Xanthomonas campestris* pv. *vitians*). (Courtesy S. T. Koike—© APS)

production of the pigment xanthomonadin). *X. campestris* pv. *vitians* can be isolated from symptomatic lettuce leaves on general or selective media and will appear in approximately 3 or more days. Because strains of the pathogen only weakly hydrolyze starch, starch-based semiselective media, such as SX and MXP, are not useful for identifying *X. campestris* pv. *vitians*. A semiselective medium containing maltose, methyl green, and antibiotics (MMG) was developed for isolation of *X. campestris* pv. *vitians*.

X. campestris pv. *vitians* can also be detected with the polymerase chain reaction (PCR) and specific primers. These include the B162 primer pair designed from a random amplified polymorphic DNA (RAPD) fragment and the RST65/RST69 primers that target the *HrpB2* gene of phytopathogenic xanthomonads.

A number of studies have revealed genetic diversity among the xanthomonads that cause BLS. Two major groups, *X. campestris* pv. *vitians* types A and B, have been recognized based on genotypic characteristics and pathogenicity. In a reclassification of the genus *Xanthomonas,* it was proposed that *X. campestris* pv. *vitians* type A strains be renamed *X. axonopodis* pv. *vitians* and that type B strains be renamed *X. hortorum* pv. *vitians*. However, the type strain of *X. campestris* pv. *vitians* (type A) is nonpathogenic on lettuce, and its relationship to BLS of lettuce remains unclear. Most of the xanthomonads that cause BLS are *X. campestris* pv. *vitians* type B. Although the type B strains may be renamed in the future, the name *X. campestris* pv. *vitians* will be used here to refer to lettuce-pathogenic type B strains. Within this group, at least three races have been identified based on interactions with different lettuce cultivars, which are either compatible (i.e., cause systemic infections) or incompatible (i.e., cause local lesions).

In agricultural settings, lettuce is the main economic crop host of *X. campestris* pv. *vitians,* although other crops, such as pepper and tomato, can support epiphytic populations of the bacterium. Epiphytic populations may be higher on pepper than tomato, indicating the greater potential for pepper (compared with tomato) to be a host of the pathogen. *X. campestris* pv. *vitians* also infects and causes leaf spots on weeds, including prickly lettuce (*Lactuca serriola,* a species of wild lettuce) and sowthistle (*Sonchus oleraceus*). Greenhouse and field studies have indicated that other weed species from the Chenopodiaceae, Polygonaceae, and Portulacaceae can support epiphytic populations of the bacterium without showing disease symptoms.

Disease Cycle and Epidemiology

Inoculum sources of *X. campestris* pv. *vitians* include contaminated seed (for direct-seeded lettuce crops), diseased transplants (grown from contaminated seed), weed hosts, and volunteer lettuce plants. Other sources can be lettuce crop debris derived from infected plants and possibly irrigation water. The epidemiological importance of bacterial survival as an epiphyte on leaves of weeds is not known and probably varies depending on the growing region.

Once *X. campestris* pv. *vitians* has been introduced onto the lettuce plant, there is an initial asymptomatic epiphytic phase, during which the bacterial population increases and may spread to other plants by splash dispersal. Disease symptoms appear when the bacterial population on leaves reaches approximately 10^7 colony forming units (CFUs)/cm^2 of tissue and is internalized.

Development of BLS is highly dependent on environmental conditions. The greatest disease severity occurs under cool temperatures (optimal ~23°C) and wet, humid conditions generated by rainfall or sprinkler irrigation. However, BLS can also develop in warmer climates and in greenhouses, suggesting that the most critical environmental factor is moisture. Following harvest of the lettuce crop, *X. campestris* pv. *vitians* can survive for a limited time on or in soil in association with crop debris. High populations of the pathogen were recovered from soil in association with lettuce residue buried for approximately 1 month after crop incorporation; much smaller populations were recovered for up to 4 months, after which the *X. campestris* pv. *vitians* population fell to an undectable level.

X. campestris pv. *vitians* can move systemically within the vascular tissue of lettuce stems. Thus, it is possible that seed can become internally infected via vascular connections or externally contaminated from contact with infected flowers, bracts, and other tissues during seed development. An outbreak of BLS in New Zealand was associated with commercial seed contaminated with *X. campestris* pv. *vitians*. Although it has been established that *X. campestris* pv. *vitians* can be seedborne in lettuce, the bacterium is not commonly recovered from commercial seed lots. This low rate of recovery from seed may reflect inefficient seed infection in the seed plant, levels of contamination below detection levels in seed lots, or production of seed in climates unfavorable for BLS. Nevertheless, it is believed that the worldwide distribution of *X. campestris* pv. *vitians* is due at least in part to long-distance spread in association with seed.

Management

An integrated management strategy is most effective for control of BLS. Lettuce types and cultivars have different levels of susceptibility, so resistant or less susceptible cultivars should be selected. Lettuce seed crops should be planted with pathogen-free seed grown in regions with arid climates and limited rainfall during seed production and produced under conditions

Fig. 72. Crisphead plants in a field severely affected by bacterial leaf spot (*Xanthomonas campestris* pv. *vitians*). (Courtesy S. T. Koike—© APS)

Fig. 73. Lesions caused by bacterial leaf spot (*Xanthomonas campestris* pv. *vitians*) on the inflorescence of lettuce plants. (Courtesy S. T. Koike—© APS)

unfavorable for BLS (e.g., watering with furrow or drip irrigation, rather than overhead irrigation).

For lettuce crop production, the planting of pathogen-free seed is an important management strategy. This is particularly critical for production of lettuce transplants in greenhouses, where conditions for disease development can be favorable. For seed lots contaminated with *X. campestris* pv. *vitians,* a treatment such as soaking seeds in 1% sodium hypochlorite for 5–20 min or 3–5% hydrogen peroxide for 5–15 min (which may slightly reduce seed germination) may help reduce the level of contamination. Dry-heat and hot-water treatments are also effective but substantially reduce seed germination.

In the greenhouse and in the field, adopting certain cultural practices can minimize the conditions favorable for BLS development—for example, reducing or eliminating overhead sprinkler irrigation in favor of bottom-water (greenhouse) and drip (field) irrigation. Prior to symptom development, foliar applications of copper-based materials mixed with dithiocarbamate fungicides (e.g., zineb and mancozeb) can slow buildup of epiphytic populations and disease development but will not prevent disease if conditions are favorable. For lettuce transplants, diseased plants should be removed and copper compounds sprayed to reduce epiphytic populations of *X. campestris* pv. *vitians.*

Weed management should be practiced in and around lettuce fields to minimize potential reservoir hosts of *X. campestris* pv. *vitians.* Because the pathogen can survive on or in soil for short periods, infested lettuce crop debris should be buried by deep plowing after harvest. Consecutive lettuce crops should not be grown in fields that have had BLS outbreaks. In such fields, a 1- or 2-year crop rotation with a nonhost of *X. campestris* pv. *vitians* should be practiced.

Selected References

Al-Saleh, M., and Ibrahim, Y. 2009. First report of bacterial leaf spot of lettuce (*Lactuca sativa*) caused by *Xanthomonas campestris* pv. *vitians* in Saudi Arabia. (Abstr.) Plant Dis. 93:107.

Barak, J. D., and Gilbertson, R. L. 2003. Genetic diversity of *Xanthomonas campestris* pv. *vitians,* the causal agent of bacterial leafspot of lettuce. Phytopathology 93:596-603.

Barak, J. D., Koike, S. T., and Gilbertson, R. L. 2001. Role of crop debris and weeds in the epidemiology of bacterial leaf spot of lettuce in California. Plant Dis. 85:169-178.

Barak, J. D., Koike, S. T., and Gilbertson, R. L. 2002. Movement of *Xanthomonas campestris* pv. *vitians* in the stems of lettuce and seed contamination. Plant Pathol. 51:506-512.

Bull, C. T., Goldman, P. H., Hayes, R., Madden, L. V., Koike, S. T., and Ryder, E. 2007. Genetic diversity of lettuce for resistance to bacterial leaf spot caused by *Xanthomonas campestris* pv. *vitians.* Plant Health Progress doi:10.1094/PHP-2007-0917-02-RS

Bull, C. T., Gebben, S. J., Goldman, P. H., Trent, M., and Hayes, R. J. 2015. Host genotype and hypersensitive reaction influence population levels of *Xanthomonas campestris* pv. *vitians* in lettuce. Phytopathology 105:316-324.

Carisse, O., Ouimet, A., Toussaint, V., and Philion, V. 2000. Evaluation of the effect of seed treatments, bactericides, and cultivars on bacterial leaf spot of lettuce caused by *Xanthomonas campestris* pv. *vitians.* Plant Dis. 84:295-299.

Daboin, C., and Tortolero, O. 1991. Mancha bacterial foliar de la lechuga en algunos campos Andinos de Venezuela. (In Spanish.) Fitopatol. Venez. 6:8-10.

Hayes, R. J., Trent, M. A., Mou, B., Simko, I., Gebben, S. J., and Bull, C. T. 2014. Baby leaf lettuce germplasm enhancement: Developing diverse populations with resistance to bacterial leaf spot caused by *Xanthomonas campestris* pv. *vitians.* HortScience 49:18-24.

Hayes, R. J., Trent, M. A., Truco, M. J., Antonise, R., Michelmore, R. W., and Bull, C. T. 2014. The inheritance of resistance to bacterial leaf spot of lettuce caused by *Xanthomonas campestris* pv. *vitians* in three lettuce cultivars. Hortic. Res. 1:14066.

Myung, I.-S., Moon, S. Y., Jeong, I. H., Lee, S. W., and Shim, H. S. 2010. Bacterial leaf spot of iceberg lettuce caused by *Xanthomonas campestris* pv. *vitians* type B, a new disease in South Korea. (Abstr.) Plant Dis. 94:790.

Ohata, K., Serizana, S., Azegami, K., and Shirata, A. 1982. Possibility of seed transmission of *Xanthomonas campestris* pv. *vitians,* the pathogen of bacterial spot of lettuce. Bull. Natl. Inst. Agric. Sci. 36:81-88.

Pernezny, K., Raid, R. N., Stall, R. E., Hodge, N. C., and Collins, J. 1995. An outbreak of bacterial spot of lettuce in Florida caused by *Xanthomonas campestris* pv. *vitians.* Plant Dis. 79:359-360.

Pernezny, K., Nagata, R., Raid, R. N., Collins, J., and Carroll, A. 2002. Investigation of seed treatments for management of bacterial leaf spot of lettuce. Plant Dis. 86:151-155.

Robinson, P. E., Jones, J. B., and Pernezny, K. 2006. Bacterial leaf spot of lettuce: Relationship of temperature to infection and potential host range of *Xanthomonas campestris* pv. *vitians.* Plant Dis. 90:465-470.

Sahin, F., and Miller, S. A. 1997. Identification of the bacterial leaf spot pathogen of lettuce, *Xanthomonas campestris* pv. *vitians,* in Ohio, and assessment of cultivar resistance and seed treatment. Plant Dis. 81:1443-1446.

Sahin, F., Abbasi, P. A., Lewis Ivey, M. L., Zhang, J., and Miller, S. A. 2003. Diversity among strains of *Xanthomonas campestris* pv. *vitians* from lettuce. Phytopathology 93:64-70.

Toussaint, V. 1999. Bacterial leaf spot, a new disease of lettuce in Quebec caused by *Xanthomonas campestris* pv. *vitians.* Phytoprotection 80:121-125.

Toussaint, V., Morris, C. E., and Carisse, O. 2001. A new semi-selective medium for *Xanthomonas campestris* pv. *vitians,* the causal agent of bacterial leaf spot of lettuce. Plant Dis. 85:131-136.

Toussaint, V., Benoit, D. L., and Carisse, O. 2012. Potential of weed species to serve as a reservoir for *Xanthomonas campestris* pv. *vitians,* the causal agent of bacterial leaf spot of lettuce. Crop Prot. 41:64-70.

Umesh, K. C., Koike, S. T., and Gilbertson, R. L. 1996. Association of *Xanthomonas campestris* pv. *vitians* with lettuce seed. (Abstr.) Phytopathology 86:S3.

(Prepared by S. T. Koike, R. L. Gilbertson, and C. T. Bull)

Bacterial Soft Rot

Bacterial soft rot is one of the most serious transit and market diseases of lettuce. Heavy losses may also occur in the field, where the disease causes a rapid wilt and collapse of crisphead and other lettuce types. Losses are frequently related to wet growing conditions. In Hawaii (United States), field losses as high as 100% can occur during the rainy season, whereas losses during drier months typically range from 10 to 25%. In Florida (United States), where unseasonal heavy rainfall may result in saturated field conditions for more than 24 h, entire fields of lettuce have been lost (Fig. 74).

Symptoms

In the field, bacterial soft rot initially appears as a rapid wilting of the outer wrapper leaves (Fig. 75). Plants at or near harvest are most susceptible. Wilting is caused by collapse of the vascular tissues, which develop a pinkish to brown discoloration (Fig. 76). As the disease progresses, the pith of the stem becomes water soaked, macerated, and greenish (Fig. 77). The gelatinlike consistency of the basal pith at this stage has given rise to the name "jelly butt"—a popular reference to the disease (Fig. 78). Eventually, the entire lettuce head may become slimy. In advanced stages of soft rot, lettuce heads collapse because of the extensive disintegration of foliar tissues (Fig. 79).

Soft rot infections that occur during postharvest transit or storage are closely associated with wounds on outer leaves. Wrapper leaves become wilted and discolored and heads become slimy as a result of the pectinolytic breakdown of foliar tissues (Fig. 80). If infection is not extensive, rotted wrapper leaves may be stripped from the head, leaving the innermost foliage intact and marketable.

Rotting of lettuce heads caused by bacterial soft rot can be differentiated from rotting caused by lettuce drop or southern blight by the absence of fungal mycelium and/or sclerotia (see earlier in Part I, the section "Diseases Caused by Fungi and Oomycetes").

Causal Organisms

Bacterial soft rot of lettuce is caused by *Pectobacterium carotovorum* subsp. *carotovorum* (syn. *Erwinia carotovora* subsp. *carotovora*). This bacterium has a wide host range, including a large number of herbaceous, dicotyledonous plants

Fig. 74. Saturated field conditions may result in heavy losses of lettuce from bacterial soft rot (*Pectobacterium carotovorum* subsp. *carotovorum*). (Courtesy S. Glucksman—© APS)

Fig. 76. (A) Vascular discoloration and **(B)** core rot of head lettuce, caused by bacterial soft rot (*Pectobacterium carotovorum* subsp. *carotovorum*). (Courtesy S. Glucksman—© APS)

Fig. 75. Wilted outer leaves of head lettuce is the initial symptom of bacterial soft rot (*Pectobacterium carotovorum* subsp. *carotovorum*). (Courtesy S. Glucksman—© APS)

Fig. 77. Discoloration and maceration of the basal pith of head lettuce caused by bacterial soft rot (*Pectobacterium carotovorum* subsp. *carotovorum*). (Courtesy R. N. Raid—© APS)

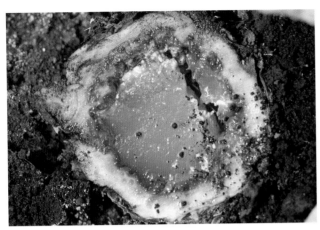

Fig. 78. Green, macerated pith tissue of head lettuce caused by bacterial soft rot (*Pectobacterium carotovorum* subsp. *carotovorum*), giving rise to the name "jelly butt." (Courtesy S. Glucksman—© APS)

Fig. 79. Collapse of a lettuce head in an advanced stage of bacterial soft rot (*Pectobacterium carotovorum* subsp. *carotovorum*). (Courtesy S. Glucksman—© APS)

Fig. 80. Slimy head of crisphead lettuce caused by pectinolytic degradation of outer leaf tissue, characteristic of postharvest development of bacterial soft rot (*Pectobacterium carotovorum* subsp. *carotovorum*). (Courtesy R. N. Raid—© APS)

(e.g., carrot, cabbage, cucurbits, celery, pepper, potato) and a limited number of monocotyledons (e.g., corn, sorghum). It is a single-celled, gram-negative, straight rod (0.5–1.0 × 1.0–3.0 μm) and is motile via peritrichous flagella. The bacterium is facultatively anaerobic, oxidase negative, and catalase positive; it reduces nitrate to nitrite, produces hydrogen sulfide from sodium thiosulfate, and produces β-galactosidase but not urease.

P. carotovorum subsp. *carotovorum* is easily cultured and produces deep pits on selective media containing polypectate, such as crystal violet pectate medium. It may be differentiated from other subspecies of the *P. carotovorum* group through additional nutritional, physiological, and biochemical tests. Pectinolytic strains of *Pseudomonas marginalis* pv. *marginalis* (see the later section "Marginal Leaf Blight"), which may also cause a soft rot on lettuce, are considered somewhat less aggressive than *P. carotovorum* subsp. *carotovorum*.

Disease Cycle and Epidemiology

Soft-rotting bacteria are considered ubiquitous and are capable of survival in soil, in aquatic environments, and in association with crop residue. They are easily disseminated by insects, splashing water, and contaminated equipment. The bacteria generally access plant tissues through wounds or natural plant openings. Soft-rotting bacteria are capable of rapid multiplication under favorable temperatures (25–30°C), and the latent period may be as short as 24 h if the inoculum concentration is high. At cool to moderate temperatures and a low inoculum concentration, the latent period may range from 2 to 3 weeks.

In the field, bacterial soft rot is most often associated with very moist to saturated soil and warm temperatures. Lettuce at or near maturity appears to be much more susceptible than lettuce at an early growth stage, presumably because excessive moisture remains in the canopy for a longer period of time. Postharvest infection is frequently related to improper handling and storage conditions. For example, excessive wounding during harvest or transport, using contaminated water in cooling or washing, and storing lettuce at higher than recommended temperatures are three factors commonly linked to major outbreaks of soft rot in transit or storage.

Bacterial soft rots typically result in more extensive trimming losses than storage decays caused by fungi, such as *Botrytis cinerea*.

Management

Management strategies for bacterial soft rot include rotating crops, providing good soil drainage, using furrow and drip irrigation, and applying fertilizers and pesticides properly to keep crops growing vigorously. In general, management should focus on avoiding crop injuries and excessive moisture conditions within the canopy.

Technological advances in shipping and storage have greatly diminished the incidence and severity of bacterial soft rot occurring at terminal markets. For example, quick removal of field heat by vacuum-cooling, maintenance of transit temperatures below 5°C, and extensive use of refrigeration by wholesalers and retailers all provide conditions less favorable for soft rot.

Prophylactic foliar applications of copper bactericides and soil fumigation have limited effectiveness in controlling soft rot. In fact, disease incidence is frequently higher in fumigated fields. Some lettuce cultivars appear to be more tolerant to soft rot than others, but this subject needs further research.

Selected References

Ceponis, M. J., Kaufman, J., and Butterfield, J. E. 1970. Relative importance of gray mold and bacterial soft rot of western lettuce on the New York market. Plant Dis. Rep. 54:263-265.

Cho, J. J. 1977. Control of bacterial leaf spot of crisphead type lettuce in Hawaii. Plant Dis. Rep. 61:783-787.

Cho, J. J. 1979. Evaluation of bacterial soft rot-tolerant crisphead lettuce cultivars in Hawaii. Univ. Hawaii Agric. Exp. Stn. Tech. Bull. 102.

Cho, J. J., and Talede, K. Y. 1976. Evaluation of lettuce varieties for resistance to bacterial soft rot. Hortic. Dig. 35:4-5.

Perombelon, M. C. M. 1980. Ecology of the soft rot *Erwinias.* Annu. Rev. Phytopathol. 18:361-387.

Schaad, N. W., Jones, J. B., and Chun, W. 2001. Laboratory Guide for Identification of Plant Pathogenic Bacteria. 3rd ed. American Phytopathological Society, St. Paul, MN.

Silva, A. M. F., Oliverra, W. J., Mariano, R. L. R., and Barbosa, E. B. 2014. Lettuce genotype resistance to "soft rot" caused by *Pectobacterium carotovorum* subsp. *carotovorum.* Sci. Agric. 71:1-8.

(Prepared by R. N. Raid)

Corky Root

Corky root of lettuce has been reported from most lettuce-producing areas in western Europe, North America, South America, Australia, and New Zealand. The disease has had serious effects on lettuce production under relatively high temperatures in Australia, California (United States), Florida (United States), and Italy. In severely infested fields in California and Florida, yield losses from reduced head size have ranged from 30 to 70% on susceptible cultivars. The yield losses are caused by reduced efficiency of water and nutrient uptake by diseased roots. The introduction of resistant lettuce cultivars in the 1990s reduced losses from corky root. Similarly, switching to production of baby lettuce in California and Spain has reduced losses, because the crop is harvested before corky root causes damage.

Symptoms

The initial symptom of corky rot is the formation of discrete, yellow lesions on the taproot and the main lateral roots (Fig. 81). On susceptible cultivars, these lesions develop into bands around the roots. After approximately 3 weeks, the lesions become greenish brown. Longitudinal ridges eventually develop on the taproot and the main lateral roots. Isolated corky areas are swollen compared with healthy areas of the roots. The root cortex may become brown and hollow, and a severely infected root will become brittle and can be pinched off, leaving only a small stump of the taproot (Fig. 81).

Aboveground symptoms develop only when the disease is extremely severe. In such cases, the lower leaves display interveinal chlorosis, wilting, and necrosis, and the head remains small.

The symptoms of corky root are sometimes confused with those caused by ammonium toxicity. However, the typical symptoms of ammonium toxicity include a reddish discoloration of the cortex and sometimes the central core of the taproot. The corky, longitudinal ridges on the taproot surface of roots affected by ammonium toxicity are narrower than those caused by bacterial corky root.

Causal Organisms

Corky root is caused by aerobic, gram-negative bacteria in the genus *Rhizorhapis* and the closely related genera *Rhizorhabdus, Sphingobium,* and *Sphingopyxis* but not *Sphingomonas.* (Note that the genus *Rhizorhapis* was formerly called *Rhizomonas;* however, the latter name was previously assigned to a protozoan, thereby requiring the change.) The species most commonly isolated from lettuce roots with corky root disease is *Rhizorhapis suberifaciens.* Most strains of *R. suberifaciens* are pathogenic to lettuce, but nonpathogenic strains have also been found.

The genus *Rhizorhapis* belongs to ribosomal DNA (rRNA) superfamily IV, or the alpha-4 subclass of Proteobacteria. It is closely related to the genera *Novosphingobium, Rhizorhabdus, Sphingobium, Sphingomonas,* and *Sphingopyxis,* which are common soil bacteria. They all belong to the family *Sphin-* *gomonadaceae.* Members of this family have cell walls that consist of glycosphingolipids. The fatty acid composition is characterized by relatively large amounts of 2-hydroxyl tetradecanoic acid (C14:02OH).

Many of the bacterial strains that cause corky root are oligotrophic; that is, they grow slowly and only on media with low carbon concentrations (~1 g/L or less). Thus, it is difficult to isolate the pathogen from infected tissue. Although a special medium (S-medium) with low carbon was developed, it is not truly selective, and isolating the pathogen remains an art (requiring the recognition of very firm, small colonies and the use of a phase contrast microscope to recognize the size and shape of bacterial cells). After about 1 week, the colonies are approximately 1 mm in diameter. Colonies of various species of *Rhizorhapis* and closely related genera are firm, initially smooth but later wrinkled, and cream to yellow colored; they sometimes produce a brown pigment on S-medium. The most common isolates of *R. suberifaciens* are creamy white.

Monoclonal antibodies are available for the identification of *R. suberifaciens.* The 16S rRNA genes of several isolates have been sequenced, and primers are available for use in the quantitative polymerase chain reaction (qPCR) for the identification of *R. suberifaciens.*

Disease Cycle and Epidemiology

The host range of *R. suberifaciens* is limited to members of the tribe Cichorieae of the family Asteraceae, which includes lettuce, endive, sowthistle (*Sonchus oleraceus*), and prickly lettuce (*Lactuca serriola,* a species of wild lettuce). However, *R. suberifaciens* has also been isolated from the roots of

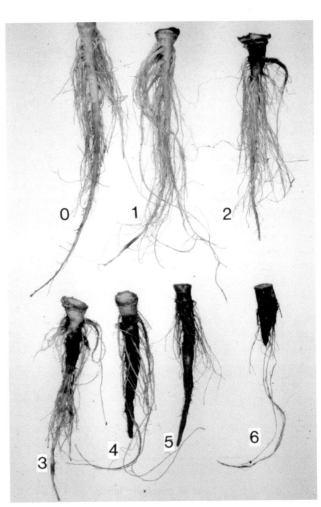

Fig. 81. The progression of corky root (*Rhizorhapis* sp.) symptoms is illustrated by this severity scale on crisphead lettuce. (Courtesy A. H. C. van Bruggen—© APS)

various nonhost species, indicating that it may be a common rhizosphere inhabitant. For example, *R. suberifaciens* is able to survive on barley roots, although the population on barley is not as high as on the roots of lettuce or prickly lettuce. The population of the pathogen was found to be higher on a susceptible lettuce cultivar than on a resistant cultivar or on prickly lettuce. As symptoms develop, the pathogen population generally decreases over time and is replaced by secondary microorganisms, such as *Cladosporium* and *Alternaria* spp.

Symptoms of corky root are enhanced as the temperature increases from 10 to 33°C. The optimum temperature for growth of *R. suberifaciens* is 33°C, and the maximum temperature for growth is 36°C. The bacterium is killed at 37°C. The relationship between soil water potential and corky root development has not been studied in detail. However, corky root is enhanced by excess moisture, and the disease is less severe under drip than furrow irrigation.

The incidence and severity of corky root are also enhanced by applications of inorganic nitrogen (N) fertilizer in the range of 70 to 210 kg N/ha, regardless of the form that is applied. However, the increase in disease is related to the soil concentration of nitrate, rather than ammonium. Organically managed fields are less prone to development of corky root. Low severity of corky root in organic farms may also be related to greater microbial activity and diversity; an inverse relationship has been demonstrated between soil microbial activity and corky root severity.

Lettuce plants are more susceptible to *R. suberifaciens* after application of the herbicide pronamide at the commonly used concentrations (1.1–2.2 kg of active ingredient per hectare).

Management

Resistant cultivars are widely available for several different lettuce types (e.g., crisphead, butterhead, romaine, and leaf lettuce). The resistance is recessive and monogenic and attributed to the *cor* gene. Although resistance is broadly effective, at some locations, there are strains of *R. suberifaciens* that are virulent on resistant cultivars or breeding lines. Thus, monogenic resistance may not be durable in the long term. Efforts to identify additional sources of resistance are ongoing.

Crop rotation with sugarcane has been shown to significantly reduce corky root of susceptible lettuce cultivars in Florida. Yields of susceptible cultivars slowly decrease after the first crop of lettuce following sugarcane. Thus, it is economically feasible to grow three or four lettuce crops with susceptible cultivars. Afterward, resistant cultivars should be planted.

Turning over a rye cover crop 3 weeks before planting lettuce can also reduce the development of corky root, but such cover cropping must be complemented with other cultural practices (e.g., reducing the amount of nitrogen fertilizer) to further reduce disease. Improved disease reduction from applying slow-release nitrogen (sulfur-coated urea) compared with side dressings of ammonium nitrate or ammonium sulfate has also been reported.

Planting a cover crop may enhance soil microbial activity and diversity and thus competition or antibiosis against virulent strains of *R. suberifaciens*. In addition to providing competition from nonrelated microorganisms, nonpathogenic strains of *R. suberifaciens* and related species or genera may provide specific inhibition of pathogenic strains. One nonpathogenic isolate of *R. suberifaciens* from Florida proved to be a very effective biological control agent of highly virulent strains of *R. suberifaciens* and related genera in natural field soil in California.

Corky root can also be reduced by improving soil drainage—for example, by growing lettuce on raised beds or by reducing the amount of irrigation water. Corky root is less severe in drip-irrigated than in furrow-irrigated fields. Reducing the number of furrow irrigation events can also decrease development of the disease.

Substantial control of corky root can be obtained by using transplants instead of direct-seeding, because transplants do not have well-developed taproot systems. Yields of transplanted lettuce crops can be significantly higher than those of direct-seeded crops, particularly when corky root is severe in the latter.

Corky root can be managed effectively using various fumigants, but these chemicals are not registered for lettuce production. Incorporation of crucifer residues may reduce development of the disease, although rotation with broccoli, for example, has not provided the desired level of control.

A potential alternative may be biological soil disinfestation (BSD), which is also called "anaerobic soil disinfestation" (ASD). BSD was developed for production of various other vegetable and fruit crops and has proved to be effective at controlling pathogens of these crops. Under this method, easily decomposable organic matter is worked into the soil, moistened, and then covered by impermeable plastic, which promotes anaerobic decomposition and the formation of toxic organic acids (e.g., acetic and n-butyric acids). BSD has not been developed for lettuce production.

Selected References

Brown, P. R., and Michelmore, R. W. 1988. The genetics of corky root resistance in lettuce. Phytopathology 78:1145-1150.

Bull, C., Goldman, P. H., and Martin, K. J. 2014. Novel primers and PCR protocols for the specific detection and quantification of *Sphingobium suberifaciens* in situ. Mol. Cell. Probes 28:211-217.

Francis, I. M., Jochimsen, K. N., de Vos, P., and van Bruggen, A. H. C. 2014. Reclassification of rhizosphere bacteria including strains causing corky root of lettuce as *Rhizorhapis suberifaciens* gen. nov., *Sphingobium mellinum* sp. nov., *Sphingobium xanthum* sp. nov., *Sphingopyxis* sp., and *Rhizorhabdus argenteus* gen. nov., sp. nov. Int. J. Syst. Evol. Microbiol. 64:1340-1350.

Mou, B., Hayes, R. J., and Ryder, E. J. 2007. Crisphead lettuce breeding lines with resistance to corky root and lettuce mosaic virus. HortScience 42:701-703.

Subbarao, K. V., Hubbard, J. C., and Schulbach, K. F. 1997. Comparison of lettuce diseases and yield under subsurface drip and furrow irrigation. Phytopathology 87:877-883.

van Bruggen, A. H. C. 2014. The strains of *Rhizorhapis* and related genera isolated from lettuce roots that were used to develop specific primers for *Rhizorhapis suberifaciens*. Mol. Cell. Probes 28:218-219.

van Bruggen, A. H. C., and Francis, I. M. 2015. Case investigation and forensic evidence for a new plant disease: The case of lettuce corky root. Plant Dis. 99:300-309.

van Bruggen, A. H. C., Francis, I. M., and Jochimsen, K. N. 2014. Non-pathogenic rhizosphere bacteria belonging to the genera *Rhizorhapis* and *Sphingobium* provide specific control of lettuce corky root disease caused by the same but not different genera. Plant Pathol. 63:1384-1394.

van Bruggen, A. H. C., Ochoa, O., Francis, I. M., and Michelmore, R. W. 2014. Differential interactions between strains of *Rhizorhapis, Sphingobium, Sphingopyxis* or *Rhizorhabdus* and accessions of *Lactuca* spp. with respect to severity of corky root disease. Plant Pathol. 63:1053-1061.

van Bruggen, A. H. C., Francis, I., and Krag, R. 2015. The vicious cycle of lettuce corky root disease: Effects of farming system, nitrogen fertilizer and herbicide. Plant Soil 388:119-132.

(Prepared by A. H. C. van Bruggen)

Marginal Leaf Blight

Marginal leaf blight of lettuce was first described in 1918 in Kansas (United States) and referred to as "Kansas disease of lettuce." It has since been reported from many parts of the world, including Argentina, Europe (Belgium and England), India, and the United States (California, Florida, and New

York). Marginal leaf blight is usually a disease of minor importance, but economic losses can occur under wet weather conditions. In these situations, necrosis and wilting of leaves may render affected lettuce heads unmarketable.

Symptoms

Marginal leaf blight usually occurs during periods of wet weather—typically, in the spring and early summer. The initial symptom is the development of localized areas of wilting along the margins of leaves (Fig. 82). This symptom is followed by the appearance of brown to black, necrotic lesions in the wilted areas, resulting in narrow, brown to black lesions that extend up or down relative to the sites of the initial lesions. A distinctive darkening of leaf veins develops in the areas of the lesions; this symptom is associated with enhanced wilting and water soaking of the interveinal areas. During periods of rain and high humidity, the lesions become soft and slimy, and bacteria may ooze from infected veins. Under dry conditions, infected tissue turns brown or black and then becomes dry and papery. In some cases, entire leaves may be affected.

Marginal leaf blight usually affects the leaves toward the outside of the plant, but these may not be the oldest leaves. Infected leaves tend to be of the same age and whorl. The disease is usually confined to the leaves; however, under continuous wet conditions, lesions may extend down the petiole into the pith of the stem, producing a butt rot.

Causal Organism

Marginal leaf blight is caused by *Pseudomonas marginalis* pv. *marginalis,* which is a strictly aerobic, pectinolytic, gram-negative, rod-shaped bacterium. The bacterium measures $0.7–0.8 \times 2.0–2.8$ μm and has one to three polar flagella. *P. marginalis* pv. *marginalis* forms fast-growing, slimy, white to yellow colonies on King's medium B and produces a diffusible yellow-green pigment that fluoresces green under ultraviolet light. The LOPAT profile of *P. marginalis* pv. *marginalis* is (1) levan positive, (2) oxidase positive, (3) potato rot positive and pectinolytic, (4) arginine dihydrolase positive, and (5) negative for the hypersensitive response (HR) in tobacco. (LOPAT is a series of determinative tests of plant-pathogenic *Pseudomonas* spp.) The bacterium hydrolyzes gelatin but not

starch and grows at 4°C but not at 41°C. It is positive for nitrate reductase, denitrification, and β-glucosidase, but it does not accumulate poly-β-hydroxybutyrate (PHB) and is ice-nucleation negative. The bacterium utilizes 2-ketogluconate, mannitol, sorbitol, sucrose, and trehalose as sole carbon sources but not D(-)-tartrate, D-arabinose, D-aspartate, and L-rhamnose.

The fluorescent plant-pathogenic bacteria *P. cichorii* and *P. viridiflava* are often co-isolated with *P. marginalis* pv. *marginalis* from the same lesions. However, these bacteria can be differentiated from *P. marginalis* pv. *marginalis* because *P. viridiflava* is oxidase negative and *P. cichorii* is arginine dihydrolase negative.

P. marginalis pv. *marginalis* is ubiquitous in many agricultural fields and causes disease on many vegetable crops (>50 species), including lettuce, chicory, endive, escarole, cabbage, cucumber, onion, and potato.

Disease Cycle and Epidemiology

Soil, contaminated debris, and reservoir hosts are the typical sources of inoculum for *P. marginalis* pv. *marginalis* in the field. Water splashed from rain or sprinkler irrigation disseminates the bacterium from the soil, debris, or reservoir hosts to the leaves of lettuce plants in the field. The bacterium enters through wounds and natural openings, such as leaf hydathodes, during periods of high leaf wetness. Subsequent development of symptoms of marginal leaf blight in the lettuce field will depend on levels of moisture following rainfall or sprinkle irrigation.

Management

Lettuce cultivars have different levels of susceptibility to marginal leaf blight. Thus, if possible, growers should select less susceptible varieties during seasons when wet conditions are expected to occur. The use of furrow or drip irrigation, instead of sprinkler irrigation, will reduce the frequency of leaf wetness periods and slow bacterial spread and multiplication and subsequent disease development. Providing adequate air movement in the field and between plants facilitates the drying of leaves after wet periods and will also reduce disease development and severity.

Crop rotation of at least 2 years will allow for the breakdown of debris and greatly reduce the level of inoculum in the soil.

Selected References

Berger, R. D. 1967. Marginal leaf blight of lettuce. Proc. Fla. State Hortic. Soc. 80:134-138.

Bradbury, J. F. 1986. Guide to Plant Pathogenic Bacteria. CAB International Mycological Institute, Kew, Surrey, UK.

Brown, N. A. 1918. Some bacterial diseases of lettuce. J. Agric. Res. 13:367-388.

Burkholder, W. H. 1954. Three bacteria pathogenic on head lettuce in New York State. Phytopathology 44:592-596.

Fahy, P. C., and Persley, G. J. 1983. Plant Bacterial Diseases: A Diagnostic Guide. Academic Press, New York.

Miller, S. A. 1980. Susceptibility of lettuce cultivars to marginal leaf blight caused by *Pseudomonas marginalis* (Brown 1918) Steven 1925. N.Z. J. Exp. Agric. 8:169-171.

(Prepared by E. L. Little and R. L. Gilbertson)

Varnish Spot

Varnish spot of lettuce was first described in 1977 in California (United States), where it can be an economically important disease of mature crisphead lettuce. Symptoms generally occur on the inner leaves, whereas the outer leaves usually show no symptoms; therefore, the disease may not be identified until harvest. Occasionally, an entire field is abandoned because of a high incidence of varnish spot. Varnish spot occurs worldwide

Fig. 82. Wilting along the margins of leaves is the initial symptom of marginal leaf blight of lettuce (*Pseudomonas marginalis* pv. *marginalis*). (Courtesy R. N. Raid—© APS)

in most lettuce-producing areas, including Australia (where it can be found in all states), Brazil, Canada, Italy, Turkey, and the United States. In Australia, the incidence of the disease ranges from 0 to 20%.

Symptoms

The symptoms of varnish spot occur only on the inner leaves of lettuce cultivars that form heads; thus, the disease is typically not observed in leaf lettuce types. In head lettuce, symptoms may not be observed until harvest, when the heads are cut and the outer leaves are removed (Fig. 83). The disease is characterized by shiny, dark-brown, firm, necrotic lesions on or along the midribs or veins. The lesions are initially small (a few millimeters in diameter) but later expand and coalescence. The areas along the veins are most often affected, but necrotic areas can expand and cover large areas of leaves. Varnish spot lesions are moist and dark brown to black but typically do not show rotting. Older lesions may dry out and become papery (Fig. 84).

The firmness and lack of rotting differentiate varnish spot from the slimy, rotting symptoms associated with bacterial soft rot (caused by *Pectobacterium carotovorum* subsp. *carotovorum*). In addition, it should be noted that the varnish spot pathogen can also induce leaf spot symptoms in lettuce and chicory, but the disease is not economically important.

Causal Organism

Varnish spot is caused by *Pseudomonas cichorii*, which is a fluorescent pseudomonad. It is a strictly aerobic, gram-negative rod (0.8 × 1.2–3.5 μm) with multiple polar flagella. The bacterium forms round, smooth, mucoid, light-yellow, convex colonies on King's medium B after 3 days of growth, and it produces

Fig. 83. Internal symptoms of varnish spot (*Pseudomonas cichorii*) on crisphead lettuce. (Courtesy S. T. Koike—© APS)

Fig. 84. Varnish spot lesions on crisphead lettuce (*Pseudomonas cichorii*). (Courtesy S. T. Koike—© APS)

a diffusible green pigment on this medium that fluoresces when exposed to ultraviolet light. The LOPAT profile of *P. cichorii* is (1) levan negative, (2) oxidase positive, (3) potato rot negative and not pectolytic, (4) arginine dihydrolase negative, and (5) positive for the hypersensitive reaction (HR) in tobacco. (LOPAT is a series of determinative tests for plant-pathogenic *Pseudomonas* spp.) *P. cichorii* does not accumulate poly-β-hydroxybutyrate (PHB) or hydrolyze starch or gelatin, and it is negative for nitrate reductase, denitrification, and ice-nucleation activity. It does not grow at 41°C. It utilizes 2-ketogluconate, mannitol, meso-tartrate, and D-aspartate as sole carbon sources but not geraniol, benzoate, cellobiose, sorbitol, trehalose, sucrose, D(-)-tartrate, D-arabinose, and L-rhamnose.

In addition to lettuce, *P. cichorii* can infect and cause disease in numerous other crops, including chicory, endive, cabbage, cauliflower, chrysanthemum, tobacco, and celery.

Disease Cycle and Epidemiology

P. cichorii is common in the soil and as an epiphyte on leaves. It can reach a high population in the soil in association with crop debris. Varnish spot occurs when water contaminated with *P. cichorii* is used to sprinkler-irrigate a lettuce crop, especially during head formation. The bacterium also can be introduced to lettuce plants via splashing of contaminated soil or debris onto leaves. Other possible sources of inoculum are seeds, transplants, reservoir (weed) hosts, and insects. Spread of the bacteria on lettuce plants occurs via splashing or wind-driven irrigation water and rain. Long periods of leaf wetness favor the buildup of the *P. cichorii* population on leaves.

As a lettuce plant with a population of *P. cichorii* grows and forms a head, the bacteria infect and cause disease on the inner leaves. Infection can occur directly via the stomates of unwounded leaves but is facilitated by wounds, such as growth cracks and damage caused by cultivation and insect feeding (e.g., thrips). Depending on the weather conditions, symptoms may appear 1–5 days after inoculation. The pathogen grows at temperatures between 5 and 35°C (optimum 26°C).

Varnish spot lesions may develop secondary infections by soft-rotting bacteria, resulting in a slimy, wet rot of leaf tissue. This can complicate identification of the primary causal agent of the disease.

Management

Irrigation water is important both as an inoculum source and for creating favorable conditions for disease development. Therefore, furrow or drip irrigation should be used instead of sprinkler irrigation. If sprinkler irrigation must be used, it should be done such that leaf wetness is minimized, especially within 3 weeks of harvest. Fields should be established in well-drained soils and in locations in which there is good air movement. (Air movement will reduce humidity and leaf wetness, which are important for disease development.)

In locations in which the disease has caused economic losses, the irrigation water used for growing transplants or plants in the field should be tested for *P. cichorii*. Treatment of irrigation water with copper compounds (e.g., copper oxychloride) may reduce the level of bacteria.

Lettuce cultivars vary in susceptibility to varnish spot; thus, growing less susceptible varieties may reduce disease development, particularly during periods when conditions are favorable for the disease. Avoiding continuous cropping of lettuce and other susceptible hosts and not growing susceptible crops side by side can reduce the bacterial population and subsequent disease development. Crop rotation (ideally, 2 years) out of hosts of *P. cichorii* will reduce the level of inoculum in the soil.

Selected References

Aysan, Y., Sahin, S., Ulke, G., and Sahin, F. 2003. Bacterial rot of lettuce caused by *Pseudomonas cichorii* in Turkey. Plant Pathol. 52:6782.

Bleyart, P., Vaerenbergh, J., and van Kint, S. 1999. Identification of *Pseudomonas* spp. as the causal organism and of sulfate as the promoting factor of midrib rot in butterhead lettuce. Parasitica 55:73-83.

Bradbury, J. F. 1986. Guide to Plant Pathogenic Bacteria. CAB International Mycological Institute, Kew, Surrey, UK.

Burkholder, W. H. 1954. Three bacteria pathogenic on head lettuce in New York State. Phytopathology 44:592-596.

Dhanvantari, B. N. 1990. Occurrence of bacterial stem rot caused by *Pseudomonas cichorii* in greenhouse-grown lettuce in Ontario. (Abstr.) Plant Dis. 74:394.

Fahy, P. C., and Persley, G. J. 1983. Plant Bacterial Diseases: A Diagnostic Guide. Academic Press, New York.

Grogan, R. G., Misaghi, I. J., Kimble, K. A., Greathead, A. S., Ririe, D., and Bardin, R. 1977. Varnish spot, destructive disease of lettuce in California caused by *Pseudomonas cichorii*. Phytopathology 67:957-960.

Hikichi, Y., Saito, A., and Suzuki, K. 1996. Infection sites of *Pseudomonas cichorii* into head leaf of lettuce. Ann. Phytopathol. Soc. Jpn. 62:125-129.

Hikichi, Y., Saito, A., and Suzuki, K. 1996. Relationship between population dynamics of *Pseudomonas cichorii* on lettuce and disease incidence of bacterial rot of lettuce. Ann. Phytopathol. Soc. Jpn. 62:141-146.

Shirata, A., Ohata, K., Serzawa, S., and Tsuchiya, Y. 1982. Relationship between lesion development by *Pseudomonas cichorii* and growth stage and leaf position of lettuce and its infection mechanism. Bull. Natl. Inst. Agric. Sci. 36:61-73.

Watson, A. 2005. Scoping Study on the Management of Varnish Spot in Field and Hydroponic Lettuce. Proj. VG03003. NSW Department of Primary Industries, Horticulture Australia, Ltd., Sydney, New South Wales.

(Prepared by E. L. Little and R. L. Gilbertson)

Diseases Caused by Phytoplasmas

Lettuce Yellows (Aster Yellows), Lettuce Phyllody, and Australian Lettuce Phyllody

Phytoplasmas that cause disease in lettuce differ genetically depending on their geographical origins. In Canada, the United States, and most of Europe, lettuce yellows (formerly known as "aster yellows") is caused by a phytoplasma that belongs to the provisional species 'Candidatus Phytoplasma asteri' (aster yellows phytoplasma). This species contains many genetically diverse strains and affects a wide variety of wild and cultivated plants, including more than 300 species of vegetables, weeds, and ornamentals. In Iran, lettuce phyllody is caused by a phytoplasma that belongs to the pigeon pea witches'-broom group, and in Australia, the phytoplasma that causes Australian lettuce phyllody is in the faba bean phyllody group. Losses from diseases caused by phytoplasmas in lettuce are sporadic.

Symptoms

Levels of phytoplasma infection vary depending on the growth stage of the lettuce plant and the strain of phytoplasma. With lettuce yellows, when young plants are infected, they are generally stunted and chlorotic. They also have pale heart leaves, which never expand normally but instead remain small and abnormal (Fig. 85, part A). When older plants are infected, the inner heart leaves can be chlorotic (pale green), and the outer leaves are yellow and sometimes twisted. Latex droplets are often exuded along the midribs of the undersurfaces of leaves of both young and old plants.

With lettuce phyllody, plants are stunted and chlorotic, have deformed leaves, and develop a proliferation of buds in the crowns. Lettuce plants exhibiting phyllody often die because of the disease.

In lettuce yellows and lettuce phyllody, plants grown for seed can also show virescence (i.e., greening of the flowers) and phyllody (i.e., abnormal development of a floral organ, such as a flower petal, into a leaf) (Fig. 85, part B).

Causal Agents

Phytoplasmas (formerly referred to as "mycoplasmalike organisms," or MLOs) are small (0.5–1.0 µm) microorganisms (prokaryotes) that reproduce by division or budding in the phloem sieve elements of host plants, as well as in their leafhopper vectors. Phytoplasmas are pleomorphic, lack a

Fig. 85. **A,** Gross symptoms on lettuce, with plant distortion caused by lettuce yellows. **B,** Orange or pink latex blisters caused by lettuce yellows ('Candidatus Phytoplasma asteri,' or aster yellows phytoplasma). (Courtesy S. T. Koike—© APS)

TABLE 1. Phytoplasmas That Cause Diseases in Lettuce[a]

Pathogen Common Name (Scientific Name)	RFLP[b] Group	Primary Leafhopper Vector	Distribution	Disease Caused
Aster yellows phytoplasma ('*Candidatus* Phytoplasma asteri')	16SrI-A	*Macrosteles quadrilineatus*	Canada, United States (Ohio, Oklahoma, Texas, midwestern states)	Lettuce yellows
Aster yellows phytoplasma ('*Candidatus* Phytoplasma asteri')	16SrI-B	*Macrosteles quadrilineatus*	Italy, United States (California, New York, Ohio, Texas, midwestern states)	Lettuce yellows
Pigeon pea witches'-broom group	16SrIX	*Neoaliturus fenestratus*	Iran	Lettuce phyllody
Faba bean phyllody group	16SrII	Unknown	Australia	Australian lettuce phyllody

[a] Courtesy C. Blomquist—© APS.
[b] Restriction fragment length polymorphism.

cell wall, and have never been grown in culture. Because of their size, they can be visualized only using electron microscopy, light microscopy, and fluorescent DNA staining (4',6-diamidino-2-phenylindole [DAPI]) techniques). Detection of phytoplasmas can be confirmed by bioassay, enzyme-linked immunosorbent assay (ELISA), DNA hybridization techniques, and polymerase chain reaction (PCR) (the most widely used technique for detection).

Taxonomically, phytoplasmas are categorized according to their similarities in restriction enzyme digest patterns and in sequences of ribosomal DNA (rDNA). The diagnostic rDNA fragments are obtained by using PCR and phytoplasma rDNA primers and digesting the amplified DNA fragment with a panel of restriction enzymes or sequencing it and comparing the sequence with the sequences of known phytoplasmas. Phytoplasma isolates with similar restriction digestion patterns belong to the same restriction fragment length polymorphism (RFLP) group; these groups have been designated with roman numerals (Table 1).

Disease Cycle and Epidemiology

The aster yellows phytoplasma is vectored by many different species of leafhopper, but the most important is the aster leafhopper, *Macrosteles quadrilineatus* (syn. *M. fascifrons*) (Fig. 86). In parts of the U.S. Midwest and Texas, aster yellows infection of lettuce is linked to leafhopper migration.

After an incubation period of approximately 20 days, the leafhopper transmits the phytoplasma in a propagative manner and remains infective for up to 100 days (essentially, the life of the insect). In the spring, infected female leafhoppers migrate north with prevailing southern or western winds into fields of lettuce and other crops. These leafhoppers have previously acquired the phytoplasma by feeding on infected weeds and crops. Infected females feed, transmit the phytoplasma,

Fig. 86. Aster leafhopper (*Macrosteles quadrilineatus*), the primary vector of the aster yellows phytoplasma ('*Candidatus* Phytoplasma asteri'). (Photo by J. K. Clark; Reproduced by permission of University of California Statewide IPM Project)

and lay eggs on young lettuce plants. Lettuce is a preferred feeding and egg-laying host of the aster leafhopper, not an incidental host. This affects the epidemiology of lettuce yellows and makes it different from diseases of hosts that are not the preferred feeding hosts. Leafhopper populations peak on lettuce in late summer and then decline, possibly because of the leafhoppers' migrating south and a reduction in host quality as lettuce matures. Infected plants tend to be clustered in the field, and disease incidence can range from 0 to 100%.

In the far western and eastern United States, where aster leafhopper migration is not known to occur, local leafhopper vectors acquire the phytoplasma from many infected perennial and biennial crops and weed hosts such as sowthistle (*Sonchus oleraceus*), dandelion (*Taraxacum officinale*), Queen Anne's lace (*Daucus carota*), Russian thistle (*Salsola tragus*), and prickly lettuce (*Lactuca serriola,* a wild species of lettuce).

In Iran, lettuce phyllody is transmitted by another leafhopper, *Neoaliturus fenestratus*. Disease incidence is higher in late summer and early fall, presumably because of an increase in the vector population and an increase in inoculum levels in host plants. Important weed hosts are prickly lettuce and sowthistle.

The vector of the faba bean phyllody phytoplasma, which causes Australian lettuce phyllody, is not known (Table 1).

Management

Management of lettuce yellows and yellows phyllody is not usually needed in areas that are outside leafhopper migration. When needed, strategies include managing weed hosts near lettuce fields and controlling vectors with insecticides. All lettuce cultivars are susceptible to these diseases.

In parts of the northern Midwest of the United States, where lettuce yellows and aster yellows in carrot are recurring economic problems, the infectivity of the aster leafhopper is measured using a bioassay of captured leafhoppers on China aster. An aster yellows index (AYI) is calculated using a combination of the susceptibility of lettuce, the number of leafhoppers present, and the percentage of infective leafhoppers. The AYI is the percent infectivity of the aster leafhopper population multiplied by the number of aster leafhoppers present in 100 insect net sweeps. Because lettuce is highly susceptible, insecticidal treatment is recommended if the AYI is equal to or greater than 25.

Leafhopper abundance can vary between crop years and within a single growing season, and leafhopper infection varies yearly. Thus, applying insecticide only when the index threshold is reached can reduce the amount of insecticide used for leafhopper control compared with routine spraying. To narrow the treatment window and further reduce insecticide use, research has focused on treating lettuce with insecticide only when both the leafhopper count and rate of phytoplasma infection are above certain thresholds.

Once a lettuce plant is infected with a phytoplasma, there is no known cure.

Selected References

Beanland, L., Madden, L. V., Hoy, C. W., Miller, S. A., and Nault, L. R. 2005. Temporal distribution of aster leafhopper sex ratios and spatial pattern of aster yellows phytoplasma disease in lettuce. Ann. Entomol. Soc. Amer. 98:756-762.

Frost, K. E., Esker, P. D., Van Haren, R., Kotolski, L., and Groves, R. L. 2013. Seasonal patterns of aster leafhopper (Hemiptera: Cicadellidae) abundance and aster yellows phytoplasma infectivity in Wisconsin carrot fields. Econ. Entomol. 42:491-502.

Lee, I. M., Bottner-Parker, K. D., Zhao, Y., Davis, R. E., and Black, M. C. 2014. Aster yellows group (16SrI), subgroups 16Sr-I-A and 16SrI-B, phytoplasmas associated with lettuce yellows in Texas. New Dis. Rep. 29:5.

Salehi, M., Izadpanah, K., Nejat, N., and Siampour, M. 2007. Partial characterization of phytoplasmas associated with lettuce and wild lettuce phyllodies in Iran. Plant Pathol. 56:669-676.

Seemuller, E., Marcone, C., Lauer, U., Ragozzino, A., and Goschl, M. 1998. Current status of molecular classification of the phytoplasmas. J. Plant Pathol. 80:3-26.

(Prepared by C. Blomquist)

Diseases Caused by Viruses

Like most cultivated plants, lettuce can be infected by a range of plant viruses; approximately 30 viruses have been reported to infect cultivated lettuce. Most of these viruses do not usually cause economic damage. However, under favorable conditions, some can cause substantial economic losses.

Viruses are obligate parasites that require plants for their replication, and they "trick" host cells into synthesizing viral nucleic acids and proteins. Infection of plants with most viruses results in the development of disease symptoms, which vary considerably depending on the virus, the lettuce type and cultivar, and the environmental conditions under which plants are grown. Common symptoms observed when lettuce plants are infected with a virus include stunting of growth and crumpling/crinkling, distortion, mosaic/mottling, necrosis, ring spots, vein swelling, and yellowing of leaves.

A plant virus is composed of one or more nucleic acids (either RNA or DNA) enclosed in a protective protein shell (capsid), which together are referred to as a "virus particle" or "virion." The shape and size of a virion can be icosahedral (spherical), bacilliform (bullet shaped), or rod shaped, and a rod-shaped virion can be rigid (straight) or flexuous. The nucleic acid is the genetic information of a virus and can be single- or double-stranded RNA or DNA; for some viruses, the viral genome may be divided between or among more than one nucleic acid species (a multipartite genome). The genomes of the majority of lettuce-infecting viruses are plus-sense, single-stranded RNA. Lettuce-infecting rhabdoviruses have negative-sense, single-stranded RNA genomes. No lettuce-infecting viruses with double-stranded RNA or DNA genomes have been identified.

Plant viruses are spread from plant to plant in several ways. The most important and common method is via insect vectors, including aphids, beetles, leafhoppers, mealybugs, thrips, and whiteflies. The most common insect vectors of lettuce-infecting viruses are species of aphids. Lettuce viruses can also be transmitted by fungi and nematodes and on or in seed, in pollen, by contact, and by soil and water.

The management of viruses is most effective when an integrated approach is used. Such an approach may involve planting virus-free seed or transplants, using virus-resistant cultivars, removing virus-infected plants (i.e., rogueing), monitoring and managing insect vectors, managing reservoir (weed) hosts, rotating crops, and providing host-free periods. The measures used for integrated management will depend on the biological properties of the virus targeted for control.

The first step in determining if a disease of lettuce (or any other plant) is caused by a virus is to examine the symptoms and compare them with photographs of symptoms of known viruses. The descriptions and photographs in this section of the compendium will help in making an accurate diagnosis of potential virus diseases. An initial diagnosis of a virus disease is often followed up with one or more specific tests. Testing may involve mechanical (sap) inoculation of indicator plants or observation of leaf-dip preparations with an electron microscope. However, serological (antibody-based) tests, such as enzyme-linked immunosorbent assay (ELISA) and lateral-flow devices (immunostrips), and nucleic acid-based tests, such as polymerase chain reaction (PCR) and reverse transcription-(RT-) PCR and sequencing, are more precise and commonly used. The types of tests available for many of the lettuce viruses in this compendium are indicated in the following sections on specific viruses. Lateral-flow tests can be conducted quickly and usually provide results in a short amount of time, and they can be used in the field without specialized equipment and with minimal training. The other tests require specialized equipment and trained personnel and are typically done in government, private (e.g., diagnostics and seed companies), and university laboratories. Proper identification of a suspected virus disease is essential for knowing the potential for economic loss and, if necessary, the approach or approaches to use for disease management.

Among the important viruses that infect lettuce, the seed- and aphid-transmitted *Lettuce mosaic virus* (LMV) is distributed worldwide and historically has caused the greatest economic losses. However, it can be effectively managed through an integrated management strategy involving planting virus-free lettuce seed, using resistant cultivars, managing reservoir host plants, and providing lettuce-free periods. Lettuce big vein, caused by the *Mirafiori lettuce big-vein virus* (which is transmitted by a soilborne *Olpidium* fungus), is a common and distinctive disease of lettuce in some growing regions. The thrips-transmitted tospoviruses—*Tomato spotted wilt virus, Tomato chlorotic spot virus, Groundnut ringspot virus,* and *Impatiens necrotic spot virus*—have emerged as important viral pathogens of lettuce in a number of production areas in North America and South America. Table 2 presents a list of lettuce-infecting viruses according to their vectors, classifications, and symptoms.

(Prepared by R. L. Gilbertson)

Alfalfa Mosaic

Alfalfa mosaic is caused by *Alfalfa mosaic virus* (AMV) and is a minor disease of lettuce. It was first reported in Arizona (United States) in 1965 in a field of crisphead lettuce located near an alfalfa field and has since been reported sporadically in North America (United States: Arizona and California) and Europe (France and Spain). The disease occurs most commonly in lettuce fields established adjacent to or near alfalfa fields.

Symptoms

Leaves of lettuce plants infected with AMV develop a striking bright-yellow mosaic or calico pattern (Fig. 87). Older

TABLE 2. Viruses and Phytoplasmas That Infect Lettuce and Other Leafy Green Crops (grouped by types of vectors)[a]

APHID VECTORS

Virus (Acronym)	Transmission Type	Genus (Family)	Primary Symptom Type(s)[b]	Other Modes of Transmission[c]	Important Vector Species[d]	Section in This Book
Alfalfa mosaic virus (AMV)	Nonpersistent	Alfamovirus (Bromoviridae)	Y, Mos, Mot, EV, St	M, S[e]	Aphis craccivora, Myzus persicae	Alfalfa Mosaic
Beet western yellows virus (BWYV)	Persistent	Polerovirus (Luteoviridae)	Chl, Y, CS, Br	NA	Myzus persicae	Beet Western Yellows
Beet yellow stunt virus (BYSV)	Semipersistent	Closterovirus (Closteroviridae)	Chl, Y	NA	Hyperomyzus lactucae, Macrosiphum euphorbiae, Myzus persicae	Beet Yellow Stunt
Bidens mottle virus (BiMoV)	Nonpersistent	Potyvirus (Potyviridae)	Mos, Mot, VC	M	Nasonovia ribisnigri, Aphis craccivora, Myzus persicae	Bidens Mottle
Broad bean wilt virus (BBWV)	Nonpersistent	Fabavirus (Secoviridae)	LD, Mot, VN, NS, RHF	M	Aphis craccivora, Hyperomyzus lactucae, Macrosiphum euphorbiae	Broad Bean Wilt
Cucumber mosaic virus (CMV)	Nonpersistent	Cucumovirus (Bromoviridae)	Mos, Mot, LD, St	M	Myzus persicae, Aphis craccivora, Aphis gossypii, Hyperomyzus lactucae, Macrosiphum euphorbiae, Myzus ornatus, Myzus persicae	Cucumber Mosaic
Dandelion yellow mosaic virus (DaYMV)	Semipersistent	Sequivirus (Sequiviridae)	Bz, VC, VN	M	Nasonovia ribisnigri, Aulacorthum solani, Myzus ascalonicus, Myzus ornatus	Dandelion Yellow Mosaic
Lettuce mosaic virus (LMV)	Nonpersistent	Potyvirus (Potyviridae)	Mos, Mot, VC, Chl, Y, N, NS, St, RHF	M, P, S	Myzus persicae, Aulacorthum solani, Acyrthosiphon lactucae, Aphis craccivora, Aphis gossypii, Hyperomyzus lactucae, Macrosiphum euphorbiae, Myzus persicae	Lettuce Mosaic
Lettuce mottle virus (LeMoV)	Nonpersistent	Sequivirus (Sequiviridae)	Mos, Mot, LD, N, RHF	M	Nasonovia ribisnigri	Lettuce Mottle
Lettuce necrotic yellows virus (LNYV)	Persistent, Propagative	Cytorhabdovirus (Rhabdoviridae)	Bz, N, St, LD, Chl, Mot	M	Hyperomyzus lactucae, Hyperomyzus carduellinus, Hyperomyzus lactucae	Lettuce Necrotic Yellows
Sonchus yellow net virus (SYNV)	Persistent, Propagative	Nucleorhabdovirus (Rhabdoviridae)	VC, St, Y, LS, Chl, N	M	Aphis coreopsidis	Sonchus Yellow Net
Sowthistle yellow vein virus (SYVV)	Persistent, Propagative	Nucleorhabdovirus (Rhabdoviridae)	VC, Y	M	Hyperomyzus lactucae	Sowthistle Yellow Vein
Turnip mosaic virus (TuMV)	Nonpersistent	Potyvirus (Potyviridae)	LS, Chl, Mot, Ruf, LD, CS, NS	M	Aphis craccivora, Brevicoryne brassicae, Macrosiphum euphorbiae, Myzus persicae	Turnip Mosaic

WHITEFLY VECTORS

Virus (Acronym)	Transmission Type	Genus (Family)	Primary Symptom Type(s)[b]	Other Modes of Transmission[c]	Important Vector Species[d]	Section in This Book
Lettuce chlorosis virus (LCV)	Semipersistent	Crinivirus (Closteroviridae)	Y, Br, VC, LD, RHF	NA	Bemisia tabaci (biotypes A and B)	Lettuce Chlorosis
Lettuce infectious yellows virus (LIYV)	Semipersistent	Crinivirus (Closteroviridae)	Y, Br, VC, LD, RHF	NA	Bemisia tabaci (biotype A)	Lettuce Chlorosis

THRIPS VECTORS

Virus (Acronym)	Transmission Type	Genus (Family)	Primary Symptom Type(s)[b]	Other Modes of Transmission[c]	Important Vector Species[d]	Section in This Book
Groundnut ringspot virus (GRSV)	Persistent, propagative	Tospovirus (Bunyaviridae)	Bz, St, Y, NS, N, RHF	M	Frankliniella occidentalis, Frankliniella schultzei	Tomato Spotted Wilt
Impatiens necrotic spot virus (INSV)	Persistent, propagative	Tospovirus (Bunyaviridae)	St, RS, Y, N, RHF, NS	M	Frankliniella intonsa, Frankliniella occidentalis	Impatiens Necrotic Spot

	Transmission Type	Genus (Family)	Primary Symptom Type(s)[b]	Other Modes of Transmission[c]	Important Vector Species[d]	Section in This Book
Tobacco streak virus (TSV)	Thrips-feeding, pollen-mediated	*Ilarvirus (Bromoviridae)*	NS, NStr, N, Ruf, RS	M, P, S[e]	*Frankliniella occidentalis*, *Thrips tabaci*	Tobacco Streak
Tomato chlorotic spot virus (TCSV)	Persistent, propagative	*Tospovirus (Bromoviridae)*	Bz, St, Y, NS, N, RHF	M	*Frankliniella occidentalis*, *Frankliniella schultzei*	Tomato Spotted Wilt
Tomato spotted wilt virus (TSWV)	Persistent, propagative	*Tospovirus (Bunyaviridae)*	Bz, St, Y, NS, N, RHF	M	*Frankliniella bispinosa*, *Frankliniella fusca*, *Frankliniella intonsa*, *Frankliniella occidentalis*, *Frankliniella schultzei*, *Thrips setosus*, *Thrips tabaci*	Tomato Spotted Wilt

LEAFHOPPER VECTORS

Phytoplasma	Transmission Type	Genus (Family)	Primary Symptom Type(s)[b]	Other Modes of Transmission[c]	Important Vector Species[d]	Section in This Book
'Candidatus Phytoplasma asteri' (Lettuce yellows phytoplasma)	Propagative	Phytoplasma	St, Chl, LD	NA	*Macrosteles quadrilineatus*	Lettuce Yellows (Aster Yellows), Lettuce Phyllody, and Australian Lettuce Phyllody
Lettuce phyllody phytoplasma	Not determined	Phytoplasma	St, Chl, LD	NA	*Neoaliturus fenestratus*	Lettuce Yellows (Aster Yellows), Lettuce Phyllody, and Australian Lettuce Phyllody

CHYTRID FUNGI VECTORS

Virus (Acronym)	Transmission Type	Genus (Family)	Primary Symptom Type(s)[b]	Other Modes of Transmission[c]	Important Vector Species[d]	Section in This Book
Lettuce big-vein associated virus (LBVaV)	F[f]	*Varicosavirus* (Unassigned)	Symptomless	NA	*Olpidium virulentus*	Lettuce Big Vein
Mirafiori lettuce big-vein virus (MLBVV)	F[f]	*Ophiovirus (Ophioviridae)*	EV, VC, VB, St, RHF, Ruf	M	*Olpidium virulentus*	Lettuce Big Vein

NEMATODE VECTORS

Virus (Acronym)	Transmission Type	Genus (Family)	Primary Symptom Type(s)[b]	Other Modes of Transmission[c]	Important Vector Species[d]	Section in This Book
Tobacco rattle virus (TRV)	Semipersistent	*Tobravirus (Virgaviridae)*	LS, LD, Mos, Mot, RS	M	*Paratrichodorus* spp., *Trichodorus* spp.	Tobacco Rattle
Tobacco ringspot virus (TRSV)	Semipersistent	*Nepovirus (Secoviridae)*	RS, Y, Mot, Mos, St	M, P, S[e]	*Xiphinema americanum*	Tobacco Ringspot

UNKNOWN VECTORS

Virus (Acronym)	Transmission Type	Genus (Family)	Primary Symptom Type(s)[b]	Other Modes of Transmission[c]	Important Vector Species[d]	Section in This Book
Moroccan pepper virus (MPV)	No known vector	*Tombusvirus (Tombusviridae)*	St, N, Y, VC, VN, RHF	M	Not applicable	Lettuce Dieback
Tomato bushy stunt virus (TBSV)	No known vector	*Tombusvirus (Tombusviridae)*	St, N, Y, VC, VN, RHF	M	Not applicable	Lettuce Dieback

[a] Courtesy W. M. Wintermantel and R. L. Gilbertson.
[b] Some of the symptoms listed may be specific to lettuce. Symptom key: Br = Brittle leaf, Bz = Bronzing, Chl = Chlorosis, CS = Chlorotic spots, En = Enations, EV = Enlarged veins, LC = Leaf curl, LD = Leaf distortion, LS = Leaf spots, Mot = Mottle, Mos = Mosaic, N = Necrosis, NS = Necrotic spots, NStr = Necrotic streaking, RHF = Reduced head formation, RS = Ring spots, Ruf = Ruffling of margins, St = Stunting, VB = Vein banding, VC = Vein clearing, VN = Vein necrosis, Y = Yellowing.
[c] Transmission key: M = Mechanical transmission, P = Pollen transmission, S = Seed transmission, NA = No alternate mode of transmission.
[d] Vectors listed in this table but not the text include those that are important in certain geographic regions.
[e] Seed transmitted in crops other than lettuce.
[f] F = Fungus.

Fig. 87. Characteristic bright-yellow mosaic or calico pattern on a crisphead lettuce plant infected with *Alfalfa mosaic virus*. (Courtesy R. L. Gilbertson—© APS)

Fig. 88. Older romaine lettuce leaves with enlarged veins, caused by *Alfalfa mosaic virus*. (Courtesy S. T. Koike—© APS)

Fig. 89. Stunted growth of a romaine lettuce plant (right), caused by *Alfalfa mosaic virus* infection, compared with growth of a healthy plant (left). (Courtesy S. T. Koike—© APS)

leaves show a yellow to white, chalky mottle and enlarged veins (Fig. 88). Infected plants may be stunted, particularly those infected at an early stage of growth (Fig. 89). Because of the striking yellow mosaic symptoms in leaves, the disease is sometimes referred to as "calico."

Causal Agent

AMV is a plus-sense, single-stranded, multipartite RNA virus and is the type and only member of the genus *Alfamovirus* in the family *Bromoviridae*. AMV virions are bullet shaped (bacilliform) and have four sizes: 18 × 30, 35, 43, and 56 nm. Like other bromoviruses, AMV has a multipartite genome that is divided among three different-sized, plus-sense, single-stranded RNAs: RNA-1 (~3.7 kb), RNA-2 (~2.6 kb), and RNA-3 (~2.2 kb). Each is individually encapsidated into different-sized virions. A subgenomic RNA (~0.9 kb), transcribed from RNA-3, encodes the capsid protein and is separately encapsidated into the smallest (18 × 30 nm) virion. The capsid protein activates gene expression from the genomic RNAs and thus is required for infectivity. Numerous strains of AMV with distinct biological properties have been described.

The host range of AMV is extremely wide. As many as 150 plant species in 22 families are reported to be infected in nature, and an additional 430 plant species in 51 families can be infected experimentally.

AMV is transmitted by at least 22 species of aphids, including the green peach aphid (*Myzus persicae*), in a nonpersistent (styletborne) manner. Thus, the virus is acquired and transmitted in seconds. In some hosts, such as alfalfa, AMV is pollen borne and seed transmitted, but seed transmission has not been demonstrated in lettuce. AMV is transmitted mechanically (via sap) but not by plant-to-plant contact.

AMV can be detected using serological methods, such as enzyme-linked immunosorbent assay (ELISA), and using reverse transcription-polymerase chain reaction (RT-PCR) and sequencing.

Disease Cycle and Epidemiology

Alfalfa mosaic is infrequently observed in lettuce crops, and therefore, lettuce does not play an important role in the disease cycle. Because AMV is not thought to be seed transmitted in lettuce, the primary inoculum source is aphids that carry the virus after acquiring it from infected crop and weed plants. The most important of these are perennials, especially alfalfa, and outbreaks of alfalfa mosaic in lettuce are often correlated with the proximity of the lettuce fields to alfalfa fields.

After AMV has been introduced into a lettuce field by viruliferous aphids, spread within the field depends on the subsequent level of aphid activity.

Management

Management measures are usually not warranted for AMV in lettuce. To prevent the disease from developing, lettuce should not be planted adjacent to alfalfa fields. There are no reports of resistance in lettuce to AMV infection.

Selected References

Jaspars, E. M. J., and Bos, L. 1980. Alfalfa mosaic virus. Descriptions of Plant Viruses, no. 229 (no. 46 rev.). Commonwealth Mycological Institute, Kew, Survey, UK.

Stone, W. J. H., and Nelson, M. R. 1966. Alfalfa mosaic virus (calico) of lettuce. Plant Dis. Rep. 50:629-631.

(Prepared by R. L. Gilbertson)

Beet Western Yellows

Beet western yellows, caused by *Beet western yellows virus* (BWYV), is widely distributed throughout many parts of the United States and has been associated with lettuce production since at least the 1950s. The virus is responsible for yield and quality losses in lettuce throughout the world and is one of several viruses that cause yellowing symptoms.

Symptoms

The symptoms and rate of symptom development of beet western yellows vary depending on the lettuce cultivar, stage of plant growth when infected, and climatic conditions. Initial symptoms may develop from 12 to 30 days following inoculation of BWYV by aphids. The rate of symptom development depends on the stage of plant growth at infection and light intensity.

The initial symptom of BWYV infection is the formation of mild, chlorotic spots in interveinal areas, especially at the tips of middle-aged and older leaves. The interveinal areas become yellow (chlorotic), and older leaves become an intense yellow to nearly white. The major veins remain green (Fig. 90). Older infected leaves also become thick and brittle. Infected plants are not visibly reduced in size but may become unmarketable because of brittle leaves and foliar discoloration.

Symptoms of beet western yellows resemble those associated with magnesium and iron deficiency. Studies have suggested that co-infection of BWYV with *Lettuce mosaic virus* may make crisphead lettuce plants more susceptible to the development of internal rib necrosis, although severity may vary by cultivar.

Causal Agent

BWYV is a plus-sense, single-stranded RNA virus and a member of the genus *Polerovirus* in the family *Luteoviridae*. BWYV virions are icosahedral and approximately 26 nm in diameter. The genome consists of a single plus-sense, single-stranded RNA of 5,666 nucleotides. The virion is composed of two capsid proteins: a major capsid protein of approximately 22 kilodaltons (kDa) and a minor capsid protein of 75 kDa.

BWYV is closely related to several other *Polerovirus* spp., but only BWYV and some isolates of *Turnip yellows virus* are known to infect lettuce. Serological tests, such as enzyme-linked immunosorbent assay (ELISA), can confirm a polerovirus infection, but because of the high degree of similarity among the capsid proteins of several poleroviruses, confirmation of the virus species requires the use of molecular detection methods, such as reverse transcription-polymerase chain reaction (RT-PCR) and sequencing.

Epidemiology

The best-studied vector of BWYV is the green peach aphid (*Myzus persicae*), but at least eight other species of aphids are also known to transmit the virus. BWYV is transmitted in a persistent (circulative) manner within the aphid vector, but the virus does not replicate in the aphid. BWYV can be acquired by aphids during feeding on an infected source plant for as little as 5 min and can be transmitted by feeding for a period as short as 10 min. However, efficient virus acquisition and transmission requires feeding for several hours. The virus must circulate through the body of the insect, and following a latent period of 12–24 h, transmission can occur. BWYV can persist in some aphid species for more than 50 days—essentially, for the life of the insect. These vectors retain the ability to transmit BWYV after molting but do not transmit the virus to their progeny.

The host range of BWYV is very broad; more than 146 species in 23 families have been reported to be susceptible. There are different variants or strains of BWYV, and they have distinct host ranges. In addition to lettuce, several other crops can be infected by BWYV, including beet and Swiss chard (*Beta vulgaris*), broccoli and cauliflower, spinach, pea, and potato. These hosts can serve as inoculum sources for aphids to acquire BWYV. Some common weed hosts include wild crucifers such as London rocket (*Sisymbrium irio*), shepherd's purse (*Capsella bursa-pastoris*), common mallow (*Malva parviflora*), and fiddleneck (*Amsinckia* spp.), as well as many wild species in the Asteraceae and Solanaceae. Diagnostic species include shepherd's purse, old-man-in-the-Spring or groundsel (*Senecio vulgaris*), and miner's lettuce (*Claytonia perfoliata*).

BWYV is not mechanically (sap) transmissible, nor is it seed-borne or seed transmitted in lettuce.

Management

Beet western yellows does not usually cause economically significant damage to lettuce crops, and management is typically not warranted. BWYV is extremely difficult to control. Doing so involves eliminating reservoir hosts, and BWYV has an extensive host range among weed and crop plants. Even so, weeds that are known reservoir hosts of the virus should be eliminated. To reduce virus spread from crops infected with BWYV to new lettuce plantings, the latter should be separated by as much space and time as possible. Reducing aphid populations through insecticide treatment programs or biological control methods will reduce but not eliminate transmission of the virus from reservoir hosts or crops to lettuce.

Crisphead lettuce cultivars generally have higher levels of resistance to BWYV than romaine and butterhead cultivars. Resistance to BWYV has been identified in wild *Lactuca* spp.

Selected References

Beuve, M., Stevens, M., Liu, H.-Y., Wintermantel, W. M., Hauser, S., and Lemaire, O. 2008. Biological and molecular characterization of an American sugar beet-infecting *Beet western yellows virus* isolate. Plant Dis. 92:51-60.

D'Arcy, C. J., Torrance, L., and Martin, R. R. 1989. Discrimination among luteoviruses and their strains by monoclonal antibodies and identification of common epitopes. Phytopathology 79:869-873.

Duffus, J. E. 1960. Radish yellows, a disease of radish, sugar beet, and other crops. Phytopathology 50:389-394.

Duffus, J. E. 1960. Two viruses that induce symptoms typical of "June yellows" in lettuce. Plant Dis. Rep. 44:406-408.

Duffus, J. E. 1977. Aphids, viruses, and the yellow plague. Pages 361-383 in: Aphids as Virus Vectors. K. F. Harris and K. Maramorosch, eds. Academic Press, New York.

Duffus, J. E., and Russell, G. E. 1975. Serological relationship between beet western yellows and beet mild yellowing viruses. Phytopathology 65:811-815.

Falk, B. W., and Duffus, J. E. 1984. Identification of small single and double-stranded RNAs associated with severe symptoms in beet western yellows virus-infected *Capsella bursa-pastoris*. Phytopathology 74:1224-1229.

Govier, D. A. 1985. Purification and partial characterization of beet mild yellowing virus and its serological detection in plants and aphids. Ann. Appl. Biol. 107:439-447.

Lewellen, R. T. 2004. Registration germplasm lines C67/2, C69/2, C78/3, and C80/2 with resistance to virus yellows and rhizomania. Crop Sci. 44:358-359.

Fig. 90. Crisphead lettuce infected with *Beet western yellows virus*, showing foliar chlorosis with the major veins remaining green. (Courtesy J. E. Duffus)

Maisonneuve, B., Chovelon, V., and Lot, H. 1991. Inheritance of resistance to beet western yellows virus in *Lactuca virosa* L. HortScience 26:1543-1545.

Mayo, M. A., and W. A. Miller. 1999. The structure and expression of Luteovirus genomes. Pages 23-42 in: The Luteoviruses. H. G. Smith and H. Barker, eds. CAB International, Wallingford, UK.

Mayo, M. A., and Ziegler-Graff, V. 1996. Molecular biology of luteoviruses. Adv. Virus Res. 46:413-460.

Pink, D. A. C., Walkey, D. G. A., and McClement, S. J. 1991. Genetics of resistance to beet western yellows virus in lettuce. Plant Pathol. 40:542-545.

Russell, G. E. 1958. Sugar beet yellows: A preliminary study of the distribution and interrelationships of viruses and virus strains found in East Anglia, 1955-57. Ann. Appl. Biol. 46:393-398.

Zink, F. W., and Duffus, J. E. 1972. Association of beet western yellows and lettuce mosaic viruses with internal rib necrosis of lettuce. Phytopathology 62:1141-1144.

(Prepared by J. E. Duffus;
revised by W. M. Wintermantel)

Beet Yellow Stunt

Beet yellow stunt virus (BYSV) is a potentially destructive yellows-type virus that affects lettuce and other plants in the family Asteraceae. Infections of lettuce by BYSV have been reported from California (United States) and England. Although beet yellow stunt has been responsible for substantial losses in some lettuce fields in California since the 1960s, it has never been a widespread problem.

Symptoms

The initial symptom of BYSV infection is chlorosis of the older leaves, similar to that induced by *Beet western yellows virus*. In addition, the outer leaves may fold back. As an infected plant grows, the older leaves develop a pronounced yellowing (Fig. 91).

A plant infected at an early stage of growth may collapse prematurely and die prior to head formation. In such a case, symptoms of beet yellow stunt may be confused with the collapse symptoms observed in lettuce drop disease (caused by *Sclerotinia* spp.). The phloem tissue of a BYSV-infected plant is extremely necrotic and displays distinct brown zones extending into the crown tissue when the stem and crown are cut longitudinally (Fig. 92).

Causal Agent

BYSV is a plus-sense, single-stranded RNA virus and a member of the genus *Closterovirus* in the family *Closteroviridae*. BYSV virions are long, flexuous, filamentous rods. A single virion is approximately 12.5 × 1,400.0 nm, and it is composed of a single major capsid protein with a molecular weight of approximately 24.5 kilodaltons. The genome is composed of a single species of plus-sense, single-stranded RNA of approximately 18,000 nucleotides. The virus genome has been only partially sequenced and is organized similarly to the genomes of other members of the genus *Closterovirus*.

Epidemiology

BYSV is transmitted by aphids in a semipersistent manner. The sowthistle aphid (*Hyperomyzus lactucae*) is the most efficient vector (Fig. 93). Its preferred host is common sowthistle (*Sonchus oleraceus*), and it feeds only transiently on lettuce. The virus is transmitted less efficiently by the green peach aphid (*Myzus persicae*), the currant-lettuce aphid (*Nasonovia ribisnigri*), and the potato aphid (*Macrosiphum euphorbiae*). Most aphids cease to transmit the virus 1–2 days after acquisition, but the virus can persist for up to 4 days in some species. BYSV is not transmitted transstadially (i.e., after molting).

Common sowthistle is the principal reservoir of BYSV and the primary reproductive host of the sowthistle aphid. Thus,

Fig. 92. Vascular discoloration of lettuce root, caused by *Beet yellow stunt virus*. (Courtesy J. E. Duffus)

Fig. 91. Yellowing of older leaves in crisphead lettuce, caused by *Beet yellow stunt virus*. (Courtesy W. M. Wintermantel)

Fig. 93. Sowthistle aphid (*Hyperomyzus lactucae*). (Courtesy D. Gibson and J. Fletcher—© APS)

70

a high incidence of BYSV infection in lettuce occurs only in areas in which common sowthistle is abundant. In addition to common sowthistle, prickly lettuce (*Lactuca serriola*), a species of wild lettuce, is commonly infected. BYSV has also been reported to infect plants in the families Asteraceae, Chenopodiaceae, Geraniaceae, Portulacaceae, and Solanaceae.

Like other members of the family *Closteroviridae*, BYSV is not transmitted mechanically (sap) or via seed.

Management

Beet yellow stunt is not a common disease of lettuce, and management is generally not necessary. Resistant cultivars are not available.

To minimize losses from beet yellow stunt, lettuce fields should not be established adjacent to crops with BYSV-infected plants or areas with high populations of common sowthistle plants. In areas in which beet yellow stunt has caused losses, reservoir hosts (e.g., common sowthistle and prickly lettuce) should be controlled, and aphid populations in and around fields should be managed with insecticides.

Selected References

Duffus, J. E. 1972. Beet yellow stunt, a potentially destructive virus disease of sugar beet and lettuce. Phytopathology 62:161-165.

Duffus, J. E. 1979. Beet yellow stunt virus. Descriptions of Plant Viruses, no. 207. Commonwealth Mycological Institute, Kew, Surrey, UK.

Hoefert, L. L., Esau, K., and Duffus, J. E. 1970. Electron microscopy of *Beta* leaves infected with beet yellow stunt virus. Virology 42:814-824.

Karasev, A. V., Nikolaeva, O., Koonin, E. V., Gumpf, D. J., and Garnsey, S. M. 1994. Screening of the Closterovirus genome by degenerate primer-mediated polymerase chain reaction. J. Gen. Virol. 75:1415-1422.

Karasev, A. V., Nikolaeva, O., Mushegian, A. R., Lee, R. F., and Dawson, W. O. 1996. Organization of the 3'-terminal half of *Beet yellow stunt virus* genome and implications for the evolution of closteroviruses. Virology 221:199-207.

Reed, R. R., and Falk, B. W. 1989. Purification and partial characterization of beet yellow stunt virus. Plant Dis. 73:358-362.

(Prepared by J. E. Duffus; revised by W. M. Wintermantel)

Bidens Mottle

Bidens mottle virus (BiMoV) is one of many viruses that can cause mosaic and/or mottle symptoms in leaves of infected lettuce plants. Bidens mottle was first described in Florida (United States) in the late 1960s, where it caused mottling symptoms in lettuce, escarole, and endive. The virus was subsequently found infecting numerous weeds and ornamentals. In 2012, BiMoV was detected in stunted lettuce plants with distorted growth and mosaic symptoms in Taiwan.

Symptoms

Lettuce plants infected with BiMoV are stunted, especially when plants are infected at a young age, and the leaves develop mosaic/mottle symptoms (Fig. 94). In some cases, vein clearing or necrosis may also be observed in leaves.

These symptoms are similar to those induced by other lettuce-infecting potyviruses, such as *Lettuce mosaic virus* (LMV) and *Turnip mosaic virus* (TuMV), and the cucumovirus *Cucumber mosaic virus* (CMV).

Causal Agent

BiMoV is a plus-sense, single-stranded RNA virus and a member of the genus *Potyvirus* in the family *Potyviridae*. It has long, flexuous, rod-shaped virions (~13 × 720 nm) and a sin-gle approximately 10-kb, plus-sense, single-stranded genomic RNA, which is translated into a polyprotein.

BiMoV has a relatively wide host range, which includes both crops and weeds; hosts include 32 species in 28 genera in eight families. In addition to lettuce, BiMoV infects crops such as escarole, endive, and sunflower; weeds such as hairy beggarticks (*Bidens pilosa*) and Virginia pepperweed (*Lepidium virginicum*); and ornamentals such as elegant zinnia (*Zinnia elegans*), tropical whiteweed (*Ageratum conyzoides*), and marigold (*Calendula* spp.).

The virus is transmitted by several species of aphids in a nonpersistent (styletborne) manner. Adults and nymphs of the green peach aphid (*Myzus persicae*) are particularly efficient vectors of BiMoV. The virus is also mechanically (sap) transmissible. In contrast to LMV, BiMoV is not seed transmitted in hairy beggarticks or lettuce.

BiMoV is serologically distinct from other lettuce-infecting potyviruses, such as LMV and TuMV. It can be readily identified using serological tests, such as enzyme-linked immunosorbent assay (ELISA), and using reverse transcription-polymerase chain reaction (RT-PCR) and sequencing. BiMoV can also be identified by infection of certain differential hosts (e.g., sunflower and zinnia).

Disease Cycle and Epidemiology

In Florida, BiMoV occurs naturally in several annual and perennial weeds, including hairy beggarticks and Virginia pepperweed, which serve as reservoirs. In addition, BiMoV can infect ornamental bedding plants such as elegant zinnia and tropical whiteweed, which also can serve as inoculum sources for lettuce. Because BiMoV is not seedborne, the primary inoculum source is infected weed and ornamental reservoir hosts, from which aphids acquire the virus and transmit it to lettuce. The virus is subsequently spread in lettuce fields by viruliferous aphids.

In Florida, BiMoV commonly occurs in mixed infections with LMV. In one study of the relative incidences of these viruses, LMV was predominant in commercial lettuce fields (>90% incidence), whereas BiMoV was more prevalent in escarole fields (62% incidence). In field experiments, a higher incidence of BiMoV in lettuce was observed. Thus, in Florida, LMV appears to be more important in lettuce, although BiMoV also has the potential to cause losses.

Management

Eradication of local BiMoV reservoir hosts (especially weeds along ditch banks) is recommended as a general virus management strategy. Most commercial lettuce cultivars are susceptible to BiMoV, but the romaine-type cultivar Valmaine is resistant.

Fig. 94. Stunted growth of crisphead lettuce plants caused by *Bidens mottle virus* (lower left), *Lettuce mosaic virus* (upper right), and both viruses (lower right) compared with a healthy plant (upper left). (Courtesy T. A. Zitter—© APS)

Selected References

Chen, Y. K., and Lee, J. Y. 2012. First report of *Bidens mottle virus* causing mosaic and leaf distortion in garland chrysanthemum and lettuce in Taiwan. (Abstr.) Plant Dis. 96:464.

Christie, S. R., Edwardson, J. R., and Zettler, F. W. 1968. Characterization and electron microscopy of a virus isolated from *Bidens* and *Lepidium*. Plant Dis. Rep. 52:763-768.

Logan, A. E., Zettler, F. W., and Christie, S. R. 1984. Susceptibility of *Rudbeckia, Zinnia, Ageratum,* and other bedding plants to Bidens mottle virus. Plant Dis. 68:260-262.

Purcifull, D. E., Christie, S. R., Zitter, T. A., and Bassett, M. J. 1971. Natural infection of lettuce and endive by Bidens mottle virus. Plant Dis. Rep. 55:1061-1063.

Youssef, F., Marais, A., and Candresse, T. 2008. Partial genome sequence of Bidens mottle virus sheds light on its taxonomy. Arch. Virol. 153:227-228.

Zitter, T. A., and Guzman, V. L. 1974. Incidence of lettuce mosaic and Bidens mottle viruses in lettuce and escarole fields in Florida. Plant Dis. Rep. 58:1087-1091.

(Prepared by B. W. Falk; revised by R. L. Gilbertson)

Broad Bean Wilt

Broad bean wilt, caused by *Broad bean wilt virus* (BBWV), was first described in broad bean, or faba bean (*Vicia faba*), in Australia in 1947. The first reported infection of lettuce was in 1971 in New York (United States), where the virus also infects bean, pea, and spinach. After *Cucumber mosaic virus* (CMV), BBWV is the second most important virus of lettuce in New York State. Infections of lettuce have also been reported from eastern Germany and southern France. BBWV has a very wide host range and has been reported to infect various crops in Africa, Asia (especially China), Australia, Europe, North America, and South America.

Symptoms

Plants of susceptible lettuce cultivars respond to BBWV infection with varying degrees of foliar malformation, chlorotic mottle, brownish veinal necrosis, and interveinal necrotic pitting. Infected plants are stunted and produce small, poorly formed heads with loose leaves (Fig. 95). When exposed to stress caused by low nighttime and high daytime temperatures, infected plants develop a prominent reddish-brown color at the margins of affected leaves. Plants of cultivars with resistance retain their normal size and vigor and may be symptomless or show only a mild and often transient chlorotic mottle.

Fig. 95. Crisphead lettuce with small, poorly formed heads and loose leaves, caused by *Broad bean wilt virus*. (Courtesy T. A. Zitter—© APS)

In some cases, the symptoms induced by BBWV may be similar to those caused by CMV and by *Lettuce mosaic virus*. Positive identification of BBWV requires the use of diagnostic hosts and serological or molecular tests. In hosts other than lettuce, the symptoms of BBWV infection can vary seasonally and may disappear soon after infection.

Causal Agent

BBWV is a plus-sense, single-stranded RNA virus and a member of the genus *Fabavirus* in the family *Secoviridae*. BBWV virions are icosahedral and approximately 25 nm in diameter. Each is composed of two capsid proteins, which are 22 and 44 kilodaltons. The genome is bipartite, composed of two species of plus-sense, single-stranded RNA: RNA-1 (~6 kb) and RNA-2 (~3.5 kb). The two RNAs are encapsidated separately, and both are required for infectivity. Inclusion bodies are produced in infected plant cells—including amorphous X bodies near the nucleus, tubular crystals, and tubes and scrolls containing virus particles—and they can be used in diagnosis.

Considerable genetic diversity exists among isolates of BBWV that infect various crop plant species worldwide. Two serotypes of BBWV have been identified: BBWV-1 and BBWV-2. The type species from Australia was identified as a strain of BBWV-1. BBWV-1 isolates have been reported to infect broad bean, narrowleaf or buckthorn plantain (*Plantago lanceolata*), nasturtium (*Tropaeolum* spp.), parsley, pea, and spinach, whereas BBWV-2 isolates have been reported to infect broad bean, lettuce, narrowleaf plantain, and pea. In general, BBWV-1 isolates are more prevalent in Europe, whereas BBWV-2 isolates occur in Asia, Australia, and North America. Based on differences in serological reactions and nucleotide sequences, BBWV-1 and BBWV-2 have been recognized as distinct species in the genus *Fabavirus*.

Although BBWV-2 has been reported to infect lettuce, the host ranges of BBWV-1 and BBWV-2 overlap, and finding that BBWV-1 isolates also infect lettuce would not be unexpected. Furthermore, although the biological properties described in the remainder of this section relate to BBWV-2, many are shared with BBWV-1.

BBWV-2 has an extremely wide host range, including 177 species in 39 families; the hosts are mostly dicotyledonous plants but also include a few monocots. The principal families with important crop species are Asteraceae, Chenopodiaceae, Fabaceae, and Solanaceae. In addition to lettuce, other important susceptible crops include broad bean, common bean, cowpea, pepper, soybean, and spinach. Diagnostic hosts include broad bean (systemic symptoms); lambsquarters (*Chenopodium album*) and goosefoot (*C. amaranticolor*) (local lesions and systemic symptoms); and the tobacco species *Nicotiana glutinosa* (chlorotic ring spots and systemic symptoms).

In nature, BBWV-2 is transmitted by various species of aphids in a nonpersistent (styletborne) manner. The most efficient aphid vector is the green peach aphid (*Myzus persicae*). The cowpea aphid (*Aphis craccivora*) and the potato aphid (*Macrosiphum euphorbiae*) are also good vectors, and the sowthistle aphid (*Hyperomyzus lactucae*) may be a vector, as well. BBWV-2 is readily transmitted mechanically (via sap) but not by plant-to-plant contact. These is no evidence that BBWV-2 is seedborne in lettuce or most other species, although there was a report of seed transmission of a Syrian isolate at a very low frequency (0.4–0.6%).

BBWV-2 can be identified through the inoculation of diagnostic indicator host plants. However, the most effective and precise methods for identification involve serology, such as enzyme-linked immunosorbent assay (ELISA) with BBWV-2-specific antisera, as well as polymerase chain reaction (PCR) and sequencing.

Disease Cycle and Epidemiology

BBWV overwinters in a number of weeds, including common or broadleaf plantain (*Plantago major*) and narrowleaf plantain, and it survives during the season in spiny or prickly sowthistle (*Sonchus asper*) and redroot amaranth or pigweed (*Amaranthus retroflexus*). As noted previously, it is efficiently spread to lettuce crops via several aphid species. The relative incidence of BBWV-2 in the field is a function of the frequency and proximity of reservoir hosts (and infected crop plants) and the migration and populations of aphid vectors.

In cases in which the initial infection of a lettuce crop occurs early in the season, secondary spread within fields may develop and produce economic damage. However, such situations have been limited to occasional fields in some years in New York.

Management

The application of mineral oil sprays that interfere with virus transmission and insecticides that reduce aphid populations can slow the spread of BBWV in areas in which broad bean wilt is economically important. However, the most effective management strategy is to plant resistant cultivars. Resistance to BBWV-2 has been reported; in resistant cultivars, the virus titer is reduced, and in some lines, symptoms are absent. Resistance in *Lactuca* spp. appears to be recessive.

Selected References

Bruckart, W. L., and Lorbeer, J. W. 1975. Recent occurrences of cucumber mosaic, lettuce mosaic, and broad bean wilt viruses in lettuce and celery fields in New York. Plant Dis. Rep. 59:203-206.

Kobayashi, Y. O., Nakano, M., Kashiwazaki, S., Naito, T., Mikoshiba, Y., Shiota, A., Kameya-Iwaki, M., and Honda, Y. 1999. Sequence analysis of RNA-2 of different isolates of broad bean wilt virus confirms the existence of two distinct species. Arch. Virol. 144:1429-1438.

Provvidenti, R., Robinson, R. W., and Shail, J. W. 1984. Incidence of broad bean wilt virus in lettuce in New York State and sources of resistance. HortScience 19:569-570.

Stubbs, L. L. 1947. A destructive vascular wilt virus disease of broad bean (*Vicia faba* L.) in Victoria. J. Dep. Agric. Victoria 46:323-332.

Taylor, R. H., and Stubbs, L. L. 1972. Broad bean wilt virus. Descriptions of Plant Viruses, no. 81. Commonwealth Mycological Institute, Kew, Surrey, UK.

Uyemoto, J. K., and Provvidenti, R. 1974. Isolation and identification of two serotypes of broad bean wilt virus. Phytopathology 64:1547-1548.

(Prepared by T. A. Zitter; revised by R. L. Gilbertson)

Cucumber Mosaic

Cucumber mosaic, caused by *Cucumber mosaic virus* (CMV), is usually a minor disease of lettuce, but it can be a significant problem in some temperate lettuce-growing regions. The disease has been reported in Australia, Europe (Belgium, England, Germany, Italy, and Spain), New Zealand, and numerous states in the United States. In New York State, cucumber mosaic is the most important viral disease of lettuce, and fields with 100% incidence have been reported.

Symptoms

Lettuce plants infected with CMV are usually stunted, and leaves show varying degrees of light-green to yellow mosaic/mottling, as well as crinkling, distortion, and necrotic spots (Figs. 96 and 97). The intensity of the mosaic/mottling is related to the lettuce cultivar and the environmental conditions. For example, symptoms of CMV in lettuce tend to be more severe in the fall in the northeastern United States and in Europe, when day-to-night temperatures tend to fluctuate. The leaves of crisphead lettuce plants infected at an early stage of growth become severely stunted, and plants develop small, unmarketable heads (Fig. 98).

Fig. 96. Necrotic spots on romaine lettuce leaves, caused by *Cucumber mosaic virus*. (Courtesy S. T. Koike—© APS)

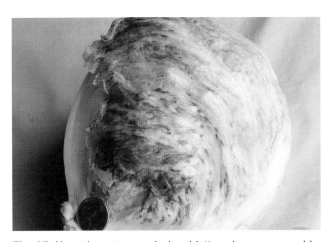

Fig. 97. Necrotic spots on crisphead lettuce leaves, caused by *Cucumber mosaic virus*. (Courtesy S. T. Koike—© APS)

Fig. 98. Chlorotic leaves and stunted growth of a romaine lettuce plant infected with *Cucumber mosaic virus* (right) compared with a healthy plant (left). (Courtesy S. T. Koike—© APS)

Symptoms induced in lettuce by CMV are difficult to differentiate from those induced by *Lettuce mosaic virus*. Diagnosis is further confounded by the fact that mixed infections of these and other viruses are common. Mixed infections tend to result in more severe stunting and yellowing of leaves than infections with individual viruses.

Causal Agent

CMV is a plus-sense, single-stranded RNA virus and the type species of the genus *Cucumovirus* in the family *Bromoviridae*. CMV virions are icosahedral (spherical) and measure 28–30 nm in diameter. The genome of CMV is tripartite and divided among three plus-sense, single-stranded RNAs, designated RNA-1 (~3.4 kb), RNA-2 (~3.0 kb), and RNA-3 (~2.2 kb); all three are required for systemic infection of a plant. RNA-1 and -2 encode proteins involved in viral replication, whereas RNA-3 encodes the 3a protein involved in movement and a subgenomic RNA (RNA-4 [~1.0 kb]), from which the capsid protein is translated. An additional subgenomic RNA is responsible for translation of the 2b silencing suppressor protein. RNA-1 and -2 are individually packaged into virions, whereas RNA-3 and -4 are packaged together into another virion. Thus, there are three types of virions, but all are similar in appearance and sedimentation coefficient (weight).

Numerous strains of CMV have been reported, and two subgroups (I and II) have been described based on serological and sequence properties. Subgroup I isolates are the most common, but relatively little is known about the CMV strains that infect lettuce. Finally, associated with some CMV strains is an additional small RNA referred to as the "satellite RNA," which is encapsidated within virions formed by the CMV capsid protein and totally dependent on the CMV helper virus for replication. The presence of the satellite RNA generally results in a reduction in symptom severity, but for some satellites, symptom severity is enhanced.

CMV has an extremely wide host range, including more than 1,200 species of dicotyledonous and monocotyledonous crop, weed, and ornamental plants. In nature, the virus is transmitted by more than 75 aphid species, including the green peach aphid (*Myzus persicae*) and the cotton aphid (*Aphis gossypii*). Transmission occurs in a nonpersistent (styletborne) manner; the virus is acquired and transmitted in 5–10 sec and retained for 1–2 h. The virus is also readily transmitted mechanically (via sap). Seed transmission has been reported in as many as 19 hosts but not in lettuce.

CMV can be detected by using serological methods, such as enzyme-linked immunosorbent assay (ELISA) and lateral-flow devices (immunostrips); by using reverse transcription-polymerase chain reaction (RT-PCR) and sequencing; and by identifying diagnostic symptoms in certain indicator plants.

Disease Cycle and Epidemiology

The primary inoculum sources of CMV infections in lettuce are nearby infected weed, ornamental, and crop plants. Infected perennial ornamental and weed hosts may be particularly important. For example, outbreaks of cucumber mosaic in lettuce in Arizona (United States) were associated with the proximity of fields to ornamental plants in housing developments. Because the virus is transmitted by aphids in a nonpersistent manner, spread may occur rapidly, particularly if aphid populations are large. Once introduced, the virus can be spread efficiently within a field by aphids, but it is not believed to be transmitted by touch or plant-to-plant contact.

Thus, the incidence CMV infection in lettuce is correlated with proximity to weed and crop reservoirs and with aphid activity. In general, the highest incidences of CMV infection occur in lettuce fields near fields of other infected crops (e.g., cucurbits) and near residential areas that have extensive plantings of ornamentals.

Management

Cucumber mosaic is difficult to control because of the wide host range of CMV and the nonpersistent mode of aphid transmission. Management strategies in lettuce are not generally implemented, because the virus is usually a minor problem in most production areas. To avoid introducing CMV into new plantings by viruliferous aphids, lettuce fields should not be planted next to or near old or recently harvested lettuce or cucurbit fields known to have CMV-infected plants (minimum separation of 100 m [300 feet]). In addition, annual and perennial weeds should be eliminated from areas surrounding fields.

Applications of stylet oils that interfere with virus transmission have been reported to slow the spread of CMV within a field, but frequent applications are needed to achieve reasonable control. Application of systemic insecticides, such as neonicotinoids, has also been reported to slow the spread of viruses transmitted by aphids in a nonpersistent manner.

Resistance to CMV was identified in a species of wild lettuce, *Lactuca saligna* (plant introduction [PI] 261653), from Portugal. Through pedigree selection from an interspecific cross of cultivar Ithaca × PI 261653, the CMV-resistant cultivar Saladcrisp was generated and released. Although a number of naturally occurring CMV strains can overcome the resistance in Saladcrisp, additional sources of resistance have not been identified.

Selected References

Bruckart, W. L., and Lorbeer, J. W. 1975. Recent occurrences of cucumber mosaic, lettuce mosaic and broad bean wilt viruses in lettuce and celery fields in New York. Plant Dis. Rep. 59:203-206.

Moreno, A., de Blas, C., Biurrun, R., Nebreda, M., Palacios, I., Duque, M., and Fereres, A. 2004. The incidence and distribution of viruses infecting lettuce, cultivated *Brassica* and associated natural vegetation in Spain. Ann. Appl. Biol. 144:339-346.

Nelson, M. R., and McKittrick, R. T. 1969. Epidemiology of cucumber mosaic and other virus diseases of lettuce in Arizona. Plant Dis. Rep. 53:27-29.

Provvidenti, R. R., Robinson, W., and Shail, J. W. 1980. A source of resistance to a strain of cucumber mosaic virus in *Lactuca saligna* L. HortScience 15:528-529.

Robinson, R. W., and Provvidenti, R. 1993. Breeding lettuce for viral resistance. Pages 61-79 in: Resistance to Viral Diseases of Vegetables. M. M. Kyle, ed. Timber Press, Portland, OR.

Thompson, A. D., and Proctor, C. H. 1966. Cucumber mosaic virus in lettuce. N.Z. J. Agric. Res. 9:142-144.

(Prepared by R. L. Gilbertson)

Dandelion Yellow Mosaic

Dandelion yellow mosaic, caused by *Dandelion yellow mosaic virus* (DaYMV), was first reported in lettuce and dandelion (*Taraxacum officinale*) in the United Kingdom in 1944. It has since been reported from other countries in Europe, including Denmark, Finland, Germany, the Netherlands, Sweden, and the former Czechoslovakia. Although symptoms of the disease can be severe, the incidence is usually not high and economic losses are rare. The highest incidences of dandelion yellow mosaic have been reported from the United Kingdom (Hertfordshire and Rothamsted); economic losses have occurred occasionally, particularly in lettuce cultivars with resistance to *Lettuce mosaic virus* (LMV). The disease has not been reported outside Europe.

Symptoms

Young leaves of DaYMV-infected lettuce plants initially show bronzing. This symptom is followed by the development of veinal chlorosis and necrosis, which may become pronounced. In addition, leaves often develop blistering and yellow mottling.

Infected plants are typically stunted and have distorted leaves, especially those infected at an early stage of growth. Dandelion yellow mosaic can be observed in lettuce plants grown in the greenhouse or in the field, but it tends to be most damaging in the field.

The virus also infects two species of wild lettuce: *Lactuca serriola* (prickly lettuce), which develops a green mottle in younger leaves, and *L. virosa,* which develops yellow blotches.

Causal Agent

DaYMV is a plus-sense, single-stranded RNA virus and a member of the genus *Sequivirus* in the family *Sequiviridae.* The virions are icosahedral (spherical) and approximately 30 nm in diameter. The genome is composed of one plus-sense, single-stranded RNA of approximately 10 kb.

In addition to the natural hosts lettuce and dandelion, the host range of DaYMV includes plants in six families, including lambsquarters (*Chenopodium album*) and goosefoot (*C. amaranticolor*) and the tobacco species *Nicotiana clevelandii* and *N. benthamiana.* In nature, the virus is transmitted by several species of aphids, including the green peach aphid (*Myzus persicae*), in a semipersistent manner. The virus is also mechanically transmissible (via sap) but not easily. There is no evidence of seed transmission.

Detection of the virus can be accomplished using enzyme-linked immunosorbent assay (ELISA) or using reverse transcription-polymerase chain reaction (RT-PCR) and sequencing.

Disease Cycle and Epidemiology

DaYMV has been reported only in Europe. Outbreaks of dandelion yellow mosaic are generally associated with proximity to infected dandelion plants, which serve as a reservoir for the virus and aphids. In areas in which DaYMV-infected dandelions are plentiful and aphid populations are large, the incidence of DaYMV in lettuce plants can be relatively high. Because of the severe symptoms induced by the virus, economic losses may occur in lettuce fields in these areas.

DaYMV is one of the viruses that will infect and cause symptoms in cultivars with resistance to LMV.

Management

In areas with a history of yield losses caused by dandelion yellow mosaic, dandelion plants should be removed in and around fields and insecticides should be used for aphid control. Harvested fields with infected plants should be promptly plowed under, and new lettuce fields should not be established adjacent to or near fields with DaYMV-infected plants. Lettuce plants should not be moved from areas known to have DaYMV to areas in which the virus is not found.

Selected References

Bos, L., Huijberts, N., Huttiga, H., and Maat, D. Z. 1983. Further characterization of dandelion yellow mosaic virus from lettuce and dandelion. Neth. J. Plant Pathol. 89:207-222.

Brcák, J. 1979. Czech and Scandinavian isolates resembling dandelion yellow mosaic virus. Biol. Plant. 21:298-301.

Kassanis, B. 1947. Studies on dandelion yellow mosaic virus and other virus diseases of lettuce. Ann. Appl. Biol. 34:412-421.

Moore, W. C. 1946. A virus disease of *Cos*-lettuce (Dandelion yellow mosaic virus). Trans. Br. Mycol. Soc. 29:252-253.

(Prepared by P. Guzman; revised by R. L. Gilbertson)

Impatiens Necrotic Spot

Lettuce can be infected by a number of tospoviruses, depending on the region of production. The most common and economically important of these is *Tomato spotted wilt virus* (TSWV—see the later section "Tomato Spotted Wilt"). However, in the mid-2000s, severe tospovirus-like symptoms appeared in commercial lettuce fields in the Salinas Valley of California (United States). Diagnostic tests revealed that the causal agent was *Impatiens necrotic spot virus* (INSV)—a tospovirus typically associated with ornamental plants. Since this initial report, outbreaks of impatiens necrotic spot disease have continued to occur in coastal lettuce-growing areas of California, sometimes causing economic losses. INSV has also been reported to infect lettuce in Italy. Thus, INSV is emerging as a pathogen of crop plants as well as ornamentals.

Symptoms

Symptoms of INSV infection in lettuce are similar to those caused by other tospoviruses, including TSWV. Infected plants are stunted, and leaves show tan to dark-brown spots or ring spots and varying degrees of yellowing and necrosis with the leaves curling down (Figs. 99 and 100). Plants infected at a young age are severely stunted and necrotic and sometimes die. Older plants show varying degrees of stunting and distorted growth, and the leaves show extensive marginal necrosis (as necrotic spots coalesce), distortion, wilting, and yellowing. Infected plants generally fail to produce marketable heads (Fig. 101).

Causal Agent

INSV is an ambisense, single-stranded RNA virus and a member of the genus *Tospovirus* in the family *Bunyaviridae.* Tospovirus virions are pleomorphic, spherical particles and

Fig. 99. Necrosis and distortion of leaf lettuce, caused by *Impatiens necrotic spot virus.* (Courtesy S. T. Koike—© APS)

Fig. 100. Necrosis and distortion of romaine lettuce, caused by *Impatiens necrotic spot virus.* (Courtesy S. T. Koike—© APS)

Fig. 101. Severe stunting of romaine lettuce, caused by *Impatiens necrotic spot virus*. (Courtesy S. T. Koike—© APS)

roughly 80–120 nm in diameter; each virion is covered by an envelope consisting of a host-derived, lipid bilayer membrane. The tospovirus genome consists of three ambisense, single-stranded RNAs of a total size of approximately 16 kb. The small (S) RNA (2.9 kb) encodes the viral nucleocapsid (N) protein (29 kilodaltons [kDa]) and a nonstructural (NSs) protein; the middle (M) RNA (4.8 kb) encodes a precursor of the two glycoproteins (G1 [78 kDa] and G2 [58 kDa]) and a nonstructural (NSm) movement protein; and the large (L) RNA (8.9 kb) encodes the viral RNA polymerase (~200 kDa). The virion consists of a core composed of the ribonucleoproteins in the form of the three RNAs individually encapsidated by the N protein, a few molecules of the polymerase, and the outerhost, membrane-derived envelope, from which project the viral glycoproteins embedded in the membrane.

Like TSWV, INSV has a wide host range that includes crop plants (e.g., lettuce, pepper, potato, spinach, and tomato), as well as ornamentals and weeds. Like other tospoviruses, INSV is transmitted by thrips in a persistent, propagative manner. However, unlike TSWV, which is transmitted by at least seven species of thrips, INSV is transmitted primarily by the western flower thrips (*Frankliniella occidentalis*) and to a lesser extent by the European flower thrips (*F. intonsa*). In the outbreaks of impatiens necrotic spot in lettuce in California, the western flower thrips has been the primary vector of the virus. INSV is also mechanically (sap) transmissible, although long-term propagation of the virus requires transmission by thrips at regular intervals. There is no evidence that INSV is seed transmitted in any host.

Because the symptoms induced in lettuce (and other crops) by different tospoviruses are similar, diagnostic tests must be used to identify the species involved. Detection of INSV can be accomplished using serological methods, including enzyme-linked immunosorbent assay (ELISA) and lateral-flow devices (immunostrips), and using reverse transcription-polymerase chain reaction (RT-PCR) and sequencing. Indeed, the identification of INSV in lettuce plants with tospovirus symptoms in the Salinas Valley resulted from the initial negative results with a TSWV lateral-flow device and subsequent positive results with an INSV device. A precise and sensitive INSV RT-PCR test was subsequently developed for detecting the virus in lettuce and other crops.

Disease Cycle and Epidemiology

INSV infections in lettuce and other crops may represent "spillover" from infected ornamental plants, either in the greenhouse or in the field. Indeed, in the Salinas Valley, INSV had been documented to infect ornamentals in greenhouses and container-grown plants well before outbreaks of disease in lettuce occurred in the field. In this case, evidence that the INSV

isolates infecting lettuce were similar to those infecting ornamentals came from the results of molecular tests (RT-PCR and sequencing).

Outbreaks of impatiens necrotic spot in lettuce and other crops in Salinas Valley fields are believed to reflect an increased population of or changes in the behavior of the western flower thrips. Weeds infected with INSV (many of which are symptomless) and possibly ornamentals serve as reservoirs for both INSV and thrips populations. Viruliferous adult thrips from these reservoirs fly to lettuce plants and transmit INSV during feeding on the plants' epidermal and mesophyll cells. New generations of viruliferous adult thrips that have developed on infected lettuce plants spread INSV within fields or from one field to another. It is important to emphasize that for adult thrips to become viruliferous, they must acquire the virus as larvae; thus, the presence of INSV-infected reservoir hosts or crop plants is critical for the generation of viruliferous adults and the subsequent outbreak of disease.

Thus, outbreaks of impatiens necrotic spot in lettuce—which tend to develop in the spring and early summer in California—likely occur when conditions are favorable for the growth and infection of reservoir weed hosts and the buildup of thrips populations.

Management

An integrated pest management (IPM) strategy is required for effective management of impatiens necrotic spot, as it is for tomato spotted wilt. Also, as is true for TSWV and other tospoviruses, no INSV-resistant lettuce cultivars are commercially available.

Many of the same strategies can be used to manage tomato spotted wilt and impatiens necrotic spot in lettuce. Strategies include planting virus- and thrips-free lettuce transplants, planting new fields upwind or separated from established fields of lettuce and other crops with INSV-infected plants, managing weeds and other virus reservoirs, and promptly plowing and destroying crop residues after the harvest of lettuce fields to reduce INSV inoculum levels and thrips populations.

Monitoring and managing thrips populations with insecticides is also important. Doing so can be difficult, however, given limitations in the efficacy of available insecticides, difficulty delivering material to areas in which thrips aggregate, insecticide resistance in the western flower thrips, and reintroduction of winged adults by wind (e.g., in the Salinas Valley of California).

Selected References

Gilbertson, R. L., Batuman, O., Webster, C. G., and Adkins, S. 2015. Role of the insect supervectors *Bemisia tabaci* and *Frankliniella occidentalis* in the emergence and global spread of plant viruses. Ann. Rev. Virology 2:67-93.

Kuo, Y.-W., Gilbertson, R. L., Turini, T., Brennan, E. B., Smith, R. F., and Koike, S. T. 2014. Characterization and epidemiology of outbreaks of *Impatiens necrotic spot virus* on lettuce in coastal California. Plant Dis. 98:1050-1059.

Vicci, V., and Bellardi, M. G. 1997. Infections of *Impatiens necrotic spot virus* on lettuce in Italy. Inf. Fitopatol. 47:55-57.

(Prepared by R. L. Gilbertson and S. T. Koike)

Lettuce Big Vein

Lettuce big vein is an important soilborne virus disease that affects lettuce production throughout the world. The disease has been recognized for decades, but the virus that causes the disease, which is transmitted by a chytrid fungus, was only identified in 2002. Although lettuce big vein is one of the most widespread and common diseases of lettuce, effective management remains elusive because limited control measures are available.

Symptoms

The most common symptom of lettuce big vein is a clearing and swelling of the veins (Fig. 102). When the vein-clearing and -swelling symptoms become intense, affected leaves pucker slightly, and the leaf margins exhibit a ruffled appearance (Fig. 103). Lettuce plants infected at an early stage of growth can be severely stunted, and maturity can be delayed. Heads may not develop fully in infected crisphead lettuce plants, resulting in upright outer leaves (Fig. 104).

The primary cause of economic damage from lettuce big vein is reduced head formation. If plants are infected in the late rosette stage, head size will not be significantly reduced and the lettuce will be marketable (although vein-clearing and -swelling symptoms may be conspicuous).

Causal Agent

Two negative-sense, single-stranded RNA viruses are associated with big-vein disease of lettuce: *Mirafiori lettuce big-vein virus* (MLBVV; genus *Ophiovirus,* family *Ophioviridae*) and *Lettuce big-vein associated virus* (LBVaV; genus *Varicosavirus,* family unassigned). Ophiovirus virions are highly flexuous, naked nucleocapsids approximately 3–4 nm in diameter that appear as open, circular structures, whereas varicosavirus virions are rod shaped and measure 18 × 320–360 nm.

Although both viruses are usually found associated with lettuce big-vein disease, MLBVV has been established as the causal agent. Thus, lettuce plants inoculated with MLBVV—whether by mechanical inoculation with sap or through transmis-

sion by the fungus *Olpidium virulentus*—developed symptoms of lettuce big vein in the absence of LBVaV. Although LBVaV does not induce symptoms of big-vein disease, it may contribute in some manner to disease development.

The genome of MLBVV is composed of four negative-sense, single-stranded RNAs: one large RNA of approximately 7.8 kb, which encodes the proteins involved in virus replication, and three smaller RNAs of 1.4–1.8 kb, each of which encodes one or two proteins. The MLBVV capsid protein is serologically related to but genetically distinct from those of other members of the genus *Ophiovirus,* including *Lettuce ring necrosis virus* (LRNV), which causes a disease similar to lettuce big vein in European production regions. The genome of LBVaV is composed of two negative-sense, single-stranded RNAs: RNA-1 (6.8 kb) and RNA-2 (6.1 kb).

Detection of a wide range of MLBVV strains can be accomplished with antisera raised against the capsid protein. Additionally, MLBVV and LBVaV can be detected using nucleic acid-based methods, such as northern blot hybridization analysis, and using reverse transcription-polymerase chain reaction (RT-PCR) and sequencing.

Although MLBVV can be mechanically (sap) and graft transmitted in the laboratory, the natural mode of transmission in the field is via a fungal vector. Both MLBVV and LBVaV are transmitted in nature by the unicellular, holocarpic, soilborne chytrid fungus *O. virulentus.* (Studies have determined that *O. virulentus* is clearly distinct from *O. brassicae,* the name by which the vector was previously known, and that *O. virulentus*

Fig. 103. Crisphead lettuce with ruffled leaf margins and vein swelling, both symptoms of lettuce big vein (caused by *Mirafiori lettuce big-vein virus*). (Courtesy S. T. Koike—© APS)

Fig. 102. Vein-clearing symptoms of lettuce big-vein disease (caused by *Mirafiori lettuce big-vein virus*) on **(A)** romaine and **(B)** crisphead lettuce. (**A,** Courtesy S. T. Koike—© APS; **B,** Courtesy R. J. Hayes)

Fig. 104. Vein clearing and upright outer leaves disrupting head formation of crisphead lettuce, characteristic of lettuce big vein (caused by *Mirafiori lettuce big-vein virus*). (Courtesy E. A. Kurtz—© APS)

is the primary species that transmits MLBVV to lettuce.) *O. virulentus* is widely distributed throughout the world and can persist in soils for very long periods of time. Zoospores of *O. virulentus* infect the epidermal cells of the roots of young lettuce seedlings, and the fungal infection is restricted to the roots. With adequate soil moisture, the fungal thallus forms sporangia, which release abundant zoospores. The zoospores (~3 μm in diameter) have single posterior whiplash flagella. The thallus can also form thick-walled, resistant sporangia, which are capable of surviving in the soil for many years.

Disease Cycle and Epidemiology

Symptoms of lettuce big vein are most prevalent in lettuce fields during the spring, because symptom development is favored by cool temperatures and wet soils. Air temperature is more important than soil temperature. Symptoms develop most readily if the air temperature remains lower than 16°C, whereas a constant temperature of 22°C or higher has been found to inhibit symptom development.

O. virulentus is readily spread by soil and irrigation water. Zoospores remain motile in soil extracts for several hours, especially when temperatures are cool. Large numbers of *O. virulentus* resting sporangia can be found in infested soils to depths up to 90 cm, and seedlings can be infected as early as 8 days after planting. Disease symptoms appear approximately 18 days after infection.

If environmental conditions are suitable, infection can reach 100% of the plants in a field. The number of symptomatic plants within an infested field is often variable, however.

Management

O. virulentus, the vector of MLBVV, can be effectively controlled by applying fungicides to or fumigating the soil. However, in most situations, these practices are prohibitively expensive. In addition, the wide distribution of the virus and the vector throughout most of the world's lettuce-producing regions would likely result in new infestations developing within a few cropping cycles.

All types of cultivated lettuce are susceptible to and develop symptoms of lettuce big vein to some extent. Certain cultivars, such as Pacific and Pavane, were found to exhibit reduced incidences of infected plants when grown in infested soils, but these cultivars were not immune and infected plants developed typical disease symptoms. Progress toward developing commercially acceptable resistant cultivars has been slow—in part because of the complexity of the vector–virus relationship and in part because knowledge of the causal agent was limited until the early 2000s.

The identification of MLBVV as the causal agent of big-vein disease has facilitated screening of wild *Lactuca* germplasm accessions for sources of resistance. Several accessions of *L. virosa* have been identified with high levels of resistance to MLBVV infection and lettuce big vein symptom development. Resistance from *L. virosa* has been introgressed into *L. sativa,* although commercial cultivars with this resistance have not been developed.

Selected References

Campbell, R. N., and Grogan, R. G. 1963. Big-vein virus of lettuce and its transmission by *Olpidium brassicae.* Phytopathology 53:252-259.

Campbell, R. N., Grogan, R. G., and Purcifull, D. E. 1961. Graft transmission of big vein of lettuce. Virology 15:82-85.

Hayes, R. J., Wintermantel, W. M., Nicely, P. A., and Ryder, E. J. 2006. Host resistance to *Mirafiori lettuce big-vein virus* and *Lettuce big-vein associated virus* and virus sequence diversity and frequency in California. Plant Dis. 90:233-239.

Hayes, R. J., Ryder, E. J., and Wintermantel, W. M. 2008. Genetic variation for big-vein symptom expression and resistance to *Mirafiori lettuce big-vein virus* in *Lactuca virosa* L., a wild relative of cultivated lettuce. Euphytica 164:493-500.

Huijberts, N., Blystadm D. R., and Bos, L. 1990. Lettuce big-vein virus: Mechanical transmission and relationships to tobacco stunt virus. Ann. Appl. Biol. 116:463-475.

Jagger, I. C., and Chandler, N. 1934. Big vein, a disease of lettuce. Phytopathology 24:1253-1256.

Lot, H., Campbell, R. N., Souche, S., Milne, R. G., and Roggero, P. 2002. Transmission by *Olpidium brassicae* of *Mirafiori lettuce virus* and *Lettuce big-vein virus,* and their roles in lettuce big-vein etiology. Phytopathology 92:288-293.

Maccarone, L. D. 2013. Relationships between the pathogen *Olpidium virulentus* and viruses associated with lettuce big-vein disease. Plant Dis. 97:700-707.

Sasaya, T., and Koganezawa, H. 2006. Molecular analysis and virus transmission tests place *Olpidium virulentus,* a vector of *Mirafiori lettuce big-vein virus* and Tobacco stunt virus, as a distinct species rather than a strain of *Olpidium brassicae.* J. Gen. Plant Pathol. 72:20-25. doi:10.1007/s10327-005-0239-7

Sasaya, T., Fujii, H., Ishikawa, K., and Koganezawa, H. 2008. Further evidence of *Mirafiori lettuce big-vein virus* but not of *Lettuce big-vein associated virus* with big-vein disease in lettuce. Phytopathology 98:464-468.

Vetten, H. J., Lesemann, D. E., and Dalchow, J. 1987. Electron microscopical and serological detection of virus-like particles associated with lettuce big-vein disease. J. Phytopathol. 120:53-59.

(Prepared by B. W. Falk; revised by W. M. Wintermantel)

Lettuce Chlorosis

Lettuce chlorosis is caused by *Lettuce chlorosis virus* (LCV), a whitefly-transmitted virus that emerged in the southwestern desert region of the United States in the early 1990s. The appearance of LCV was associated with a change in the predominant form of the sweetpotato whitefly (*Bemisia tabaci*) in the region: the displacement of biotype A by the invasive biotype B.

LCV induces yellowing symptoms in lettuce similar to those induced by *Lettuce infectious yellows virus* (LIYV), an economically important virus of lettuce and cucurbit production during the 1980s that was transmitted by *B. tabaci* biotype A. However, following introduction of biotype B in the early 1990s, LIYV has not been detected from fields in the southwestern United States, presumably because of the inability of biotype B to transmit the virus.

LCV was likely present before the emergence of biotype B but not detected because of having similar virions and symptoms as LIYV. Thus, with the change in *B. tabaci* biotypes, LCV became the only "yellowing virus" to affect lettuce and sugarbeet in the southwestern United States. Although LCV is not uncommon in the region, it is generally not economically important.

Symptoms

Lettuce plants infected with LCV are stunted, and their leaves can show vein clearing. However, the most prominent symptoms are the striking yellowing, thickening, and brittleness of leaves (Figs. 105 and 106). Infected lettuce plants may also exhibit leaf rolling, and some varieties may display enhanced reddening of leaves. Plants infected at any early stage of growth will not form marketable heads.

As discussed previously, the symptoms induced by LCV infection in lettuce are virtually identical to those induced by LIYV. However, because LIYV and the *B. tabaci* biotype A vector have not been found in fields since the early 1990s, these symptoms are indicative of an LCV infection.

Causal Agent

LCV is a plus-sense, single-stranded RNA virus and a member of the genus *Crinivirus* in the family *Closteroviridae.* The virions of LCV are long, flexuous, filamentous rods that measure 12 × 800–850 nm. The viral genome is bipartite and composed of two plus-sense, single-stranded RNAs: RNA-1 (8,591 nucleotides) and RNA-2 (8,556 nucleotides). As with other members of the genus *Crinivirus*, RNA-1 encodes proteins involved in virus replication and suppression of gene silencing, whereas RNA-2 encodes structural proteins involved in virion formation, whitefly transmission, and movement. Although LCV and LIYV produce similar symptoms in lettuce, they are genetically distinct *Crinivirus* species.

LCV has a relatively wide host range that includes at least 31 plant species in 13 families, but lettuce and sugarbeet are the most economically important hosts. Additional host plants include spinach and the weed species silverleaf nightshade (*Solanum elaeagnifolium*), sharpleaf or Wright's groundcherry (*Physalis wrightii*), prickly lettuce (*Lactuca serriola*, a species of wild lettuce), and common mallow (*Malva parviflora*). In contrast to LIYV, LCV does not infect plants in the family Cucurbitaceae.

LCV is transmitted in a semipersistent manner by *B. tabaci* biotypes A and B and with approximately equal efficiency. This is a major difference between LCV and LIYV; the latter is transmitted very poorly by *B. tabaci* biotype B. LCV can be acquired and transmitted by whiteflies during a feeding period as short as 1 h, but efficient transmission requires a considerably longer feeding period and optimal virus acquisition occurs after a 24-h feeding period. The virus persists in whiteflies up to 4 days, and there is a gradual reduction in transmission efficiency after removal from the source plant. Like other criniviruses, LCV is not mechanically (sap) transmissible, nor is there any evidence that the virus is seed transmissible.

Fig. 105. Yellow, thickened leaves of crisphead lettuce, caused by *Lettuce chlorosis virus*. (Courtesy J. E. Duffus)

Fig. 106. Yellowing of older leaves of crisphead lettuce, caused by *Lettuce chlorosis virus*. (Courtesy G. J. Holmes—© APS)

Detection of LCV is best accomplished using molecular methods. Reverse transcription-polymerase chain reaction (RT-PCR) using virus-specific primers and northern blot hybridization analysis are the most efficient methods for detection and differentiation of LCV from other related viruses. Antisera against LCV have been produced and can differentiate it from distantly related viruses, but some cross-reactivity can occur with related virus species.

With the exception of an LCV strain identified in Europe (Spain) in 2014 that does not infect lettuce, the virus remains localized to the southwestern United States.

Disease Cycle and Epidemiology

Weed reservoir hosts are the most likely source of primary inoculum for LCV infecting lettuce crops. Whiteflies acquire the virus from these reservoir hosts and transmit it after flying to and feeding on lettuce plants. Infected lettuce plants serve as secondary inoculum sources for spread via whiteflies within and between lettuce fields. In a given season, the incidence of LCV infection in a lettuce crop is a function of the number and proximity of fields to reservoir hosts and the sizes of whitefly populations.

In the southwestern United States, infection of lettuce crops with LCV is most prevalent during the late fall, when whitefly populations are large and winter crops are being established. The incidence is usually much lower for crops planted later, because whitefly populations decline to low levels during the winter. This decline reduces the potential for virus transmission from older infected lettuce plants to emerging young plants in newly planted fields during the spring.

Management

Lettuce chlorosis is not considered a serious problem in lettuce unless plants are infected with LCV at any early stage of growth. In areas in which disease pressure is a concern, the weed reservoirs that serve as primary inoculum sources of LCV should be eliminated. Growers should also avoid planting new lettuce crops adjacent to or near fields with LCV-infected plants.

In addition, insecticides (particularly systemic neonicotinoids) should be applied to reduce whitefly populations. Doing so will reduce insect-feeding damage on lettuce and slow the rate of disease development in the field, but it will not prevent infection from occurring. Although controlling whiteflies can be important for early season lettuce crops in general, specific measures to control LCV in midwinter production are not usually implemented because of low vector pressure.

Selected References

Duffus, J. E., Liu, H.-Y., Wisler, G. C., and Li, R. 1996. Lettuce chlorosis virus—A new whitefly transmitted closterovirus. Eur. J. Plant Pathol. 102:591-596.

McLain, J., Castle, S., Holmes, G., and Creamer, R. 1998. Physicochemical characterization and field assessment of lettuce chlorosis virus. Plant Dis. 82:1248-1252.

Ruiz, M. L., Simón, A., García, M. C., and Janssen, D. 2014. First report of *Lettuce chlorosis virus* infecting bean in Spain. (Abstr.) Plant Dis. 98:857.

Salem, N. M., Chen, A. Y. S., Tzanetakis, I. E., Mongkolsiriwattana, C., and Ng, J. C. K. 2009. Further complexity of the genus *Crinivirus* revealed by the complete genome sequence of *Lettuce chlorosis virus* (LCV) and the similar temporal accumulation of LCV genomic RNAs 1 and 2. Virology 390:45-55.

Wintermantel, W. M., and Hladky, L. L. 2010. Methods for detection and differentiation of existing and new *Crinivirus* species through multiplex and degenerate primer RT-PCR. J. Virol. Meth. 170:106-114.

(Prepared by J. E. Duffus and G. C. Wisler; revised by W. M. Wintermantel)

Lettuce Dieback

Two related viruses—*Tomato bushy stunt virus* (TBSV) and *Moroccan pepper virus* (MPV)—cause the disease lettuce dieback in California and Arizona (United States). Lettuce dieback is characterized by stunting and yellowing, necrosis, and death of lettuce plants. This disease is most commonly observed in low-lying areas with poor drainage, in areas near rivers, on recently flooded land, and in areas in which soil has been dredged from rivers or ditches and spread onto adjacent fields.

Both viruses have also been associated with escarole yellows, a disease of escarole and endive that is characterized by necrosis and yellowing (Fig. 107) and found in the eastern United States. However, neither virus has been established as the cause of this disease.

Symptoms

Symptoms of lettuce dieback are most commonly observed on noncrisphead lettuce types, because resistance was introduced into crisphead lettuce cultivars in the 1940s. Plants with lettuce dieback typically show some degree of necrosis and yellowing in the outer leaves (Fig. 108). Symptoms in the outer leaves begin with necrosis of the small veins, which expands into larger areas of necrosis and progresses along and between

the veins (Fig. 109). The necrosis gradually progresses inward toward the center of the head. Younger leaves near the center of the head may develop chlorotic flecks within the minor veins, which are visible when the leaves are held up to the light (Fig. 110). The latter symptom is most common in romaine cultivars but is also observed in leaf lettuces, with the exception of red-leaf cultivars (because of the overlapping colors in diseased and healthy leafy tissue).

Once symptoms begin to develop, growth is often reduced. Plants infected at any early stage of growth are stunted and may die, whereas plants infected at later stages show distorted growth and necrosis and are unmarketable.

Fields with outbreaks of lettuce dieback are often composed of plants of different sizes and stages of symptom development. Diseased plants may be clustered or scattered in fields, and healthy plants can be found adjacent to diseased plants (Fig. 111).

The symptoms of lettuce dieback can be confused with those of bacterial soft rot. The two diseases can be differentiated based on the plant stems and crowns; plants with dieback remain rigid and do not display rot.

Causal Agents

TBSV and MPV are plus-sense, single-stranded RNA viruses and members of the genus *Tombusvirus* in the family *Tombus-*

Fig. 107. Symptoms of escarole yellows on endive include necrosis often radiating from the center of the head, yellowing of leaf tissue, and collapse of plants. This disease is associated with *Moroccan pepper virus* and *Tomato bushy stunt virus,* although a causative relationship has not been determined. (Courtesy W. M. Wintermantel)

Fig. 109. Romaine lettuce with veinal necrosis that is expanding along and between the veins, typical of lettuce dieback (caused by *Tomato bushy stunt virus* or *Moroccan pepper virus*). (Courtesy W. M. Wintermantel)

Fig. 108. Lettuce dieback (caused by *Tomato bushy stunt virus* or *Moroccan pepper virus*) on romaine lettuce, showing yellowing and necrosis of outer leaves. (Courtesy W. M. Wintermantel)

Fig. 110. Inner leaf of leaf lettuce with chlorotic flecking, symptomatic of lettuce dieback (caused by *Tomato bushy stunt virus* or *Moroccan pepper virus*). (Courtesy W. M. Wintermantel)

viridae. TBSV is the type member of the genus *Tombusvirus*. The virions of these tombusviruses are icosahedral (spherical) and approximately 30 nm in diameter. The viral genome is a single plus-sense, single-stranded RNA of 4.7–4.8 kb.

The natural host range of each virus is relatively narrow among agricultural crops. TBSV infects a wide range of experimental hosts, but most of these hosts do not become infected systemically. Less is known about the host range of MPV, but in addition to lettuce, natural infections of eggplant, escarole, pelargonium (*Pelargonium* spp.), pepper, and tomato have been reported.

Neither TBSV nor MPV has a known vector. Natural transmission to lettuce occurs through the soil. The mode of infection has not been determined, but it is suspected that the virus enters the plant through wounds and natural openings in the roots. Each virus can be transmitted easily to lettuce by rubbing sap on the leaves, but unlike natural infection, this mode of transmission only produces lesions on the inoculated leaves; it does not lead to systemic infection of the lettuce plant. Seed transmission is considered rare for TBSV in any host plant, but it has not been evaluated in lettuce. A limited evaluation of lettuce seed from plants infected with MPV found no transmission from seed.

Serological methods can be used differentiate MPV from TBSV, but the virus titer in infected plants can be low even when the plants show obvious symptoms. Thus, the most efficient and accurate means of identifying these and other tombusviruses is to use molecular methods, such as reverse transcription-polymerase chain reaction (RT-PCR) and sequencing. The sequence of the capsid protein is highly variable and can be used to identify and differentiate *Tombusvirus* spp.

Disease Cycle and Epidemiology

Tombusviruses are exceptionally stable, and infectivity can be maintained for a long period in a field in which the viruses have infected lettuce plants. TBSV has also been isolated from water collected from rivers and lakes. Thus, it is thought that the exceptional stability of TBSV and MPV virions facilitates their movement through irrigation water, in animal feces, and on plant material and agricultural equipment. The virions then gain access to the roots of plants through wounds or natural openings to cause infection.

There is a substantial environmental component to the development of lettuce dieback symptoms in plants grown in fields with a history of TBSV or MPV. Preliminary studies have found that soils associated with fields with high incidences of disease have poor drainage, along with elevated salinity and nitrates. Although it is not known how these factors or combinations of these factors may influence disease development, growers should avoid planting susceptible lettuce cultivars in soils with poor drainage and a history of either TBSV or MPV.

Fig. 111. Lettuce dieback (caused by *Tomato bushy stunt virus* or *Moroccan pepper virus*) on a cluster of romaine lettuce plants, showing stunting and necrosis. (Courtesy W. M. Wintermantel)

Management

Management of lettuce dieback can be accomplished by not planting susceptible cultivars in previously flooded fields and other areas known to predispose plants to disease. Another management strategy is to plant resistant cultivars. All modern crisphead lettuce cultivars carry the dominant resistance gene, *Tvr1*, which provides a highly stable source of resistance. This gene has been present in crisphead lettuce since the 1940s, although it was not characterized until much later. An increasing number of romaine, leaf, and other specialty lettuces also carry this gene, which provides stable resistance to both TBSV and MPV.

Selected References

Fisher, H. U., and Lockhart, B. E. L. 1977. Identification and comparison of two isolates of tomato bushy stunt virus from pepper and tomato in Morocco. Phytopathology 67:1352-1355.

Grube, R. C., Wintermantel, W. M., Hand, P., Aburomia, R., Pink, D. A. C., and Ryder, E. J. 2005. Genetic analysis and mapping of resistance to lettuce dieback: A soilborne disease caused by tombusviruses. Theor. Appl. Genet. 110:259-268.

Jagger, I. C., Whitaker, T. W., Uselman, J. J., and Owen, W. M. 1941. The Imperial strains of lettuce. U.S. Dep. Agric. Circ. 596.

Obermeier, C., Sears, J. L., Liu, H.-Y., Schlueter, K. O., Ryder, E. J., Duffus, J. E., Koike, S. T., and Wisler, G. C. 2001. Characterization of distinct tombusviruses that cause diseases of lettuce and tomato in the western United States. Phytopathology 91:797-806.

Simko, I., Pechenick, D. A., McHale, L. K., Truco, M. J., Ochoa, O. E., Michelmore, R. W., and Scheffler, B. E. 2009. Association mapping and marker-assisted selection of the lettuce dieback resistance gene Tvr1. BMC Plant Biol. doi:10.1186/1471-2229-9-135

Wintermantel, W. M., and Bachinsky, D. 2014. First report of *Moroccan pepper virus* in association with yellows on escarole in the United States and the world. (Abstr.) Plant Dis. 98:1448.

Wintermantel, W. M., and Hladky, L. L. 2013. Complete genome sequence and biological characterization of *Moroccan pepper virus* (MPV) and reclassification of Lettuce necrotic stunt virus as MPV. Phytopathology 103:501-508.

(Prepared by W. M. Wintermantel)

Lettuce Mosaic

Lettuce mosaic, caused by *Lettuce mosaic virus* (LMV), is the most common and economically important viral disease affecting lettuce worldwide. It was first described in 1921 in Florida (United States) and has since been reported from most of the world's lettuce-growing areas, including Australia, China, Iran, Israel, Japan, and New Zealand; countries in Europe and South America; and many states in the United States. Lettuce mosaic has been particularly damaging to lettuce production in Europe and the United States, but implementation of management practices has substantially reduced losses. All types of lettuce are susceptible, including crisphead, romaine, butterhead, and leaf lettuces.

Symptoms

The symptoms of lettuce mosaic vary depending on the cultivar or type of lettuce, the age of the plant when infected, and the environmental conditions. In general, infected plants show some degree of stunting and leaf or head distortion and deformation. Symptoms in leaves include mosaic/mottling, vein clearing, and yellowing (Fig. 112). Young plants that originate from infected seed will be stunted and have irregularly shaped leaves with a light-green mottle or mosaic. Symptoms of mosaic/mottling are typically more pronounced in leaf lettuce than in crisphead lettuce cultivars, and symptoms are more noticeable under cool and cloudy weather conditions (e.g., in the spring). Vein clearing and necrotic flecks or spots between the veins and at the leaf tips may also appear on the leaves of infected plants (Fig. 113). In highly susceptible cultivars, necrotic spots may expand into large areas of necrosis, especially at the leaf margins, giving leaves a scorched appearance. The necrotic-type symptoms tend to develop under warmer conditions (e.g., during the summer).

Lettuce plants infected at later stages of growth often develop a light-green to yellow mottling of leaves, which becomes especially noticeable after plants flower (bolt). Flowering lettuce plants infected with LMV are stunted, and the leaves are chlorotic and have a scorched appearance. Necrotic lesions sometimes develop on the flowers and stems.

In crisphead lettuce cultivars, LMV-infected plants are stunted, and the leaves are distorted and display a light-green mosaic/mottle. The outer leaves often show a diagnostic downward rolling of the leaf tips (Fig. 114). Crisphead lettuce plants infected at a young age fail to form heads or produce small, unmarketable heads. In plants infected at later stages of growth, the mosaic/mottling symptoms may become mild or disappear, and in these cases, the most diagnostic symptom is the downward curling of the leaf tips. Diagnosis of LMV-infected plants can be difficult in these cases.

The symptoms of LMV can be similar to those induced by other viruses, such as *Cucumber mosaic virus* (CMV) and *Turnip mosaic virus* (TuMV). Lettuce plants infected with CMV tend to have a more pronounced mosaic/mottle, and infected crisphead lettuce plants do not have the downward curling of outer leaves that characterizes LMV-infected plants. The leaves of TuMV-infected plants have light-green to yellow (chlorotic) spots, and symptoms are often pronounced on older leaves.

Diagnostic tests are usually needed to confirm LMV infection in lettuce. LMV can be detected using serological methods, such as enzyme-linked immunosorbent assay (ELISA) and lateral-flow devices (immunostrips), and using reverse transcription-polymerase chain reaction (RT-PCR) and sequencing. The development of lateral-flow devices for CMV and LMV has allowed for rapid in-field diagnosis of these viruses in lettuce and other crops.

Causal Agent

LMV is a plus-sense, single-stranded RNA virus and a typical member of the genus *Potyvirus* in the family *Potyviridae*. The virions are flexuous rods that measure approximately 13×750 nm, and the genome is composed of a single approximately 10-kb, plus-sense, single-stranded RNA, which is expressed as a polyprotein.

LMV has a relatively wide host range that includes as many as 23 species in eight families. In nature, LMV predominantly infects members of the lettuce family (Asteraceae), including the crop plants lettuce, endive, and escarole; noncultivated plants (weeds) such as wild lettuce species *Lactuca virosa* and *L. serriola* (prickly lettuce), bristly oxtongue (*Picris echioides*), old-man-in-the-Spring or groundsel (*Senecio vulgaris*), and spiny or prickly sowthistle (*Sonchus asper*); and ornamentals such as African marigold (*Tagetus erecta*), African or Cape daisy (*Osteospermum* spp.), aster, cineraria (*Cineraria* spp.), gazania (*Gazania* spp.), and zinnia. Of particular importance are perennial weed and ornamental hosts, which can serve as reservoirs of inoculum for infection of lettuce plantings. The most susceptible and commonly infected crops are chicory, endive, escarole, and lettuce; however, other crops may also be infected, including pea, safflower (*Carthamus tinctorius*), and spinach. Plants infected with LMV under experimental conditions—including lambsquarters (*Chenopodium album;* local lesions), goosefoot (*C. amaranticolor;* local lesions and systemic symptoms), common globe amaranth (*Gomphrena globosa;* local lesions), and the tobacco species *Nicotiana benthamiana* (systemic symptoms)—may be useful for diagnosis; lettuce and *N. benthamiana* are suitable propagative hosts.

In nature, LMV is transmitted in a nonpersistent manner by many species of aphids, including the cotton aphid (*Aphis gossypii*), the potato aphid (*Macrosiphum euphorbiae*), and the green peach aphid (*Myzus persicae*). The green peach aphid is the most important vector.

LMV is the only economically important virus of lettuce that is seed transmitted. The rate of seed transmission is a function of the cultivar and the age at which the plant is infected. The seed transmission rate usually ranges from 1 to 10%, although

Fig. 112. Chlorosis and necrosis of romaine lettuce, caused by *Lettuce mosaic virus.* (Courtesy S. T. Koike—© APS)

Fig. 113. Necrosis, mottling, and distortion of romaine lettuce leaves, caused by *Lettuce mosaic virus.* (Courtesy S. T. Koike—© APS)

Fig. 114. Downward rolling of leaves and stunted growth of crisphead lettuce, caused by *Lettuce mosaic virus.* (Courtesy S. T. Koike—© APS)

higher rates (~30%) can occur. LMV can be detected in the ovules and pollen of infected plants; thus, it infects the seed rather than contaminates it. The virus is also readily mechanically (sap) transmissible.

LMV can be detected using serological methods, such as enzyme-linked immunosorbent assay (ELISA) and lateral-flow devices (immunostrips), and using reverse transcription-polymerase chain reaction (RT-PCR) and sequencing. The development of lateral-flow devices for CMV and LMV has allowed for rapid in-field diagnosis of these viruses, which cause similar symptoms in lettuce plants.

Strains of LMV can be differentiated based on interaction with the recessive allelic resistance genes, *mol¹* (previously referred to as the "g gene") and *mol²*, and based on analysis of the genetic sequence of the virus. These LMV resistance genes have been cloned and shown to be allelic and to encode forms of the translation initiation factor eIF4E. The common strains of LMV are unable to infect *mol¹*- and *mol²*-containing varieties and are prevalent in the United States. In Europe, resistance-breaking LMV strains have emerged, most likely because of the widespread deployment of these resistance genes as a management strategy. Resistance-breaking strains that are seed transmitted have been labeled "moST" strains (i.e., mol-breaking Seed-Transmitted) to differentiate them from other resistance-breaking strains that are not seed transmitted.

The genetic diversity in LMV has important practical consequences in terms of developing disease management strategies (see the section "Management"). In the United States, LMV isolates that were associated with symptoms of necrosis in lettuce were believed to be highly virulent, genetically distinct strains. However, subsequent studies revealed that they were isolates of common LMV and that the necrosis symptom was associated with environmental conditions and the lettuce cultivar.

Disease Cycle and Epidemiology

Seed is the most important primary inoculum source of LMV, but ornamental and weed reservoir hosts may also be significant sources, particularly in some European countries. Outbreaks of lettuce mosaic are typically associated with planting infected seed lots, and it has been estimated that LMV infection rates greater than 0.5% can result in economic losses under favorable conditions (i.e., in the presence of large aphid populations).

Lettuce plants that have been infected with LMV from infected seed or via viruliferous aphids flying into fields from infected ornamental or weed reservoirs then serve as sources of secondary inoculum for transmission within and between fields by aphids. As stated earlier, the green peach aphid is one of the most important and efficient vectors of LMV. Secondary spread may in some cases be mediated by noncolonizing aphid species (including the green peach aphid) that pass through lettuce fields. Because LMV is transmitted in a nonpersistent manner, it requires only seconds for acquisition and transmission, allowing for rapid spread. Thus, heavy aphid activity within a field (colonizing or noncolonizing) established with LMV-infected seed can result in 100% disease incidence and substantial economic losses.

During the lettuce-growing season, LMV-infected plants in established fields can serve as sources of inoculum for newly planted fields. Overwintering of the virus occurs in infected seed and in ornamental and weed reservoirs.

Management

The most important method for managing lettuce mosaic is to plant lettuce seed that has been tested to be free of LMV infection. Classic studies conducted in the Salinas Valley of California (United States) established LMV tolerance thresholds, on which U.S. seed-testing programs are based. In the United States (e.g., California), the threshold is zero infected seeds in 30,000 tested, whereas in Europe, lower thresholds are used (e.g., zero

in 2,000). In California, lettuce production areas including Monterey and Imperial counties have ordinances that require LMV testing for all seed lots. Lots that fail to pass the test (i.e., have one or more infected seeds in 30,000) cannot be planted.

Initially, lettuce seed was tested for LMV infection by growing out seeds and visually observing seedlings for LMV symptoms or by inoculating *Chenopodium quinoa* indicator plants. Since 1983, seed testing has most commonly been done using enzyme-linked immunosorbent assay (ELISA). In Monterey County (i.e., the Salinas Valley), there is also an annual 1-month lettuce-free period (in December) and an extensive weed management program. Together, these approaches have provided effective management of lettuce mosaic since the mid-1980s (and without planting resistant cultivars). Sporadic outbreaks of lettuce mosaic in the Salinas Valley have been associated with ornamental reservoir hosts (e.g., *Gazania* spp. and *Osteospermum* spp.), but these outbreaks have not typically resulted in economic losses. Thus, the integrated management of lettuce mosaic in the Salinas Valley is a successful example in terms of applying the knowledge of the biology of a plant-infecting virus to developing an effective, long-term, sustainable approach to disease management.

In Europe, South America, and other lettuce-growing regions, lettuce mosaic is managed through a combination of planting LMV-tested seed and using resistant cultivars. Both the *mol¹* (g gene) and *mol²* genes have been incorporated into various types of lettuce. The *mol¹* gene has been used mostly in Europe and incorporated into butterhead, cos, and crisphead types, whereas the *mol²* gene has been used more extensively in the United States and incorporated into cos and crisphead types (e.g., Salinas 88 and Vanguard 75). In Europe, the management of lettuce mosaic is complicated by the occurrence of resistance-breaking strains (e.g., the moST strains), which are seed transmitted. Thus, it is critical to combine the planting of LMV-tested seed with the use of resistant cultivars.

Sanitation practices are also recommended for the effective management of lettuce mosaic, such as plowing lettuce fields promptly after harvest to prevent harvested plants from serving as sources of inoculum for newly planted fields. In areas in which lettuce mosaic is a persistent problem, aphid control is recommended; applying systemic insecticides (e.g., neonicotinoids) has been shown to slow the spread of viruses transmitted by aphids in a nonpersistent manner.

Selected References

Dinant, S., and Lot, H. 1992. Lettuce mosaic virus: A review. Plant Pathol. 41:528-542.

Falk, B. W., and Purcifull, D. E. 1983. Development and application of an enzyme-linked immunosorbent assay (ELISA) test to index lettuce seeds for lettuce mosaic virus in Florida. Plant Dis. 67:413-416.

German-Retana, S., Walter, J., and Le Gall, O. 2008. Lettuce mosaic virus: From pathogen diversity to host interactions. Mol. Plant. Pathol. 9:127-136.

Grogan, R. G. 1980. Control of lettuce mosaic with virus-free seed. Plant Dis. 64:446-449.

Horvath, J. 1991. Unknown Compositae (Asteraceae) hosts of lettuce mosaic potyvirus. Acta Phytopathol. Entomol. Hung. 26:347-351.

Krause-Sakate, R., Le Gall, O., Fakhfakh, H., Peypelut, M., Marrakchi, M., Varveri, C., Pavan, M. A., Souche, S., Lot, H., Zerbini, F. M., and Candresse, T. 2002. Molecular and biological characterization of *Lettuce mosaic virus* (LMV) isolates reveals a distinct and widespread type of resistance-breaking isolate: LMV-Most. Phytopathology 92:563-572.

Moreno, A., de Blas, C., Biurrun, R., Nebreda, M., Palacios, I., Duque, M., and Fereres, A. 2004. The incidence and distribution of viruses infecting lettuce, cultivated *Brassica* and associated natural vegetation in Spain. Ann. Appl. Biol. 144:339-346.

Moreno, A., Nebreda, M., Diaz, B. M., Garcia, M., Salas, F., and Fereres, A. 2007. Temporal and spatial spread of *Lettuce mosaic virus* in lettuce crops in central Spain: Factors involved in lettuce mosaic epidemics. Ann. Appl. Biol. 150:351-360.

Nebreda, M., Moreno, A., Perez, N., Palacios, I., Seco-Fernandez, V., and Fereres, A. 2004. Activity of aphids associated with lettuce and broccoli in Spain and their efficiency as vectors of *Lettuce mosaic virus*. Virus Res. 100:83-88.

Nicaise, V., German-Retana, S., Sanjuan, R., Dubrana, M.-P., Mazier, M., Maisonneuve, B., Candresse, T., Caranta, C., and Le Gall, O. 2003. The eukaryotic translation initiation factor 4E controls lettuce susceptibility to the potyvirus *Lettuce mosaic virus*. Plant Physiol. 132:1272-1282.

Robinson, R. W., and Provvidenti, R. 1993. Breeding lettuce for viral resistance. Pages 61-79 in: Resistance to Viral Diseases of Vegetables. M. M. Kyle, ed. Timber Press, Portland, OR.

Ryder, E. J. 1970. Inheritance of resistance to common lettuce mosaic virus. J. Am. Soc. Hort. Sci. 95:378-379.

Zerbini, F. M., Koike, S. T., and Gilbertson, R. L. 1995. Biological and molecular characterization of lettuce mosaic potyvirus isolates from the Salinas Valley of California. Phytopathology 85:746-752.

Zerbini, F. M., Koike, S. T., and Gilbertson, R. L. 1997. *Gazania* spp.: A new host of lettuce mosaic potyvirus, and a potential inoculum source for recent lettuce mosaic outbreaks in the Salinas Valley. Plant Dis. 81:641-646.

(Prepared by F. M. Zerbini and R. L. Gilbertson)

Lettuce Mottle

Lettuce mottle, caused by *Lettuce mottle virus* (LeMoV), has been reported from regions of Brazil and Chile. It was first found in the Federal District of Brazil and later in several southern (Rio Grande do Sul and Santa Catarina) and southeastern (São Paulo) states. In a survey of lettuce fields in these three Brazilian states from 2002 to 2005, approximately 10% of samples with mosaic symptoms were infected with LeMoV. (The majority of the samples were infected with *Lettuce mosaic virus* [LMV]; see the previous section, "Lettuce Mosaic.") In a survey of lettuce fields around Santiago, Chile, conducted in 2002 and 2003, a low incidence of LeMoV infection was detected in plants with mosaic symptoms. (Again, the majority were infected with LMV.) Although lettuce mottle disease is not uncommon in Brazil, it generally does not cause economic losses.

Symptoms

Lettuce plants infected with LeMoV develop vein clearing, followed by a light-green mosaic and mottling. The leaves of infected plants may be crumpled, distorted, and reduced in size (Fig. 115). Some lettuce cultivars may exhibit slight necrosis of leaves, whereas other cultivars may be symptomless. Plants infected with LeMoV produce small heads that may not be marketable.

Causal Agent

LeMoV is plus-sense, single-stranded RNA virus with icosahedral (spherical) virions approximately 30 nm in diameter. The genome is believed to be a single plus-sense, single-stranded RNA of approximately 9 kb. Analysis of the nucleotide sequence of the RNA-dependent RNA polymerase gene has suggested that LeMoV is a distinct species in the genus *Sequivirus* (family *Sequiviridae*). It is most closely related to *Dandelion yellow mosaic virus* (DaYMV), another lettuce-infecting sequivirus (see the section "Dandelion Yellow Mosaic").

The host range of LeMoV is relatively narrow, and lettuce is the only species reported to be infected in nature. Plant species in four families have been infected by LeMoV under experimental conditions, including dandelion (*Taraxacum officinale*) and common sowthistle (*Sonchus oleraceus*) (both Asteraceae); lambsquarters (*Chenopodium album*) (Chenopodiaceae), which develops local lesions on inoculated leaves and mosaic symptoms in leaves of systemically infected plants; and common globe amaranth (*Gomphrena globosa*) and slim amaranth (*Amaranthus hybridus*) (both Amaranthaceae). The host from the Solanaceae, tobacco species *Nicotiana benthamiana*, remains symptomless and can be used to differentiate LeMoV from LMV, which induces mosaic symptoms in this host.

The vector of LeMoV is the sowthistle aphid (*Hyperomyzus lactucae*) (Fig. 93). LeMoV is not transmitted by four other aphid species, including the green peach aphid (*Myzus persicae*). Transmission appears to be nonpersistent (styletborne).

LeMoV is apparently not seed transmitted. Under laboratory conditions, the virus can be mechanically (sap) transmitted to lettuce and other hosts. Detection of LeMoV can be accomplished using serological tests, such as enzyme-linked immunosorbent assay (ELISA), and using reverse transcription-polymerase chain reaction (RT-PCR) and sequencing.

Disease Cycle and Epidemiology

Lettuce is the only natural host of LeMoV, and little information is available regarding natural reservoirs of the virus. However, because LeMoV has been shown to infect dandelion and common sowthistle under experimental conditions, it is possible that weed species are reservoir hosts (as dandelion is for DaYMV in Europe). Because LeMoV is apparently not seed transmitted in lettuce, it must be acquired from infected lettuce plants or unidentified reservoir hosts by the sowthistle aphid and then transmitted to lettuce plants in newly established fields.

The disease symptoms induced by LeMoV and LMV in lettuce are similar, although LeMoV can infect LMV-resistant cultivars. In cultivars susceptible to both viruses, symptoms alone cannot be used to differentiate the viruses. Furthermore, LeMoV and LMV can occur together in a mixed infection and may even be co-transmitted by aphids. Thus, using serological or molecular tests is necessary to differentiate these viruses in areas in which they occur together (Brazil and Chile).

Management

Managing lettuce mottle through aphid control is not practical, because this disease is generally not economically important. The lack of information regarding reservoir hosts of LeMoV precludes the development of eradication programs. Thus, breeding for LeMoV resistance seems to be the optimal management approach, and cultivars with resistance are available.

Selected References

Jadao, A. S., Krause-Sakate, R., Liberti, D., Pavan, M. A., Echer, M. M., Svanella-Dumas, L., Zerbini, F. M., Candresse, T., and Le Gall, O. 2007. Further characterization of two sequiviruses infecting lettuce and development of specific RT-PCR primers. Arch. Virol. 152:999-1007.

Kitajima, E. W., Marinho, V. L. A., Lin, M. T., Gama, M. I. C. S., and de Avila, A. C. 1980. Mosaico necrotico da alface: Um virus isometrico transmitido por afideos. (In Spanish.) (Abstr.) Fitopatol. Bras. 5:409.

Fig. 115. Crumpled leaf of a lettuce seedling infected with *Lettuce mottle virus*. (Courtesy R. L. Gilbertson—© APS)

Krause-Sakate, R., Jadão, A. S., Firmino, A. C., Pavan, M.A., Zerbini, F. M., Rosales, I. M., Bustamante, P., and Le Gall, O. 2005. First report of a lettuce-infecting sequivirus in Chile. (Abstr.) Plant Dis. 89:1129.

Krause-Sakate, R., Firmino, A. C., Jadao, A. S., Pavan, M. A., da Silva, N., Hanai, S. M., Anbo, R. H., and Nietzsche, T. 2008. Occurrence of Lettuce mottle virus on three lettuce producing areas from São Paulo State. Summa Phytopathol. 34. doi:10.1590/S0100-54052008000100020

Marinho, V. L. A., and Kitajima, E. W. 1986. Virus do mosqueado da alface—Um virus isometrico transmitido por afideos. (In Spanish.) Fitopatol. Bras. 11:923-936.

Marinho, V. L. A., Lin, M. T., and Kitajima, E. W. 1986. Purificacao e sorologia do virus do mosqueado da alface. (In Spanish.) Fitopatol. Bras. 11:937-942.

Stangarlin, O. S. 1995. Identificacao dos virus causadores de mosaico em cultivares de alface (Lactuca sativa L.) resistentes ao virus do mosaico da alface nas regioes produtoras do estado de São Paulo. (In Spanish.) MS dissertation, Universidade Estadual de São Paulo, campus Botucatu.

(Prepared by E. W. Kitajima and M. A. Pavan; revised by R. L. Gilbertson)

Lettuce Necrotic Yellows

Lettuce necrotic yellows is caused by the aphid-transmitted rhabdovirus *Lettuce necrotic yellows virus* (LNYV) (see Table 2). The disease first appeared on lettuce in Australia, and the virus was subsequently described in 1963 by L. L. Stubbs and R. G. Grogan. High incidences of necrotic yellows have been reported in some regions of Australia—particularly New South Wales, where it has caused economic losses. The disease has also been reported from New Zealand and Tasmania.

Symptoms

Symptoms of LNYV infection in lettuce plants begin with the leaves becoming dull green, bronzed, or necrotic. As the infection progresses, plant growth is stunted, and the leaves become deformed and twisted and develop chlorosis or a chlorotic mottle (Fig. 116). A diseased plant may have a flattened or flaccid appearance, and it may die. A plant infected just before the onset of head formation may develop reddening and necrosis of the veins and internal necrosis. High temperatures exacerbate the wilting and dying of plants, whereas under cool conditions, plants may recover from the disease.

The symptoms of necrotic yellows may be confused with those of tomato spotted wilt and lettuce mosaic (in cases in which necrotic symptoms develop).

Fig. 116. Crisphead lettuce with chlorotic and deformed leaves, characteristic of infection with *Lettuce necrotic yellows virus.* (Courtesy J. W. Randles—© APS)

Causal Agent

LNYV is a negative-sense, single-stranded RNA virus and the type member of the genus *Cytorhabdovirus* in the family *Rhabdoviridae* (order Mononegavirales). The virions are bacilliform (bullet shaped), measure approximately 66 × 227 nm, and are covered by a host-derived, lipid bilayer membrane. In an infected cell, LNYV virions accumulate in the cytoplasm. The LNYV genome is composed of one single-stranded, negative-sense RNA of 12,807 nucleotides. The organization of the genome is similar to those of other plant and animal rhabdoviruses.

In addition to lettuce, LNYV infects other plants in the family Asteraceae, including prickly lettuce (*Lactuca serriola*, a species of wild lettuce), common sowthistle (*Sonchus oleraceus*), and black thistle (*Cirsium vulgare*). In the natural host common sowthistle, the virus induces mild or no symptoms. Plant species experimentally infected with LNYV include the tobacco species *Nicotiana glutinosa*, jimsonweed (*Datura stramonium*), pot marigold (*Calendula officinalis*), spinach, and tomato.

In nature, LNYV is transmitted by the sowthistle aphid (*Hyperomyzus lactucae*) (Fig. 93). The mode of transmission is persistent and propagative, and the virus is believed to be passed from the adult to its progeny. Another aphid species, the Asian sowthistle aphid (*H. carduellinus*), can also transmit LNYV, but it is not important in the epidemiology of the disease.

There is no evidence that LNYV is transmitted through the seeds of lettuce, common sowthistle, or *N. glutinosa*. Under laboratory conditions, LNYV is also mechanically (sap) transmitted.

LNYV can be detected using serological methods, such as enzyme-linked immunosorbent assay (ELISA), and using reverse transcription-polymerase chain reaction (RT-PCR) and sequencing.

Disease Cycle and Epidemiology

The epidemiology of lettuce necrotic yellows is closely tied to the weed host of the virus: common sowthistle. This weed serves as a major reservoir for both LNYV and the sowthistle aphid vector and is widely distributed in southern Australia. A large population of the sowthistle aphid can develop on common sowthistle plants (especially on the flower stalks) and then spread LNYV to nearby plantings of lettuce. However, because the sowthistle aphid does not reproduce on lettuce, there is little spread of LNYV within lettuce fields.

Other host plants for both LNYV and the sowthistle aphid include native sowthistle (*S. hydrophilus*) and other members of the Asteraceae, but these hosts do not seem to play a major role in the epidemiology of lettuce necrotic yellows. Thus, the incidence of the disease in lettuce is closely correlated with proximity to LNYV-infected common sowthistle plants and the migratory population of the sowthistle aphid.

The highest incidence of lettuce necrotic yellows tends to occur during the fall, when conditions are most favorable for vector development.

Management

The most effective strategy for managing lettuce necrotic yellows is to destroy or remove common sowthistle plants in and around lettuce fields; doing so eliminates the source of primary inoculum for both the virus and the vector. Controlling the aphid population with insecticides on common sowthistle plants (but not in lettuce crops) may also help manage the disease. These control measures are particularly important in the fall, when the disease is prevalent.

No resistant lettuce cultivars are available.

Selected References

Dietzgen, R. G., Callaghan, B., Wetzel, T., and Dale, J. L. 2006. Completion of the genome sequence of *Lettuce necrotic yellows virus*, type species of the genus *Cytorhabdovirus*. Virus Res. 118:16-22.

Randles, J. W., and Carver, M. 1971. Epidemiology of lettuce necrotic yellows virus in South Australia. II. Distribution of virus, host plants, and vectors. Aust. J. Agric. Res. 22:231-237.

Randles, J. W., and Crowley, N. C. 1970. Epidemiology of lettuce necrotic yellows virus in South Australia. I. Relationship between disease incidence and activity of *Hyperomyzus lactucae* (L.). Aust. J. Agric. Res. 21:447-453.

Stubbs, L. L., and Grogan, R. G. 1963. Necrotic yellows: A newly recognized virus disease of lettuce. Aust. J. Agric. Res. 14:439-459.

Stubbs, L. L., Guy, J. A. D., and Stubbs, K. J. 1963. Control of lettuce necrotic yellows virus disease by the destruction of common sow thistle (*Sonchus oleraceus*). Aust. J. Exp. Agric. Anim. Husb. 3:215-218.

Wetzel, T., Dietzgen, R. G., and Dale, J. L. 1994. Genomic organization of lettuce necrotic yellows rhabdovirus. Virology 200:401-412.

(Prepared by B. W. Falk; revised by R. L. Gilbertson)

Sonchus Yellow Net

Sonchus yellow net is caused by *Sonchus yellow net virus* (SYNV), one of the five known lettuce-infecting rhabdoviruses (see Table 2). This disease has been found only in central and southern Florida (United States) and in crisphead and romaine lettuce and weeds, including hairy beggarticks (*Bidens pilosa*), butterweed (*Packera glabella*), and various species of sowthistle (*Sonchus* spp.). SYNV is most closely related to another lettuce-infecting rhabdovirus, *Sowthistle yellow vein virus* (SYVV), but differs in a number of properties (see the section "Sowthistle Yellow Vein").

Symptoms

Lettuce plants infected with SYNV are severely stunted, and leaf symptoms include vein clearing, yellow spots, and mosaic. As an infected plant grows, the older, lower leaves may develop a diagnostic bright-yellow, interveinal spotting. Eventually, entire lower leaves may turn chlorotic, and in advanced stages of Sonchus yellow net, some of the yellowed areas may become necrotic. Under certain conditions, lettuce plants infected with SYNV can recover from disease symptoms.

Sowthistle plants infected with SYNV develop chlorotic local lesions followed by vein clearing and yellow, interveinal spots in newly emerging leaves.

Causal Agent

SYNV is a negative-sense, single-stranded RNA virus and a member of the genus *Nucleorhabdovirus* in the family *Rhabdoviridae* (order Mononegavirales). The virions are bacilliform (bullet shaped), measure approximately 94 × 248 nm, are covered by a host-derived, lipid bilayer membrane, and are found in the nuclei of infected plants. The genome is composed of one single-stranded, negative-sense RNA of approximately 13.6 kb.

SYNV has a relatively narrow host range. In nature, it infects lettuce; weeds in the family Asteraceae, such as hairy beggarticks (*Bidens pilosa*) and common sowthistle (*Sonchus oleraceus*); and the ornamental plant Madagascar widow's-thrill (*Kalanchoe blossfeldiana*), on which it induces yellow spots. Tobacco species such as *Nicotiana glutinosa* and *N. benthamiana* can be infected experimentally; these plants develop chlorotic lesions in inoculated leaves and vein netting, thickening, and downward cupping in newly emerging leaves. Lambsquarters (*Chenopodium album*) plants infected with SYNV develop tan-colored lesions in inoculated leaves and mild mottling in newly emerged infected leaves.

SYNV is transmitted by the aphid species *Aphis coreopsidis*, which colonizes hairy beggarticks, but it is not transmitted by the sowthistle aphid (*Hyperomyzus lactucae*) or by *Dactynotus* spp. aphids, which colonize sowthistle plants and transmit other lettuce-infecting rhabdoviruses. The mode of insect transmission is most likely persistent and propagative. SYNV is also mechanically (sap) transmissible. It is not seed transmitted in common sowthistle.

SYNV can be detected using serological methods, such as enzyme-linked immunosorbent assay (ELISA), and using reverse transcription-polymerase chain reaction (RT-PCR) and sequencing. Rhabdovirus virions from infected leaves can also be observed in leaf-dip preparations with an electron microscope. Although SYNV and SYVV induce similar symptoms in lettuce and common sowthistle, these viruses are serologically distinct, have different aphid vectors, and differ in sap-transmission capacity.

Disease Cycle and Epidemiology

SYNV naturally infects the weeds hairy beggarticks, common sowthistle, and butterweed, often in mixed infection with *Bidens mottle virus* (BiMoV). Viruliferous aphids acquire SYNV from infected weeds and transmit it to lettuce plants, and the leaves of infected plants typically develop bright-yellow spots. The incidence of Sonchus yellow net in lettuce is typically low, and the disease does not appear to cause economic losses in lettuce production in Florida.

Management

Because of the low incidence of Sonchus yellow net in lettuce, specific management practices focused on SYNV are not warranted. However, growers are advised to manage weeds in the family Asteraceae around lettuce fields, particularly hairy beggarticks, common sowthistle, and butterweed, which are reservoirs for SYNV and other lettuce-infecting viruses in Florida.

Selected References

Christie, S. R., Christie, R. G., and Edwardson, J. R. 1974. Transmission of a bacilliform virus of sowthistle and *Bidens pilosa*. Phytopathology 64:840-845.

Falk, B. W., Purcifull, D. E., and Christie, S. R. 1986. Natural occurrence of Sonchus yellow net virus in Florida lettuce. Plant Dis. 70:591-593.

Heaton, L. A., Hillman, B. I., Hunter, B. G., Zuidema, D., and Jackson, A. O. 1989. Physical map of the genome of Sonchus yellow net virus, a plant rhabdovirus with six genes and conserved gene junction sequences. Proc. Natl. Acad. Sci. U.S.A. 86:8665-8668.

Jackson, A. O. 1978. Partial characterization of the structural proteins of Sonchus yellow net virus. Virology 87:172-181.

Jackson, A. O., and Christie, S. R. 1979. Sonchus yellow net virus. Descriptions of Plant Viruses, no. 205. Commonwealth Mycological Institute, Kew, Surrey, UK.

(Prepared by J. E. Duffus; revised by R. L. Gilbertson)

Sowthistle Yellow Vein

Sowthistle yellow vein disease is caused by *Sowthistle yellow vein virus* (SYVV), one of the five known lettuce-infecting rhabdoviruses (see Table 2). This disease has been observed in lettuce fields in California (Salinas Valley) and Arizona (United States) since the early 1960s, and it has also been reported from the United Kingdom. In some lettuce fields in California, high incidences of sowthistle yellow vein have been associated with yield losses.

SYVV is most commonly found infecting common sowthistle (*Sonchus oleraceus*), in which it induces striking vein-clearing and vein-banding symptoms.

Symptoms

Lettuce plants infected with SYVV are often severely stunted, and they typically show symptoms of vein clearing and yellowing, especially at the margins of infected leaves (Fig. 117).

Similar symptoms are observed in common sowthistle plants infected with SYVV. Because of the severity of these symptoms, SYVV-infected lettuce plants are often unmarketable.

The initial vein-clearing symptom induced in lettuce leaves by SYVV can resemble symptoms of lettuce big-vein disease, but SYVV-infected leaves are typically more squared off and the veins are closer together and compressed. In contrast, the leaves of plants infected with *Mirafiori lettuce big-vein virus* (the virus that causes lettuce big-vein disease) tend to be normal in size and shape, and leaf margins show pronounced ruffling.

Causal Agent

SYVV is a negative-sense, single-stranded RNA virus in the genus *Nucleorhabdovirus* in the family *Rhabdoviridae* (order Mononegavirales). SYVV virions are bacilliform (bullet shaped), measure approximately 100×230 nm, and are covered by a host-derived, lipid bilayer membrane. The genome is composed of one single-stranded, negative-sense RNA of approximately 13.6 kb.

In nature, SYVV has a narrow host range that includes only common sowthistle and lettuce. The virus is transmitted by the sowthistle aphid (*Hyperomyzus lactucae*) in a persistent, propagative manner. In fact, SYVV was the first virus to be shown to replicate in aphid and plant hosts. The virus is not transmitted through seed of common sowthistle, and it is not mechanically (sap) transmissible.

SYVV virions resemble those of other lettuce-infecting rhabdoviruses, so observing bacilliform virions in leaf-dip preparations by electron microscopy is diagnostic only to the family *Rhabdoviridae*. SYVV can be identified using serological methods, such as enzyme-linked immunosorbent assay (ELISA), and using reverse transcription-polymerase chain reaction (RT-PCR) and sequencing. It can also be differentiated from other lettuce-infecting rhabdoviruses based on biological properties, such as sap transmission and host range.

Disease Cycle and Epidemiology

Infected common sowthistle plants serve as the reservoir for both SYVV and the sowthistle aphid (Fig. 93). This weed is the primary host on which the aphid vector reproduces. SYVV is acquired from infected sowthistle plants by the sowthistle aphid, and after a latent period, the virus can be retained in the insect for more than 50 days. Viruliferous aphids from infected common sowthistle plants transmit the virus to lettuce. The highest incidences of SYVV infection in lettuce occur in fields that are next to or near infected common sowthistle plants—for example, near stands of infected plants on abandoned properties, in fallow fields, and in fields of crops having poor weed control. Additional spread may occur within and between lettuce fields via viruliferous aphids from infected lettuce plants.

Management

Because the reservoir of both the virus and the aphid vector is common sowthistle, weed management in and around lettuce fields should be practiced to eliminate these reservoirs. Growers should avoid establishing new plantings of lettuce near areas with large populations of weeds and lettuce fields with SYVV-infected plants.

Selected References

Duffus, J. E., and Russell, G. E. 1969. Sowthistle yellow vein virus in England. Plant Pathol. 18:144-146.

Duffus, J. E., Zink, F. W., and Bardin, R. 1970. Natural occurrence of sowthistle yellow vein virus on lettuce. Phytopathology 60:1383-1384.

Peters, D. 1971. Sowthistle yellow vein virus. Descriptions of Plant Viruses, no. 62. Commonwealth Mycological Institute, Kew, Surrey, UK.

Richardson, J., and Sylvester, E. S. 1968. Further evidence of multiplication of sowthistle yellow vein virus in its aphid vector, *Hyperomyzus lactucae*. Virology 35:347-355.

(Prepared by J. E. Duffus; revised by R. L. Gilbertson)

Tobacco Rattle

Tobacco rattle is caused by *Tobacco rattle virus* (TRV), a nematode-transmitted virus that infects lettuce only rarely. Lettuce plants infected with TRV are associated with the presence of the stubby-root nematode vector (family *Trichodoridae*). Reports of TRV infection of lettuce have come from several parts of the world, including Bangladesh, Denmark, Italy, and the United States (California).

Symptoms

Lettuce plants infected with TRV are stunted and have distorted leaves. The most distinct symptoms of TRV infection are the development of yellow spots, mosaic/mottling, and ring spots and line patterns in infected lettuce leaves (Fig. 118).

Fig. 118. Ring spots on a romaine lettuce leaf, characteristic of infection with *Tobacco rattle virus*. (Courtesy D. E. Mayhew—© APS)

Fig. 117. Vein yellowing in a crisphead lettuce leaf, caused by *Sowthistle yellow vein virus*. (Courtesy J. E. Duffus)

Causal Agent

TRV is a plus-sense, single-stranded RNA virus and the type member of the genus *Tobravirus* in the family *Virgaviridae*. The virus has rigid rod-shaped virions of two sizes: approximately 22 × 190 nm and 15–50 × 22 nm. The genome is bipartite and composed of two plus-sense, single-stranded RNAs: RNA-1 (~6.8 kb) and RNA-2 (~4.5 kb). There are numerous strains of TRV, and the lengths of the smaller RNA and virion vary among strains.

TRV has a very wide host range and infects more than 400 species of dicot and monocotyledonous plants in more than 24 families. Hosts include numerous cultivated plants and weeds.

In nature, the vectors of TRV are various species of stubby-root nematode in the genera *Paratrichodorus* and *Trichodorus* (family *Tricodoridae*). Although TRV can be seed transmitted in some hosts, there is no evidence of seed transmission in lettuce. The virus is also readily mechanically (sap) transmissible to numerous plant species.

TRV can be detected using serological methods, such as enzyme-linked immunosorbent assay (ELISA), and using reverse transcription-polymerase chain reaction (RT-PCR) and sequencing.

Disease Cycle and Epidemiology

Infection of lettuce by TRV is mediated by the feeding of viruliferous stubby-root nematodes on the roots. TRV infects the roots of many plants, including weeds. In a field with populations of stubby-root nematodes in the soil, weeds can serve as a reservoir for TRV infection of lettuce. Nematode transmission of TRV occurs in a semipersistent manner, in which the virus is acquired and transmitted in approximately 1 h and then retained for as long as 20 weeks. Although TRV can be mechanically (sap) transmitted under experimental conditions, there is no evidence of transmission by contact.

Management

Because tobacco rattle is a minor disease of lettuce, management is not warranted. Moreover, because TRV infects the roots of many weeds in nature (including some that do not show obvious symptoms), following standard weed control practices should limit spread of the disease.

Selected References

Gold, A. H., Grogan, R., and Bardin, R. 1963. An apparent strain of tobacco rattle virus associated with a yellow spotting of lettuce. (Abstr.) Phytopathology 53:1139.

Mayhew, D. E., and Matsumoto. T. T. 1978. Romaine lettuce, a new host for tobacco rattle virus. Plant Dis. Rep. 62:553-556.

(Prepared by D. E. Mayhew;
revised by R. L. Gilbertson)

Tobacco Ringspot

Tobacco ringspot is caused by *Tobacco ringspot virus* (TRSV) and associated with the presence of dagger nematodes—the primary vectors of the virus—in the soil. The disease is rarely reported in lettuce crops, but because of the properties of the virus and the worldwide distribution of the nematode vector, it has the potential to appear in many lettuce-growing regions.

Symptoms

Lettuce plants infected with TRSV show diffuse yellow mottling, ring spots, and yellow-green calico patterns in midaged to older leaves. Mature plants are stunted and have a compressed appearance.

The symptoms of tobacco ringspot tend to be similar to those of tobacco rattle disease.

Causal Agent

TRSV is a plus-sense, single-stranded RNA virus and the type member of the genus *Nepovirus* in the family *Secoviridae* (order Picornvirales). The virus has icosahedral (spherical) virions that are 28–30 nm in diameter. Its bipartite genome is composed of two plus-sense, single-stranded RNAs: RNA-1 (~7.5 kb) and RNA-2 (~3.9 kb).

TRSV has a very wide host range that includes herbaceous and woody plants. Numerous strains of the virus have been described.

The main vector of TRSV is the dagger nematode (*Xiphinema americanum* and other species). The virus is transmitted in a semipersistent manner; acquisition and transmission occur in hours, and retention lasts for days. Both the larval and adult forms of the nematode can transmit the virus efficiently.

TRSV has also been reported to be nonspecifically transmitted by insects and mites, but the efficiency of transmission is very low. The virus is readily mechanically (sap) transmissible to numerous herbaceous hosts. It is also seed and pollen transmitted in a number of host plants. In lettuce, seed transmission rates as high as 21% have been reported.

TRSV can be detected using serological methods, such as enzyme-linked immunosorbent assay (ELISA), and using reverse transcription-polymerase chain reaction (RT-PCR) and sequencing.

Disease Cycle and Epidemiology

The appearance of tobacco ringspot disease in lettuce is unusual and occurs in fields with populations of viruliferous nematodes. The incidence of TRSV infection in a lettuce field reflects the populations of viruliferous nematodes.

TRSV-infected lettuce plants may also appear in fields planted with infected seed, although this is apparently very rare.

Management

Resistance in lettuce to TRSV is not available. Managing weeds that can serve as reservoirs of the virus (e.g., black nightshade [*Solanum nigrum*], jimsonweed [*Datura stramonium*], and lambsquarters [*Chenopodium album*]) and practices that minimize nematode populations in fields can minimize the spread of tobacco ringspot disease.

Selected References

Bardin, R. 1992. Diseases of Lettuce in the Salinas-Watsonville Area of California. Agricultural Commissioner's Office, Salinas, CA.

Stace-Smith, R. 1985. Tobacco ringspot virus. Descriptions of Plant Viruses, no. 309 (no. 17, rev.). Commonwealth Mycological Institute, Kew, Surrey, UK.

(Prepared by D. E. Mayhew;
revised by R. L. Gilbertson)

Tobacco Streak

Tobacco streak, which is caused by *Tobacco streak virus* (TSV), is characterized by extensive foliar necrosis of lettuce, escarole, and endive. This disease has been a problem since the mid-1990s for lettuce production in Florida (United States), where incidences as high as 70% have been reported from some fields. Overall, tobacco streak is of minor importance, and lettuce is considerably less susceptible than escarole and endive.

Symptoms

The characteristic symptoms of tobacco streak disease of lettuce are necrotic flecking and streaking of leaves. Infected plants are stunted, and the heads may develop a somewhat ruffled or frilly appearance (Fig. 119). Symptoms on escarole and endive include concentric, chlorotic, and necrotic rings, which produce a targetlike appearance. The leaves closest to the growing point will be distorted but may remain green for an extended time. Within several weeks of symptom development, the entire plant will become necrotic and then die.

Causal Agent

TSV is a plus-sense, single-stranded RNA virus and the type member of the genus *Ilarvirus* in the family *Bromoviridae*. TSV virions are icosahedral (spherical) and approximately 28 nm in diameter. The genome of TSV is a tripartite and divided among three plus-sense, single-stranded RNAs: RNA-1 (~3.4 kb), RNA-2 (~3.1 kb), and RNA-3 (~2.2 kb). RNA-1 and -2 encode the proteins involved in viral replication, whereas RNA-3 encodes the 3a protein involved in movement and a subgenomic RNA (RNA-4 [~1.0 kb]), from which the capsid protein is expressed. All three RNAs and a functional capsid protein, which activates viral replication, are required for infection. RNA-1 and -2 are individually packaged into virions, whereas RNA-3 and -4 are packaged together into another virion. Thus, there are three types of virions, but all are similar in appearance and sedimentation coefficient (weight).

A number of TSV strains have been identified, each with a different host range, symptomatology, physical properties, and serology. The TSV isolate from Florida appears to be similar to the TSV strain that causes red node disease of common bean. However, molecular characterization is required to establish the precise relationships among TSV strains and other *Ilarvirus* spp. TSV infects and causes diseases in asparagus, blackberry, common bean (red node disease), pea, potato, strawberry (necrotic shock), and tobacco. In some hosts, such as tobacco, the symptoms are initially severe but plants later recover, which is a host defense response mediated by gene silencing.

TSV is transmitted by thrips, including the western flower thrips (*Frankliniella occidentalis*) and the onion thrips (*Thrips tabaci*), in a pollen-mediated manner. The virus is also transmitted via seed in common bean, lambsquarters (*Chenopodium album*), and soybean and via pollen in various perennials, but this has not been demonstrated in lettuce. TSV is mechanically (sap) transmissible, although the virions are unstable in plant extracts; transmission does not occur by plant-to-plant contact.

TSV can be detected using serological methods, such as enzyme-linked immunosorbent assay (ELISA). However, the virus is poorly antigenic, and not all strains may be detected by certain antisera. Thus, molecular methods, such as reverse transcription-polymerase chain reaction (RT-PCR) and sequencing, are more reliable for detection of TSV.

Disease Cycle and Epidemiology

A number of annual and perennial weeds are hosts of TSV and probably serve as reservoirs for the virus. The incidence of tobacco streak in lettuce and escarole fields appears to be highest near the borders. Although transmission studies have not been conducted with TSV and lettuce and escarole, field observations and results from studies of other crops suggest that one or more species of thrips are involved in the spread of TSV in lettuce.

Although reported for other crops, seed transmission of the virus does not appear to be an important factor in the epidemiology of tobacco streak in lettuce.

Management

Tobacco streak is a minor disease of lettuce in most regions, and management is not warranted. In Florida, tobacco streak has been problematic only in fields surrounded by or adjacent to weedy banks of ditches. Destroying these viral reservoirs will offer some measure of control.

Selected References

Fulton, R. W. 1985. Tobacco streak virus. Descriptions of Plant Viruses, no. 307. Commonwealth Mycological Institute, Kew, Surrey, UK.

Johnson, J. 1936. Tobacco streak, a virus disease. Phytopathology 26:285-292.

Kaiser, W. J., Wyatt, S. D., and Pesho, G. R. 1982. Natural hosts and vectors of tobacco streak virus in eastern Washington. Phytopathology 72:1508-1512.

McDaniel, L. L., Raid, R. N., Elliot, C. L., Tsai, J. H., and Nagata, R. T. 1992. Purification and serological characterization of a tobacco streak virus isolate infecting field-grown escarole and lettuce. Plant Dis. 76:966-971.

Thomas, W. D., Jr., and Graham, R. W. 1951. Seed transmission of red node virus in pinto beans. Phytopathology 41:959-962.

(Prepared by R. N. Raid and R. L. Gilbertson)

Tomato Spotted Wilt

Tomato spotted wilt of lettuce, caused by *Tomato spotted wilt virus* (TSWV), and similar diseases caused by other tospoviruses—including *Groundnut ringspot virus* (GRSV), *Impatiens necrotic spot virus* (INSV), and *Tomato chlorotic spot virus* (TCSV)—can produce economic losses in lettuce crops. The losses result from the necrosis, yellowing, and wilting symptoms of infected plants and the efficient transmission of the viruses by the thrips vectors, which can lead to high rates of infection. The disease symptoms induced by TSWV, GRSV, and TCSV are similar in lettuce (and other crops); the viruses share common thrips vectors; and many aspects of the epidemiologies of the diseases caused by these viruses are similar. Therefore, these three tospoviruses will be considered together in this section.

First described in tomato in Australia in 1919, TSWV is now widespread in temperate and subtropical regions throughout the world, including Australia, Europe, Israel, North America, and South America. Losses caused by tospovirus infections in lettuce have been reported from Argentina, southern Australia, Brazil, Europe (Italy and Spain), Israel, and the United States (coastal and central California, Florida, Georgia, and Hawaii). Although tospoviruses are also economically important in Asia, the infection of lettuce crops is less common than in other

Fig. 119. Ruffled or frilly leaves of crisphead lettuce, caused by *Tobacco streak virus*. (Courtesy R. N. Raid—© APS)

regions. This may be because lettuce is grown less frequently or the types and cultivars grown are less susceptible to Asian tospoviruses; however, TSWV was identified in Asia in 2009. TSWV, GRSV, and TCSV are present in South America, and each can cause economic losses, depending on the crop and the location. GRSV has been reported to infect lettuce in Argentina, whereas TCSV has been identified as the causal agent of tospovirus disease in lettuce in Brazil. In approximately 2010, GRSV and TCSV were introduced in the United States (Florida and Ohio) and the Caribbean Basin (Puerto Rico and the Dominican Republic). TCSV has also been reported to cause disease symptoms in lettuce in Puerto Rico.

Symptoms

The leaves of a lettuce plant infected with a tospovirus initially appear bronzed and develop numerous small, necrotic lesions or spots, often associated with the veins. These lesions expand into tan or brown-to-black, necrotic spots, which may coalesce to form necrotic sections on affected leaves (Fig. 120). Plants infected at a young age may die. In older plants, the leaves show marginal wilting and yellowing, and the leaves and petioles have brown, necrotic spots. Eventually, affected areas of the leaves of older plants turn brown, collapse, and dry out and die.

A tospovirus-infected plant often has more severe symptoms on one side than the other; this results in unequal growth, which causes the petioles to curve or twist as uninfected tissue grows around diseased tissue. The midribs of leaves often develop necrotic streaks and sunken spots. Young, newly emerging leaves may exhibit numerous necrotic spots, and the hearts may turn black and die.

Symptoms of a tospovirus infection of lettuce can resemble chemical burn damage caused by excess fertilizer or pesticide. Symptoms can also resemble those of internal rib necrosis.

Causal Agents

Tospoviruses are ambisense, single-stranded RNA viruses in the genus *Tospovirus* and the family *Bunyaviridae*. TSWV is the type member of the genus, and GRSV and TCSV are distinct species with similar properties. Tospovirus virions are pleomorphic, spherical particles; each is roughly 80–120 nm in diameter and covered by an envelope consisting of a host-derived, lipid bilayer membrane.

The tospovirus genome consists of three single-stranded RNAs of a total size of approximately 16 kb. The small (S) RNA (2.9 kb) encodes the viral nucleocapsid (N) protein (29 kilodaltons [kDa]) and a nonstructural (NSs) protein; the middle

Fig. 120. Necrotic spotting and blighting in a crisphead lettuce plant infected with *Tomato spotted wilt virus*. (Courtesy R. L. Gilbertson—© APS)

(M) RNA (4.8 kb) encodes a precursor of the two glycoproteins (G1 [78 kDa] and G2 [58 kDa]) and a nonstructural (NSm) movement protein; and the large (L) RNA (8.9 kb) encodes the viral RNA polymerase (~200 kDa). The virion consists of a core composed of the ribonucleoproteins in the form of the three RNAs individually encapsidated by the N protein, a few molecules of the polymerase, and the outer host membrane-derived envelope, from which project the viral glycoproteins that are embedded in the membrane.

The host range of TSWV is among the widest of any known plant virus and includes more than 900 plant species in more than 80 families, including dicotyledonous and even some monocotyledonous plants. These host plants include cultivated crop plants, ornamentals, and noncultivated plants (weeds). GRSV and TCSV also have relatively wide host ranges, but whether these viruses infect as many plant species as TSWV has yet to be determined. It is important to emphasize, however, that many of the hosts of TSWV are experimental (i.e., infected under laboratory conditions) and may not serve an important function in the epidemiology of tomato spotted wilt disease.

In nature, TSWV is transmitted by as many as seven species of thrips (order Thysanoptera): the western flower thrips (*Frankliniella occidentalis*), the tomato thrips (*F. schultzei*), the tobacco thrips (*F. fusca*), the Florida flower thrips (*F. bispinosa*), the European flower thrips (*F. intonsa*), the onion thrips (*Thrips tabaci*), and the light-brown soybean thrips (*T. setosus*). The western flower thrips is a particularly efficient and important vector. GRSV and TCSV are efficiently transmitted by the western flower thrips and the tomato thrips, which tend to be prevalent in tropical and subtropical regions of South America, the Caribbean, and the southeastern United States (where these viruses are important). Transmission occurs by a persistent and propagative manner; thus, TSWV (and presumably GRSV and TCSV) has the capacity to replicate in both animal and plant cells.

The thrips–TSWV relationship is unique among plant virus–vector associations in that only the larval stages can acquire the virus. The virus is retained through molting (transstadial), such that only adults arising from larvae that have fed on infected plants can transmit the virus (become viruliferous). Adult thrips can transmit TSWV for life, but the virus is not passed through the eggs (transovarially). The minimum period for acquisition is 15–30 min, and the efficiency of acquisition increases following a longer feeding period. There is a latent period of 4–12 days before transmission occurs. Transmission of the virus to the plant occurs during feeding on epidermal and mesophyll cells and takes as little as 5 min.

There is no evidence of seed transmission of TSWV or other tospoviruses. They can be transmitted mechanically (via sap) under experimental conditions, but there is no evidence of transmission by plant-to-plant contact.

Detection of TSWV and other tospoviruses can be accomplished using serological methods, such as enzyme-linked immunosorbent assay (ELISA) and lateral-flow devices (immunostrips) (typically with antibodies raised against the N protein), and using reverse transcription-polymerase chain reaction (RT-PCR) and sequencing. Lateral-flow devices have been particularly useful for confirming TSWV infections in the field. At least one lateral-flow device for TSWV also detects GRSV and TCSV.

Disease Cycle and Epidemiology

A lettuce plant becomes infected with TSWV, GRSV, or TCSV when fed on by winged, viruliferous adult thrips. The species and source of the thrips depends on the geographical region and the time of year. The source of viruliferous thrips may be fields of other crops with infected plants (e.g., processing tomatoes in California) or noncultivated reservoir plants (weeds). Another source of viruliferous adults is those that emerge from pupae in soil or crop debris. Lettuce is a good host for thrips and can support large populations. After viruliferous thrips feed on a lettuce plant, disease symptoms develop in 7–14 days. Reproduction of thrips on infected lettuce plants generate new generations of winged, viruliferous adults, which can spread TSWV within and between lettuce fields.

Although larvae can transmit the virus before they pupate, winged adults are the major means by which the virus is spread. In areas in which there are sequential plantings of lettuce, high rates of infection in newly planted fields may occur because of migrations of large populations of viruliferous adult thrips (which remain infective throughout their life span) from older, established fields. In temperate areas, the cropping cycle is broken during the winter, causing a substantial drop in thrips populations. As a result, small thrips populations and a low level of TSWV inoculum are present early in the growing season.

Management

The effective management of tomato spotted wilt in lettuce (or any other crop) requires an integrated pest management (IPM) approach that is based on knowledge of the biology of the tospoviruses and the thrips vectors in a given geographical region, as there can be important differences among regions. It is particularly important to understand the sources of inoculum and the specific thrips vectors involved and their population dynamics. An effective IPM approach includes strategies for before, during, and after lettuce production:

- **Before-planting strategies:** (1) Utilize strategic field placement to avoid establishing new lettuce fields adjacent to or near fields of susceptible crops with tospovirus-infected plants. (2) Plant new fields upwind of and with adequate distance from established fields with tospovirus-infected plants. (3) Modify planting dates to avoid known periods of large thrips populations. (4) Manage the reservoir hosts of tospoviruses and thrips vectors.
- **During-the-season strategies:** (1) Plant TSWV- and thrips-free transplants. (2) Monitor or predict (e.g., using a degree-day model) the sizes of the thrips populations, and manage the populations with insecticides, especially early in the growing season to delay the development of viruliferous adult thrips. (3) Remove or rogue tospovirus-infected plants. (4) Minimize in-field cultivation practices to reduce the movement of viruliferous adult thrips from infected plants. (5) Manage weeds in and around fields.
- **After-harvest strategies:** (1) Promptly remove or destroy lettuce plants in fields following harvest (ideally, by deep plowing), and wait a minimum of 4 weeks before planting to allow adult thrips to emerge from pupae in soil or associated with crop debris. (2) Practice effective weed management in fallow fields and noncropped and idle land. (3) In tropical and subtropical regions in which there is no winter season, rotate to nonhosts of TSWV and thrips.

The specific combination of practices used in an IPM program will depend on the biology of the tospoviruses and the thrips vectors in a given growing region.

In contrast to crops such as pepper and tomato, for lettuce, there are no commercially available cultivars with resistance to TSWV or any other tospovirus. Thus, this highly desirable and effective strategy is not an option for tospovirus management in lettuce.

Selected References

Batuman, O., Campbell, A. J., Coop, L., Ullman, D. E., Gilbertson, R. L., and McRoberts, N. 2014. Using a degree day insect development model to guide strategic management of western flower thrips and *Tomato spotted wilt virus* (family *Bunyaviridae*, genus *Tospovirus*) on processing tomato in the Central Valley of California. Acta Hortic. 1069:309-314.

Best, R. J. 1968. Tomato spotted wilt virus. Pages 65-145 in: Advances in Virus Research, vol. 13. K. M. Smith and M. A. Lauffer, eds. Academic Press, New York.

Cho, J. J., Mau, R. F. L., German, T. L., Hartmann, R. W., Yudin, L. S., Gonsalves, D., and Provvidenti, R. 1989. A multidisciplinary approach to management of tomato spotted wilt virus in Hawaii. Plant Dis. 73:375-383.

Coutts, B. A., Thomas-Carroll, M. L., and Jones, R. A. C. 2004. Patterns of spread of *Tomato spotted wilt virus* in field crops of lettuce and pepper: Spatial dynamics and validation of control measures. Ann. Appl. Biol. 145:231-245.

de Jensen, C. E., and Adkins, S. 2014. First report of *Tomato chlorotic spot virus* in lettuce in Puerto Rico. (Abstr.) Plant Dis. 98:1015.

Gera, A., Kritzman, A., Cohen, J., Raccah, B., and Antignus, Y. 200. Tospoviruses infecting vegetable crops in Israel. Bull. OEPP/EPPO 30:289-292.

German, T. L., Ullman, D. E., and Moyer, J. W. 1992. Tospoviruses: Diagnosis, molecular biology, phylogeny, and vector relationships. Annu. Rev. Phytopathol. 30:315-348.

Gilbertson, R. L., Batuman, O., Webster, C. G., and Adkins, S. 2015. Role of the insect supervectors *Bemisia tabaci* and *Frankliniella occidentalis* in the emergence and global spread of plant viruses. Ann. Rev. Virol. 2: 67-93.

Pavan, M. A., Krause-Sakate, R., da Silva, N., Zerbini, F. M., and Le Gall, O. 2008. Virus disease of lettuce in Brazil. Pages 35-41 in: Plant Viruses. Global Science Books, East Sussex, UK.

Peters, D. 1998. An updated list of plant species susceptible to tospoviruses. Pages 107-110 in: Proceedings of the Fourth International Symposium on Tospoviruses and Thrips in Floral and Vegetable Crops. D Peters and R. Goldbach, eds. Wageningen, the Netherlands.

Whitfield, A. E., Ullman, D. E., and German, T. L. 2005. Tospovirus-thrips interactions. Annu. Rev. Phytopathol. 43:459-489.

Wilson, C. R. 1998. Incidence of weed reservoirs and vectors of tomato spotted wilt tospovirus on southern Tasmanian lettuce farms. Plant Pathol. 47:171-176.

(Prepared by J. J. Cho; revised by R. L. Gilbertson)

Turnip Mosaic

Turnip mosaic disease is caused by *Turnip mosaic virus* (TuMV), a potyvirus that has a worldwide distribution and is frequently encountered in temperate regions of Africa, Asia, Europe, and North America. TuMV was first associated with lettuce in 1966, when it was reported to infect plants in the Salinas Valley of California (United States). Susceptibility of lettuce to TuMV is restricted to crisphead types—in particular, those in which downy mildew resistance has been introgressed from plant introduction (PI) 91532. Thus, turnip mosaic is a minor disease of lettuce, and it is more important in escarole and endive.

Symptoms

A lettuce plant infected with TuMV initially develops numerous small, light-green to yellow, circular to elongated spots between or next to the veins of leaves (the so-called eyespot symptom stage) (Fig. 121). On a young plant, the numerous chlorotic lesions on leaves may replace the normal dark-green tissue, imparting a distinctly chlorotic appearance and a striking mottle. Such a plant will then become severely stunted and develop deformed and ruffled leaves; in some cases, a plant infected at a young age may die. A plant infected later in development will show chlorotic or necrotic spots on the lower (older) leaves, and these may coalesce to produce an overall chlorotic appearance. Newly emerging leaves will have a yellow mosaic/mottling and often inward-curved midribs and some degree of distorted growth (Fig. 122). During the reproductive phase of plant growth, necrotic lesions may develop on the seed stalk. Necrotic areas may also form on the developing involucral bracts and peduncles, and many of the floral heads will wither before they mature. Seed production from an infected plant will be greatly reduced because of the small number of seeds per flower head.

Turnip mosaic in lettuce can be distinguished from lettuce mosaic, which is caused by *Lettuce mosaic virus* (LMV), in several ways. Turnip mosaic is characterized by the presence of numerous chlorotic lesions on the lower leaves and the yellow mosaic and distortion in younger, newly emerged leaves. In contrast, an LMV-infected plant tends to develop a dull-green or yellow mosaic. Another characteristic of lettuce mosaic is the absence of a downward roll of the leaf tips.

Causal Agent

TuMV is a plus-sense, single-stranded RNA virus and a member of the genus *Potyvirus* in the family *Potyviridae*. Like all potyviruses, TuMV has virions that are long, flexuous rods and measure approximately 13 × 720 nm. The genome is one plus-sense, single-stranded RNA of approximately 10 kb that is translated into a single polyprotein and subsequently processed into smaller functional proteins. TuMV induces cylindrical and fibrous inclusions in the cytoplasm of an infected cell.

TuMV has a very wide host range, infecting more than 50 species of plants in at least 12 families of dicotyledonous plants. The virus most commonly infects cultivated and non-cultivated plants in the family Cruciferae. For example, TuMV infection causes mottling and black, necrotic spots in brussels sprouts, cabbage, and cauliflower and mosaic with leaf distortion and stunting in Chinese cabbage (*Brassica rapa* subsp. *pekinensis*), horseradish, mustard, radish, rape (*B. napus*), rutabaga (swede), turnip, and watercress. It also causes flower breaks in anemone (*Anemone* spp.), petunia, stock (*Matthiola* spp.), wallflower (*Erysimum* spp.), and zinnia. Local lesions are induced in leaves of quinoa (*Chenopodium quinoa*) and goose-foot (*C. amaranticolor*), whereas systemic mosaic is induced in the tobacco species *Nicotiana tabacum* and *N. glutinosa*.

In nature, TuMV is transmitted by more than 40 species of aphids, especially the green peach aphid (*Myzus persicae*) and the cabbage aphid (*Brevicoryne brassicae*), in a nonpersistent manner. Like LMV, TuMV is readily transmitted mechanically (via sap) to many plants. However, unlike LMV, TuMV has not been found to be seed transmissible in lettuce or other plants.

TuMV can be detected using serological methods, such as enzyme-linked immunosorbent assay (ELISA), and using reverse transcription-polymerase chain reaction (RT-PCR) and sequencing.

Disease Cycle and Epidemiology

Because TuMV has a very wide host range and can be transmitted by many aphid species, there can be many inoculum sources and opportunities for the virus to be transmitted to lettuce. The most likely inoculum sources are cruciferous weeds.

TuMV is introduced into lettuce fields via winged, viruliferous aphids from surrounding vegetation (weeds) or from established fields of crops with TuMV-infected plants. The incidence of disease will be a function of the populations of aphids and the number of fields planted with lettuce cultivars susceptible to TuMV. If the aphid populations are large and sources of inoculum are present, the incidence of turnip mosaic in a field of susceptible lettuce plants can be high. The TuMV-infected plants in such a field can then serve as a source of viruliferous aphids for subsequent spread within and between fields. The virus overwinters in perennial cruciferous weeds.

Lettuce cultivars susceptible to TuMV include Calmar, E-4, Imperial 410, Imperial Triumph, Valrio, Valtemp, and Valverde and potentially other cultivars with these lines or with prickly lettuce (*Lactuca serriola* [PI 91532]), a wild species of lettuce, in their genetic backgrounds.

Management

Because only certain lettuce cultivars are susceptible to TuMV and resistance to TuMV in lettuce is available, management of turnip mosaic can be achieved by planting nonsusceptible or resistant cultivars. Three types of resistance to TuMV occur in lettuce: (1) extreme resistance or immunity; (2) resistance that is manifested by mild symptom expression; and (3) resistance to aphids and mechanical (sap) inoculation. The most effective control measure is to plant TuMV-resistant types of lettuce (e.g., butterhead, leaf, and romaine cultivars) or resistant crisphead cultivars (e.g., Climax, Great Lakes, Merit, Vanguard, or newer cultivars with resistance). The crisphead cultivar Avoncrisp, the leaf types Red Salad Bowl and Salad Trim, the romaine type Valmaine, and a number of butterhead cultivars are resistant to both TuMV and some races of downy mildew.

In cases in which susceptible cultivars will be planted, it is important to manage weeds around fields and to avoid establishing new plantings adjacent to or near older, established plantings with TuMV-infected plants. Aphid management—particularly with newer systemic products, such as neonicotinoids—may help slow the spread of turnip mosaic in lettuce fields.

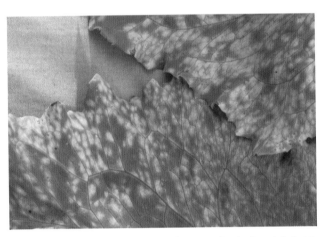

Fig. 121. Light-green spots on leaves of crisphead lettuce, caused by *Turnip mosaic virus*. (Courtesy S. T. Koike—© APS)

Fig. 122. Stunting and distortion of crisphead lettuce, caused by *Turnip mosaic virus*. (Courtesy S. T. Koike—© APS)

Selected References

Duffus, J. E., and Zink, F. W. 1969. A diagnostic host reaction for the identification of turnip mosaic virus. Plant Dis. Rep. 53:916-917.

Tomlinson, J. A. 1970. Turnip mosaic virus. Descriptions of Plant Viruses, no. 8. Commonwealth Mycological Institute, Kew, Surrey, UK.

Zink, F. W., and Duffus, J. E. 1969. Relationship of turnip mosaic virus susceptibility and downy mildew (*Bremia lactucae*) resistance in lettuce. J. Am. Soc. Hortic. Sci. 94:403-407.

Zink, F. W., and Duffus, J. E. 1970. Linkage of turnip mosaic virus susceptibility and downy mildew, *Bremia lactucae*, resistance in lettuce. J. Am. Soc. Hortic. Sci. 95:420-422.

(Prepared by J. E. Duffus; revised by R. L. Gilbertson)

Minor Viruses of Lettuce

A number of viruses that infect lettuce have been described only once and/or from a single geographical location. In some cases, these viruses have been shown only to infect lettuce experimentally, but there have been no reports of them causing economic losses in lettuce. They are therefore considered minor viruses of lettuce.

Endive necrotic mosaic virus

Endive necrotic mosaic virus (ENMV) is a potyvirus (genus *Potyvirus,* family *Potyviridae*) that was discovered in France in the mid-1990s. It was first observed on escarole and curly endive, on which it was associated with stunting of plant growth and mosaic/mottling and deformation of leaves. ENMV also infects lettuce, but only a few cultivars are susceptible. In these cultivars, infected plants are stunted and the leaves are deformed. Initially, the leaves of infected plants develop chlorotic spots and vein clearing followed by mosaic/mottle and necrosis. In lettuce, these symptoms can be confused with those induced by *Lettuce mosaic virus* (LMV) and *Turnip mosaic virus* (TuMV).

Relatively little information is available about ENMV. However, it likely shares the properties of other viruses in the genus *Potyvirus,* including having long, flexuous, rod-shaped virions (~13 × 700–750 nm) and a genome composed of one plus-sense, single-stranded RNA (~10 kb) that is translated into a polyprotein.

The vector of ENMV is likely to be one or more aphids, and transmission occurs in a nonpersistent (styletborne) manner. The importance of ENMV in lettuce production has not been established.

(Prepared by R. L. Gilbertson)

Lettuce necrotic leaf curl virus

Torradoviruses are a relatively new group of picorna-like, single-stranded, plus-sense RNA viruses; they have isometric (spherical) virions that are approximately 28–30 nm in diameter. Based on genome structure and sequence, these viruses were placed into a new genus, *Torradovirus* (family *Secoviridae*), which was named after the type member, *Tomato torrado virus* (ToTV). Most torradoviruses, including ToTV, infect tomato (or other solanaceous plants) and cause necrosis on the stems, petioles, leaves, and fruit.

In 2011, lettuce plants with symptoms of necrosis and leaf curling were observed in a single field in the Netherlands. A virus was mechanically (sap) transmitted to two species of tobacco, *Nicotiana benthamiana* and *N. occidentalis,* in which it induced stunting and local necrotic lesions and systemic necrosis. The virus was also mechanically transmitted to lettuce, in which it induced leaf mottling and deformation followed by leaf curling and necrosis. Through the use of next-generation sequencing, torradovirus sequences were identified in the leaves of infected *N. occidentalis* plants. Further characterization revealed that the virus was a new species of torradovirus, which was named *Lettuce necrotic leaf curl virus* (LNLCV).

LNLCV is a typical torradovirus in terms of having a bipartite, plus-sense, single-stranded RNA genome encapsidated in icosahedral virions approximately 28–30 nm. No vector has been identified for LNLCV. (Other torradoviruses are vectored by whiteflies.)

Attempts to find LNLCV infecting lettuce plants in the same field in the Netherlands the following growing season were unsuccessful. Thus, the importance of LNLCV as a lettuce-infecting virus is unclear.

Selected Reference

Verbeek, M., Dullemans, A. M., van Raaij, H. M. G., Verhoeven, J. T. J., and van der Vlugt, R. A. A. 2014. *Lettuce necrotic leaf curl virus,* a new plant virus infecting lettuce and a proposed member of the genus *Torradovirus.* Arch. Virol. 159:801-805.

(Prepared by R. L. Gilbertson)

Lettuce yellow mottle virus

Lettuce yellow mottle virus (LYMoV) is one of five known lettuce-infecting rhabdoviruses. In lettuce plants grown in the Rhone Valley of France, the virus was associated with the development of chlorotic spots and yellow mottling symptoms. It has bacilliform virions (65 × 300 nm) and a typical rhabdovirus genome organization. Sequence analysis of the complete genome (12,926 nucleotides) revealed that LYMoV is most closely related to *Lettuce necrotic yellows virus* (LNYV) but divergent enough to represent a new species in the genus *Cytorhabdovirus* (family *Rhabdoviridae*).

The vector of LYMoV is not known. It is mechanically (sap) transmissible to various solanaceous hosts—including the tobacco species *Nicotiana glutinosa,* in which it induces symptoms of mosaic and necrosis—but not to lettuce. The incidence of LYMoV infection in lettuce fields has been limited to a small number of plants, with no major outbreaks of disease or yield losses.

Selected Reference

Heim, F., Lot, H., Delecolle, B., Bassler, A., Krezal, G., and Wetzel, T. 2008. Complete nucleotide sequence of a putative new cytorhabdovirus infecting lettuce. Arch. Virol. 153:81-92.

(Prepared by R. L. Gilbertson)

Lettuce virus X

Lettuce virus X (LeVX) is the first potexvirus reported to infect lettuce. It was discovered surreptitiously—based on the appearance of chlorotic lesions on leaves of mechanically (sap) inoculated quinoa (*Chenopodium quinoa*) plants—during a survey of lettuce viruses in Iran. A typical potexvirus, LeVX has flexuous, rod-shaped virions (~13 × 700 nm) and a single, plus-sense RNA genome of approximately 7,200 nucleotides. The genome organization is also typical of a potexvirus.

LeVX is mechanically (sap) transmissible. In a host range study, it induced mild mottling symptoms in common bean, necrotic local lesions and top necrosis and death in nettleleaf goosefoot (*C. murale*), and no obvious symptoms in lettuce plants. The virus was not transmitted by the green peach aphid (*Myzus persicae*) or by seed.

LeVX has been found only in Tehran Province of Iran, and its distribution and prevalence should be investigated further. However, based on available information about the biology of the virus and its distribution, LeVX is unlikely to become an economically important lettuce virus.

Selected Reference

Dizadji, A., Koohi-Habibi, M., Izadpanah, K., Dietrich, C., Mossahebi, G. H., and Winter, S. 2008. Characterization of lettuce virus X, a new potexvirus infecting lettuce in Iran. Arch. Virol. 153:1867-1875.

(Prepared by R. L. Gilbertson)

Sonchus virus

Sonchus virus (SonV) is one of five rhabdoviruses that can infect lettuce. It has typical bacilliform virions and a genome composed of one negative-sense, single-stranded RNA. It is a species in the genus *Cytorhabdovirus* (family *Rhabdoviridae*).

SonV was discovered in Argentina, where it naturally infects common sowthistle (*Sonchus oleraceus*). It was experimentally transmitted to lettuce via mechanical (sap) transmission, and it induced leaf mottling and chlorotic lines, spots, and rings. Natural infection of lettuce by SonV has not been established.

Selected Reference

Vega, J., Gracia, O., Rubio-Huerto, M. and Feldman, J. M. 1976. Transmission of a bacilliform virus of sowthistle: Mitochondria modifications in the infected cells. Phytopathol. Z. 85:7-14.

(Prepared by R. L. Gilbertson)

Diseases Caused by Nematodes

Many genera of plant-parasitic nematodes are associated with lettuce production, but few have been studied in detail. Those that have been documented to reduce lettuce growth and yield include the needle nematode (*Longidorus africanus*), the lesion nematode (*Pratylenchus penetrans*), and the spiral nematode (*Rotylenchus robustus*), as well as several species of root-knot nematodes (*Meloidogyne* spp.). The needle nematode and spiral nematode are ectoparasites, which do not enter the host root tissue but instead feed on and injure the roots. The lesion nematode is a migratory endoparasite, which feeds on, moves through, and destroys the cortical root tissue. Root-knot nematodes are sedentary endoparasites.

Several other genera of nematodes have been associated with lettuce in the field: the stubby-root nematode (*Paratrichodorus minor;* formerly described as *Trichodorus christiei*); the reniform nematode (*Rotylenchulus reniformis*); the false root-knot nematode (*Nacobbus aberrans*); and stunt nematodes (*Tylenchorhynchus clarus* and *Merlinius* spp.). Limited information is available on the effects of these nematodes on lettuce growth and yield.

(Prepared by P. A. Roberts)

Lesion Nematode

The lesion nematode is a serious pest on both summer- and fall-maturing lettuce crops in Ontario (Canada) and the northeastern United States. It has not been reported in other lettuce-growing areas.

Symptoms

The primary symptom of lesion nematode infection is the presence of reddish-brown root lesions, which consist of narrow traces of damaged or dead cells. In addition to the direct effects of feeding, root discoloration is caused by the release of phenolic substances that results from interactions between plant glycosides and nematode hydrolytic enzymes. Above-ground symptoms on lettuce include stunting and leaf chlorosis. Heavily infected lettuce plants produce undersized heads. Stress factors such as drought, low temperature, and low soil fertility aggravate the damage caused by the lesion nematode.

A standard nematode extraction procedure for roots and soil, such as the mist-chamber process, may be required to confirm the presence of the lesion nematode.

Causal Organism

The lesion nematode associated with lettuce is *Pratylenchus penetrans*. This species is most prevalent in temperate regions and has an extensive host range of more than 160 plant species.

Disease Cycle and Epidemiology

The lesion nematode deposits one-celled eggs singly in cortical root tissue or in soil around the roots, depending on the location of the female. A female deposits eggs at the rate of one or two a day, with a maximum of approximately 68 eggs per female. One molt occurs in the egg, and the second-stage juvenile hatches into the soil or directly into cortical tissue. The juvenile undergoes three more molts to become an adult. All juvenile and adult stages are vermiform and able to migrate in and out of the roots. When the population density increases (usually 6–10 weeks after initial infection), many nematodes of all stages migrate out of the plant tissue and into the soil, where they remain throughout the season. Nematodes that remain in old roots at the end of the season are protected from extreme desiccation until the next growing season. Males are numerous and presumably participate in fertilization.

Temperature, soil moisture, soil type, organic soil amendments, and soil pH all influence the life cycle and rate of development of the lesion nematode. Depending on the time of planting and seasonal temperatures, one or more generations may be completed on a lettuce crop. Typically, the life cycle from adult to adult is completed in approximately 35–42 days. The optimum temperature range is 20–30°C. The lesion nematode is most mobile when 8–12% of the soil volume is air filled. The nematode reproduces optimally between a pH of 5.2 and 6.4, and it prefers coarse-textured sandy loam, silt loam, and muck soils.

An initial population density of two to six nematodes per gram of soil is considered an approximate damage threshold on summer-maturing lettuce in Ontario.

Management

Crop rotation is of little value in managing the lesion nematode because of its wide host range. Various preplant fumigants can reduce the population level, but nematicide treatment is not usually warranted for lesion nematode control. Winter fallowing has some benefit by reducing the population density.

Selected References

Olthof, T. H. A., and Potter, J. W. 1973. The relationship between population densities of *Pratylenchus penetrans* and crop losses in summer-maturing vegetables in Ontario. Phytopathology 63:577-582.

Potter, J. W., and Olthof, T. H. A. 1974. Yield losses in fall-maturing vegetables relative to population densities of *Pratylenchus penetrans* and *Meloidogyne hapla*. Phytopathology 64:1072-1075.

(Prepared by P. A. Roberts)

Needle Nematode

The needle nematode has been reported from Africa, Israel, and California (United States). Typical of many ectoparasitic nematodes, it has an extensive host range that includes avocado, sugarcane, lettuce, and many other vegetables.

Fig. 123. Reduced root system in crisphead lettuce seedlings, caused by needle nematode (*Longidorus africanus*) infection. (Courtesy F. F. Laemmien—© APS)

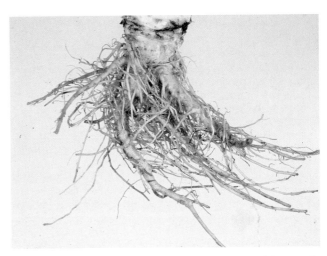

Fig. 124. Root forking in crisphead lettuce, caused by needle nematode (*Longidorus africanus*) infection. (Courtesy J. D. Radewald—© APS)

Symptoms

The most conspicuous symptom of needle nematode infection is the inhibition of root elongation. The nematode causes swelling and distortion of the regions just behind the root tips, which eventually die. The number of functional feeder roots is usually reduced, and some proliferation of lateral roots may occur to compensate for the loss of primary root growth (Fig. 123). A heavy needle nematode infection causes the root system to become branched or forked and shortened (Fig. 124).

At seedling emergence, the cotyledons cup down as though they are wilting, even when there is ample moisture. The leaves are grayish green and have chlorotic outer margins. Damage to early- and late-fall lettuce plantings can delay maturity and reduce head size. An extra harvest may be required to compensate for the lack of uniform growth.

Needle nematodes cannot be seen with the unaided eye and must be observed under a dissecting microscope for identification.

Causal Organism

Longidorus africanus was first described from Africa around sugarcane roots. It was first identified as a pathogen of lettuce in the Imperial Valley of California. As an ectoparasite, it feeds only on the root tips and never enters the root.

Disease Cycle and Epidemiology

The adult female needle nematode deposits eggs into the soil in the root zone. One molt occurs in the egg, and the second-stage juvenile hatches into the soil. The juvenile undergoes three more molts to become an adult. All juvenile and adult stages are vermiform and remain outside the root. All stages feed in the same manner on the host root tips, although no feeding occurs during molting. Males are rare and apparently not required for completing the life cycle.

The length of the life cycle of the needle nematode is influenced by temperature and host. Depending on the time of planting and seasonal temperatures, one to several generations may be completed on lettuce and other host crops. At 28°C, the needle nematode completes its life cycle on lettuce in 7–9 weeks. It can survive in moist, fallow soil at 25°C for at least 3 months and probably longer. Thus, in vegetable production areas with short cropping cycles, alternate hosts are not necessary to maintain a damaging population level.

In greenhouse inoculation tests, damage thresholds of less than two needle nematodes per 250 g of soil were recorded for dry top weights of lettuce seedlings grown in sand and inoculated at different times up to 20 days from seeding. Inoculation of 30-day-old seedlings revealed a tolerance threshold of 28 nematodes per 250 g soil. Thus, a very low needle nematode preplant population density in the soil can damage young seedlings and stunt plant growth. The distribution of the needle nematode is not influenced significantly by soil type; it is found in coarse sands to fine clay soils.

The host range of the needle nematode includes numerous field and vegetable crops, including corn, sorghum, small grains, cotton, sugarbeet, beans, cucurbits, okra (*Abelmoschus* spp.), tomato, eggplant, spinach, and carrot. Some common weeds are also hosts, such as purslane (*Portulaca* spp.) and bermudagrass (*Cynodon* spp.). Radish and broccoli are hosts, but cauliflower and cabbage are not.

Management

Seedling inoculation studies have indicated that strategies focused on avoiding early lettuce seedling exposure to the needle nematode may reduce crop damage. In the Imperial Valley of California, delaying fall planting until the soil temperature has dropped below 22°C significantly minimizes needle nematode damage to lettuce seedlings. Because of this nematode's wide host range, weeds must be eliminated from infested fields.

Preplant soil fumigation with 1,3-dichloropropene reduces the nematode population, suppresses typical symptoms of root injury, increases head weight, and hastens crop maturity.

Selected References

Flint, M. L., and Clark, J. K., eds. 1987. Integrated Pest Management for Cole Crops and Lettuce. Pub. 3307. University of California, Division of Agriculture and Natural Resources, Oakland.

Huang, X., and Ploeg, A. T. 2001. Effect of plant age and *Longidorus africanus* on the growth of lettuce and carrot. J. Nematol. 33:137-141.

Kolodge, C., Radewald, J. D., and Shibuya, F. 1987. Revised host range and studies on the life cycle of *Longidorus africanus*. J. Nematol. 19:77-81.

Radewald, J. D., Osgood, J. W., Mayberry, K. S., Paulus, A. O., and Shibuya, F. 1969. *Longidorus africanus* a pathogen of head lettuce in the Imperial Valley of southern California. Plant Dis. Rep. 53:381-384.

Radewald, J. D., Osgood, J. W., Mayberry, K. S., Paulus, A. O., Otto, H. W., and Shibuya, F. 1969. Results of a preplant fumigation trial for the control of *Longidorus africanus* on lettuce. Plant Dis. Rep. 53:519-523.

(Prepared by P. A. Roberts)

Root-Knot Nematodes

Root-knot nematodes are obligate plant parasites with worldwide distribution. Several common root-knot species are found in agricultural production systems. They have extensive, overlapping host ranges, and several parasitize lettuce.

Symptoms

The most conspicuous and diagnostic symptom of root-knot nematode infection is the development of round to spindle-shaped swellings (galls) on the roots, for which the disease is named (Fig. 125). Observing root galls on infected plants is the best way to detect the presence of root-knot nematodes in the field. The galls induced by the northern root-knot nematode (*Meloidogyne hapla*) tend to be smaller and more spherical or beadlike than those induced by other root-knot species, which often coalesce along the roots. Infected roots are usually shorter and have fewer lateral roots and root hairs than healthy roots.

Additional symptoms may also develop, such as plant stunting, yellowing, and even wilting. In addition, plant stands may be inconsistent; an infected plant stand fails to cover the planting bed as fully as a healthy stand. Finally, lettuce heads are smaller, lighter, and looser than normal.

Damage to lettuce is directly related to the size of the initial nematode population in the soil. White to dark-brown egg masses may occur on the surfaces of galled roots. An egg mass is approximately 0.5–1.0 mm in diameter, and individual eggs are sausage shaped. When a gall is cut open or teased apart, mature females within the root tissue appear as white "pearls" no more than approximately 1.5 mm long.

In areas in which the false root-knot nematode (*Nacobbus aberrans*) occurs, symptoms of root galling can be confused with infection by *Meloidogyne* spp. Confirmation by a nematologist may be required.

Causal Organisms

Parasites of lettuce include the peanut root-knot nematode (*M. arenaria*), the northern root-knot nematode (*M. hapla*), the southern or cotton root-knot nematode (*M. incognita*), and the Javanese root-knot nematode (*M. javanica*). The status of the Columbia root-knot nematode (*M. chitwoodi*) as a parasite of lettuce is not known. Four races of the southern root-knot nematode and two races of the peanut root-knot nematode have been identified by differential hosts. The host–parasite relationships between these different races and lettuce are not known.

Disease Cycle and Epidemiology

One-celled eggs are deposited by the female, which is partially or completely embedded in a root. Eggs are deposited into a gelatinous matrix that holds them together in egg masses or sacs. An egg mass may contain 100 to more than 1,000 eggs, and it may be larger than the female's body. Egg development begins within a few hours of deposition and continues until a fully formed juvenile with a visible stylet lies coiled inside the egg membrane. This is the first juvenile stage. After one molt within the egg, the second-stage juvenile hatches and moves randomly within the egg mass or migrates into the soil until it locates a root tip. Juveniles may orient toward plant roots by following gradients of attractant molecules in the rhizosphere. These juveniles usually penetrate a root just behind the root cap. Once inside, they migrate intra- and intercellularly through the root cortex. Once they come to a feeding site, they become sedentary and initiate the formation of hypertrophied, multinucleate giant cells. The nematodes enlarge, undergo three additional molts, and develop into mature females that are entirely embedded within the root tissue. Deposition of eggs in egg masses completes the cycle. The proportion of males to females increases under conditions of environmental stress. However, males are not required for completing the life cycle, since females are facultatively or obligatorily parthenogenetic.

Root-knot nematode phenology is greatly influenced by temperature. Depending on the planting time and seasonal temperatures, one or two generations per growing season may be completed on lettuce. Optimum temperature ranges are 15–25°C for the northern and Columbia root-knot nematodes and 25–30°C for the peanut, southern, and Javanese root-knot nematodes. There is very little activity by any root-knot nematodes at temperatures above 38°C or below 5°C. Generally, the minimum thresholds for root infection are 10°C for the northern root-knot nematode and 15–18°C for the peanut, southern, and Javanese root-knot nematodes.

The damage caused by root-knot nematodes is generally more severe in coarse-textured and muck soils than in clay soils. Apparently, this difference is related to the greater mobility of nematodes in water in larger, aerated pore spaces.

In field microplot tests with organic soil, damage thresholds were reported to be one or two northern root-knot nematodes per cubic centimeter of soil for lettuce grown for 8 weeks. Also, an initial population density of 28 northern root-knot nematode eggs per cubic centimeter caused up to a 64% yield loss.

Management

Ensuring sufficient soil moisture will help manage the damage caused by root-knot nematodes. When soil moisture is optimum for lettuce growth, root-knot nematodes have a less detrimental effect on the crop.

Treating the soil before planting with a nematicidal compound, such as 1,3-dichloropropene or metam sodium, reduces the nematode population. Amending the soil by incorporating Sudangrass (*Sorghum bicolor* subsp. *drummondii*) as a green manure before planting reduces northern root-knot nematode reproduction and increases lettuce head weight compared with nematode reproduction and lettuce head weight after preplant fallow or other cover crops on organic soils. Crop rotation to a nonhost (e.g., some small-grain cereals) or a weed-free summer fallow effectively reduces the nematode population. However, the extensive host range of root-knot nematodes frequently limits the choice of rotation crops and thus the practicality of this control measure.

Root-knot nematodes are not found in true seeds, but they may be found in transplant seedlings used for field planting. The production of uninfected transplants is an important management procedure.

Little information is available regarding relative host suitability and tolerance to infection among lettuce cultivars. Genetically resistant varieties are not available, although some breeding lines and wild lettuce accessions are resistant to a New York lettuce population of northern root-knot nematode.

Fig. 125. Small, beadlike galls on the roots of crisphead lettuce, caused by infection by the northern root-knot nematode (*Meloidogyne hapla*). (Courtesy S. T. Koike—© APS)

The lettuce cultivar Salinas has been reported to have some resistance compared with other cultivars.

Selected References

Flint, M. L., and Clark, J. K., eds. 1987. Integrated Pest Management for Cole Crops and Lettuce. Pub. 3307. University of California, Division of Agriculture and Natural Resources, Oakland.

Olthof, T. H. A., and Potter, J. W. 1972. Relationship between population densities of *Meloidogyne hapla* and crop losses in summer-maturing vegetables in Ontario. Phytopathology 62:981-986.

Potter, J. W., and Olthof, T. H. A. 1974. Yield losses in fall-maturing vegetables relative to population densities of *Pratylenchus penetrans* and *Meloidogyne hapla*. Phytopathology 64:1072-1075.

Radewald, J. D., Mowbray, P. G., Paulus, A. O., Shibuya, F., and Rible, J. M. 1969. Preplant soil fumigation for California head lettuce. Plant Dis. Rep. 53:385-389.

Viaene, N. M., and Abawi, G. S. 1996. Damage threshold of *Meloidogyne hapla* to lettuce in organic soil. J. Nematol. 28:537-545.

Viaene, N. M., and Abawi, G. S. 1998. Management of *Meloidogyne hapla* on lettuce in organic soil with Sudangrass as a cover crop. Plant Dis. 82:945-952.

Wong, T. K., and Mai, W. F. 1973. Pathogenicity of *Meloidogyne hapla* to lettuce as affected by inoculum level, plant age at inoculation and temperature. J. Nematol. 5:126-129.

Wong, T. K., and Mai, W. F. 1973. *Meloidogyne hapla* in organic soil: Effects of environment on hatch, movement and root invasion. J. Nematol. 5:130-138.

Wong, T. K., and Mai, W. F. 1973. Effect of temperature on growth, development and reproduction of *Meloidogyne hapla* in lettuce. J. Nematol. 5:139-142.

(Prepared by P. A. Roberts)

Spiral Nematode

The spiral nematode is an ectoparasite that may partially enter a plant's roots. This nematode has been reported as a pest of lettuce only in California (United States).

Symptoms

Nematode feeding causes cell necrosis and stunting of the root system. Lesions may coalesce and form visible necrotic areas on the roots. In a study involving field areas infested with as many as 5,000 nematodes per 100 cubic centimeters of soil collected around the roots, lettuce plants of four types (crisphead, butterhead, red leaf, and romaine) were severely stunted and yellowed.

Causal Organism

Rotylenchus robustus is the only species of the two genera of spiral nematodes (*Rotylenchus* and *Helicotylenchus*) that has been reported to parasitize lettuce. Carrot, pea, brussels sprouts, and cauliflower are all good hosts, whereas Swiss chard (*Beta vulgaris* subsp. *vulgaris*), spinach, and red beet are poor hosts. *R. robustus* has also been associated with the decline of ornamental plants.

Disease Cycle and Epidemiology

Detailed studies of the life cycle of *R. robustus* are lacking. As an ectoparasite, it remains outside the host root, feeding on any part of the root system except the root tip. It feeds on epidermal cells and root hair contents and also deeper in the roots on cortical parenchyma cells. Feeding kills and shrivels the cells, which turn yellowish and later brown. Necrosis is restricted to the vicinity of the feeding site.

Adult females lay eggs in the soil around the roots. All juvenile and adult stages remain vermiform. Males are produced and presumably participate in sexual reproduction. Reproduction of *R. robustus* on lettuce occurs equally well at 18.5 and 24.0°C.

Management

Although host range information is limited, it suggests that chenopodiaceous crops might be useful for rotation to reduce the population of *R. robustus* before lettuce is planted. Preplant soil fumigation controls *R. robustus* on lettuce and other crops.

Selected Reference

Lear, B., Johnson, D. E., and Miyagawa, S. T. 1969. A disease of lettuce associated with an ectoparasitic nematode, *Rotylenchus robustus*. Plant Dis. Rep. 53:952-954.

(Prepared by P. A. Roberts)

Stunt Nematode

The stunt nematode *Tylenchorhynchus clarus* was associated with poor lettuce growth in the Palo Verde Valley in southern California (United States) during the 1970s, but direct proof of pathogenicity has not been demonstrated. Symptoms of stunt nematode infection are nonspecific but include leaf chlorosis and stunting of both the root system and aboveground growth. The stunt nematode typically feeds on or near root tips from the root surface, stopping root elongation and growth.

Nematode reproduction was found to be greater at 24 and 27°C than at 21°C on alfalfa, a host on which the stunt nematode feeds both ecto- and endoparasitically.

In fields with initial populations of 23–203 nematodes per liter of soil, positive growth and yield responses in lettuce were achieved following the use of preplant soil fumigants.

Selected References

Noel, G. R., and Lownsbery, B. F. 1978. Effects of temperature on the pathogenicity of *Tylenchorhynchus clarus* to alfalfa and observations on feeding. J. Nematol. 10:195-198.

Radewald, J. D., Mowbray, P. G., Paulus, A. O., Shibuya, F., and Rible, J. M. 1969. Preplant soil fumigation for California head lettuce. Plant Dis. Rep. 53:385-389.

(Prepared by P. A. Roberts)

Parasitic Plant

Broomrape

Although attacks of broomrape (*Orobanche* spp., family Orobanchaceae) on lettuce have not been frequently reported in the literature, severe attacks by this parasitic plant can occur under certain circumstances and in heavily infested soils. In fact, members of the genus *Orobanche* are the most troublesome and destructive plant-parasitic plants in the temperate zones of the Northern Hemisphere and include more than 160 angiosperm parasitic species. All broomrapes are achlorophyllous holoparasites and lack photosynthetic abilities. Thus, they are totally dependent on the host for organic carbon, water, and nutrients.

Several hundred thousand hectares are infested by broomrape in a wide geographic range that includes China, Cuba, Europe, the Middle East, Russia, and the United States (California). The area threatened by broomrape includes the Mediterranean Basin and western Asia and is estimated at 16 million ha, representing approximately 1.2% of the world's arable land.

Symptoms

Infected lettuce plants show severe stunting, foliar yellowing, and loose head formation, and the plants may even die (Fig. 126, parts A and B). Plants that survive infection at early stages of growth may bolt early, making them unmarketable (Fig. 126, part C).

Infection of a lettuce plant by an *Orobanche* sp. is confirmed by the attachment of broomrape to the roots (Fig. 126, part E). The intensity of infection (based on the number of *Orobanche* shoots that have emerged close to the lettuce stem) has been reported to range from one to 20 broomrapes (flowering shoots) per lettuce plant and even higher under certain circumstances (Fig. 126, part D).

The incidence of infected lettuce plants may vary from 10 to 40% depending on the lettuce cultivar and the degree of soil infestation with broomrape seeds. Lettuce has been reported as a potential plant indicator of broomrape seed contamination in the soil, because the seeds of some broomrapes germinate between 7 and 14 days and attach very rapidly to lettuce roots between 21 and 28 days.

Causal Organisms

Lettuce can be parasitized mainly by two types of broomrape: crenate or bean broomrape (*O. crenata*) and ramose or hemp broomrape (*Phelipanche ramosa*; syn. *O. ramosa*). In addition, Egyptian broomrape (*P. aegyptiaca*; syn. *O. aegyptiaca*), nodding broomrape (*O. cernua*), small or clover broomrape (*O. minor*), and an endemic Mediterranean species of broomrape (*O. palaestina*) have been reported to infect, form tubercles, and reach the flowering shoots in lettuce plants in Israel, Jordan, and the United States. Ramose broomrape and small broomrape have been introduced and established in Cuba, Mexico, and the United States.

Crenate broomrape is an important pathogen of legumes in the Mediterranean and in warm, temperate areas of Europe, northern Africa, and the Middle East, especially in faba bean (*Vicia faba*), grasspea (*Lathyrus nissolia*), pea, and vetches (*Vicia* spp.). Other hosts of bean broomrape include wild plants in the Fabaceae and other legume crops, such as berseem clover (*Trifolium alexandrinum*), chickpea, common bean, lentil, and alfalfa. Bean broomrape can also infect plants in the Apiaceae (carrot), Asteraceae (safflower [*Carthamus tinctorius*] and treasure-flower [*Gazania rigens*]), Boraginaceae (common comfrey [*Symphytum officinale*]), and Tropaeolaceae (nasturtium [*Tropaeolum majus*]).

The broomrape inflorescence is 3.5–5.0 × 20–71 cm and formed by white, yellowish, deep orangish-brownish, or pinkish flowers arranged in spikes. The unbranched plant can reach 1 m but is usually 20–85 cm tall. Stigmata are yellow, orange, or pinkish. The corolla is 17–28 mm long, campanulate or tubular, glandular pubescent, and white (usually with lilac veins) and has divergent lips and a glabrous margin. The filaments are hairy, obliquely inserted in the corolla tube, and located 1.5–3.5 mm above the base. The calyx is 13–19 mm and has free bidentate segments and subequal teeth; it is narrowly lanceolate and has a subfiliform apex (Fig. 126, parts B and F).

Ramose broomrape infects a wide range of crop plants in the Solanaceae (eggplant, pepper, potato, tobacco, tomato), Brassicaceae (rape or rapeseed [*Brassica napus*]), Cannabaceae (marijuana or hemp [*Cannabis sativa*]), Linaceae (flax [*Linum usitatissimum*]), Fabaceae (chickpea, clover, faba bean, peanut,

lentil, pea), Apiaceae (carrot, celery, fennel [*Foeniculum vulgare*], parsnip [*Pastinaca* spp.]), and Asteraceae (lettuce and sunflower [*Helianthus* spp.]). Hemp broomrape has also been found parasitizing onion (Amaryllidaceae). This broomrape is native to Europe, the Middle East, western Asia, northern Africa, and Africa south of Ethiopia and Somalia, and it has spread to Australia, the Iberian Peninsula (Andorra, Portugal, Spain), South Africa, and the United States. The stem is 10–30 cm high (occasionally up to 50 cm); glandular pubescent; white, bluish, or purple; and often branched. The inflorescence is 2–3 × 3.5–7.0 cm and has sessile flowers that alternate irregularly in a sparse to moderately dense spike. The calyx is 4.0–7.5 mm and has four subequal triangular, acutely pointed lobes; it is usually white but sometimes dark blue. The corolla is 12–16 mm and white at the base and blue at the lobes. The anthers are generally glabrous, approximately 1 mm long, and acutely pointed at the bases.

Disease Cycle and Epidemiology

The life cycles of most holoparasitic plants in the Orobanchaceae include several key developmental phases. Before establishing the parasitic phase, seedlings develop independently from the host for a short period until they are able to attach to the host root. Seeds must undergo conditioning under suitable temperatures (optimum of 18–23°C depending on the broomrape species) and high moisture levels before germination can take place as a chemotactic response. Broomrape seeds are small (<1 mm long) (Fig. 126, part G), and each contains a small embryo (lacking a plumule and cotyledons) and a single short radicle. Nutrients stored in seeds are limited and support autonomous growth only for a few days.

The second phase in the life cycle of the parasite is the intrusive phase, which includes (a) development of a terminal haustorium at the tip of the radicle (Fig. 126, part H), (b) ingress of the haustorium into the host tissue, and (c) development of primary conductive connections with the host (Fig. 126, part E).

The final stage is the compatible phase, in which the parasite's development is coordinated with that of the host, making possible the transfer of nutrients from the host to the parasite. Development of the haustorium depends on the parasite's ability to overcome host-resistance mechanisms and to compete with host organs for available nutrients. Subsequently, the parasite develops a tubercle, which grows underground for several weeks or a month and eventually emerges from the soil near the stem of the host plant (Fig. 126, parts C and D).

Broomrapes complete their life cycle after producing flowering shoots within 7–16 weeks, depending on the species and environmental conditions (Fig. 126, parts I and J). The fruit of a single plant can contain up to 200,000 seeds. Seeds can be easily disseminated by cultivation practices, water, wind, and animals.

Management

Management of plants in the Orobanchaceae is difficult given the characteristics of their seeds: namely, that seeds are produced in large numbers and are small, long lived, and easily dispersed. A variety of agronomic and chemical measures are available for management of broomrape, but no single method is expected to effectively control this parasitic weed. Consequently, effective management requires an integrated approach that combines several methods.

Integrated management should focus on reducing the soil seed bank and limiting the production and dissemination of broomrape seed. Cultural methods of control include planting *Orobanche*-free seed, minimizing the movement of infested soil by farm machinery and vehicles, hand weeding in small farms, deep sowing, late sowing, soil solarization, and prolonged flooding.

Rotation or intercropping with trap crops and using catch crops can also reduce the number of seeds present in the soil,

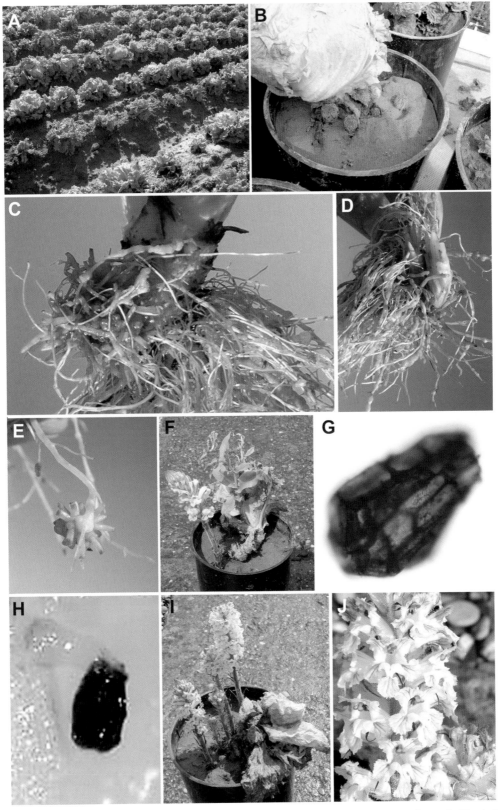

Fig. 126. Life cycle of crenate broomrape (*Orobanche crenata*) in crisphead lettuce plants. **A,** Stunted growth of plants in a field severely infected by broomrape. **B,** Apical shoot buds emerging form the soil near a lettuce plant. **C and D,** Broomrape tubercles with a prominent apical shoot bud and numerous adventitious roots of an infected lettuce plant. **E,** Lettuce plant root thickened at the site of infestation by broomrape and development of numerous adventitious roots. **F,** Broomrape flowering shoot and a lettuce plant with early induced flowering caused by infection. **G,** Broomrape seed. **H,** Germinating lettuce seedling contacting a broomrape root and anchoring radicle formation and appressorium. **I,** Flowering shoots of broomrape and a totally collapsed lettuce plant. **J,** Flowering shoot of broomrape. (Courtesy B. B. Landa—© APS)

although these methods have not been proven to be economically feasible. A trap crop comprises nonhost crops that can stimulate germination of broomrape seeds, resulting in a suicidal germination. A catch crop is composed of host plants that support parasitism but are removed from the field after the seeds germinate but before they reach the flowering and seed dispersal stages.

Soil fumigation with metam sodium, dazomet, or 1,3-dichloropropene also reduces the seed bank. Soil fumigation is usually conducted a few months before sowing the crop. Herbicides can also be applied during the cropping season if the crop is tolerant of these chemicals. Several systemic herbicides have been used to control broomrape, such as glyphosate, imidazolinones, pyrithiobac sodium, and sulfonylureas. However, their potential application depends on the availability of registration for use on lettuce and the tolerance of lettuce to them. Glyphosate-resistant lettuce has been field tested, but its usefulness for the control of broomrape has not been determined (as of early 2017). When herbicides are used, they should be applied during the underground stage of broomrape development—before the shoot has emerged and causes severe damage.

Biological control is another promising approach for controlling broomrape, although it has not been implemented effectively in the field. Larvae of the broomrape fly (*Phytomyza orobanchia*) oviposit into broomrape buds, flowers, and stems and mine broomrape shoots. The use of fungal pathogens that infect plants in the Orobanchaceae (such as *Fusarium* spp.) also has potential for management of broomrape.

Selected References

Dor, E., Eizenberg, H., Joel, D. M., Smirnov, E., Achdari G., and Hershenhorn, J. 2014. *Orobanche palaestina:* A potential threat to agricultural crops in Israel. Phytoparasitica 42:285-291.

Goldwassr, Y., and Rodenburg, J. 2013. Integrated management of parasitic weed seed bank. In: Parasitic Orobanchaceae: Parasitic Mechanisms and Control Strategies. D. M. Joel, J. G. Lytton, and J. Musselman, eds. Springer, Heidelberg, Germany.

Landa, B. B., Navas-Cortés, J. A., Castillo, P., Vovlas, N., Pujadas-Salvá, A. J., and Jiménez-Díaz, R. M. 2006. First report of broomrape (*Orobanche crenata*) infecting lettuce in southern Spain. (Abstr.) Plant Dis. 90:1112.

Parker, C. 2013. The parasitic weeds of the Orobanchaceae. In: Parasitic Orobanchaceae: Parasitic Mechanisms and Control Strategies. D. M. Joel, J. G. Lytton, and J. Musselman, eds. Springer, Heidelberg, Germany.

Pérez-de-Luque, A., Fondevilla, S., Pérez-Vich, B., Ali, R., Thoiron, S., Simier, P., Castillejo, M. A., Fernández, J. M., Jorrín, J., Rubiales, D., and Delavault, P. 2009. Understanding *Orobanche* and *Phelipanche*—Host plant interaction and developing resistance. Weed Res. 49(suppl. 1):8-22.

Pujadas, A. J. 2002. Orobanchaceae. In: Parasitic Plants of Iberian Peninsula and Balearic Islands. J. A. López-Sáez, P. Catalán, and L. Sáez, eds. Mundi-Prensa, Madrid.

Qasem, J. R. 2009. Parasitic weeds of the Orobanchaceae family and their natural hosts in Jordan. Weed Biol. Manage. 9:112-122.

Ross, K. C., Colquhoun, J. B., and Mallory-Smith, C. A. 2004. Small broomrape (*Orobanche minor*) germination and early development in response to plant species. Weed Sci. 52:260-266.

Rubiales, D., and Fernández-Aparicio, M. 2012. Innovations in parasitic weeds management in legume crops: A review. Agron. Sustain. Devel. 32:433-449.

(Prepared by B. B. Landa, S. Fondevilla,
M. Montes-Borrego, J. A. Navas-Cortés, N. Vovlas,
A. J. Pujadas-Salvá, R. M. Jiménez-Díaz, and P. Castillo)

Part II. Arthropod Pests

The animal kingdom has millions of species, and of the approximately 30 phyla of animals, the phylum Arthropoda contains the most. In fact, there are more species of arthropods than species of all the other animal phyla combined. Some unique characteristics of the Arthropoda are their exoskeletons and jointed appendages.

Among the classes of Arthropoda, these four contain species that are pests of lettuce:

- Insecta or Hexapoda (insects)
- Arachnida (arachnids)
- Symphyla (symphylans)
- Malacostraca (crustaceans)

The class Hexapoda has the most species; more than 1 million have been described, and an estimated 30 million have yet to be described. Only a very small percentage of insects and other arthropods are crop pests, and even fewer are pests of lettuce. Arthropods can cause direct injury to lettuce through feeding on leaf tissues and by removing the plant sap needed by the plant for hydration, transpiration, and growth and development. Arthropods can also cause indirect injury to lettuce through contamination with their body parts and excrement. Additionally, some species vector plant pathogens, which in turn cause damage to lettuce crops (Table 2). Arthropod pest problems of lettuce crops vary depending on the growing region and the time of year.

Among the arthropods, insects are the most common pests of lettuce. Insects that have chewing mouthparts—such as worm pests, or caterpillars, as well as beetles, crickets, and earwigs—may clip off lettuce seedlings (affecting stand establishment), consume leaf tissue, bore into lettuce heads during head development, and contaminate lettuce with their feces. Insects that have piercing–sucking mouthparts—such as aphids, leafhoppers, treehoppers, and whiteflies—may remove plant sap and vector plant viruses and phytoplasmas (Figs. 127–130). For example, leafhoppers transmit 'Candidatus Phytoplasma asteri,' the aster yellows phytoplasma, which causes lettuce yellows (formerly known as "aster yellows") disease in lettuce.

Thrips species have highly modified mouthparts for macerating plant cells and sucking up plant sap (Fig. 131). Thrips feeding causes leaf scarring, which can reduce the market acceptability of a blemished crop or even render it unmarketable. Additionally, thrips species such as the western flower thrips (*Frankliniella occidentalis*) are considered contaminants of crisphead

Fig. 128. Adult green peach aphid (*Myzus persicae*) on lettuce. (Courtesy T. M. Perring—© APS)

Fig. 129. Adult leafhopper (*Macrosteles* sp.) on crisphead lettuce. (Courtesy G. N. Oldfield—© APS)

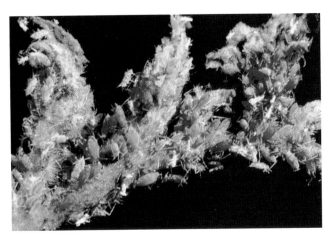

Fig. 127. Adult potato aphids (*Macrosiphum euphorbiae*) on a lettuce inflorescence. (Courtesy M. J. Blua—© APS)

Fig. 130. Sweetpotato whitefly (*Bemisia tabaci*) adult and nymphs on crisphead lettuce. (Courtesy N. C. Toscano—© APS)

101

Fig. 131. Adult western flower thrips (*Frankliniella occidentalis*) on crisphead lettuce. (Photo by J. K. Clark; Reproduced by permission of University of California Statewide IPM Project)

Fig. 133. Agromyzid leafminer "mine" on crisphead lettuce containing a dead larva (*Liriomyza* sp.). (Courtesy E. T. Natwick—© APS)

Fig. 132. "Mines" on a crisphead lettuce leaf caused by agromyzid leafminer (*Liriomyza* sp.) larvae. (Courtesy E. T. Natwick—© APS)

and leaf lettuce in some countries (e.g., Japan, Taiwan) and when detected disallow the importation of produce. Thrips are also vectors of tospoviruses, such as *Tomato spotted wilt virus* and *Impatiens necrotic spot virus*.

The following insect pests of lettuce are among the most important:

- aphids (order Hemiptera, family Aphididae)
- caterpillars (order Lepidoptera, mostly family Noctuidae)
- darkling beetles (order Coleoptera, family Tenebrionidae)
- field crickets (order Orthoptera, family Gryllidae)
- leafhoppers (order Hemiptera, family Cicadellidae)
- leafminers (order Diptera, family Agromyzidae) (Figs. 132 and 133)
- springtails (order Collembola, multiple families)
- thrips (order Thysanoptera, family Thripidae)
- whiteflies (order Hemiptera, family Aleyrodidae)

Among the insect pests, aphids are arguably the most serious because of their sheer abundance, the number of species involved, and their ability to cause all three types of damage (i.e., feeding, removing plant sap, contamination). Aphids are also the most serious vectors of lettuce-infecting viruses.

Noninsect arthropod pests of lettuce include the following:

- bulb mites (order Acari, suborder Acaridida [Astigmata], family Acaridae, genera *Rhizoglyphus* and *Tyrophagus*)
- garden symphylan (*Scutigerella immaculata:* order Symphyla, family Scutigerellidae)
- sowbug or woodlouse (*Oniscus aséllus:* order Isopoda, family Oniscidae)

All can cause serious damage to lettuce crops through direct feeding and contamination.

Insects such as field crickets, earwigs, darkling beetles, and isopods (e.g., pillbugs and sowbugs) are common arthropod pests of lettuce crops during stand establishment in some areas; they are frequently referred to as "trash" pests. Management of all trash pests begins with good weed control and sanitation practices, such as destroying crop debris in and around fields prior to planting. Insecticide bait (e.g., a carbamate or a pyrethroid) may also be used around problem fields to prevent or slow pest migration from adjacent crops.

Selected References

Blackman, R. L., and Eastop, V. F. 1984. Aphids on the World's Crops. John Wiley & Sons, New York.

Capinera, J. L. 2001. Handbook of Vegetable Pests. Academic Press, San Diego.

Koike, S. T., Gladders, P., and Paulus, A. O. 2007. Vegetable Diseases: A Color Handbook. Academic Press, San Diego.

Natwick, E. T. 2009. How to Manage Pests: Lettuce. Insects and Other Arthropods. Publ. 3450. IPM, University of California, Agriculture and Natural Resources, Davis. www.ipm.ucdavis.edu/PMG/select-newpest.lettuce.html

Palumbo, J. C., and Castle, S. J. 2009. IPM for fresh-market lettuce production in the desert southwest: The produce paradox. Pest Manag. Sci. 65:1311-1320.

Palumbo, J. C., Sanchez, C. A., and Mullis, C. H., Jr. 2002. Suppression of western flower thrips by overhead sprinkler irrigation in romaine. Pages 63-78 in: Vegetable Report 2002. AZ1292, Ser. P-131. College of Agriculture and Life Sciences, University of Arizona, Tucson. http://hdl.handle.net/10150/214950

Peters, D. 2008. Thrips as unique vectors of tospoviruses. Entomolog. Ber. 68(5):182-186.

Purcell, A. H., and Almeida, R. P. P. 2005. Insects as vectors of disease agents. Pages 1-5 in: Encyclopedia of Plant and Crop Science. R. M. Goodman, ed. CRC Press, Boca Raton, FL.

Smith, R., Cahn, M., Daugovish, O., Koike, S. T., Natwick, E., Smith, H., Subbarao, K., Takele, E., and Turini, T. 2011. Leaf lettuce production in California. Publ. 7216. Vegetable Research and Information Center, Agriculture and Natural Resources, University of California, Davis. http://anrcatalog.ucanr.edu/pdf/7216.pdf

Statewide Integrated Pest Management (IPM) Program. 1985. Integrated Pest Management for Cole Crops and Lettuce. Publ. 3307. IPM, University of California, Agriculture and Natural Resources, Davis. http://ipm.ucanr.edu/IPMPROJECT/ADS/manual_colecropslettuce.html

Turini, T., Cahn, M., Cantwell, M., Jackson, L., Koike, S., Natwick, E., Smith, R., Subbarao, K., and Takele, E. 2011. Iceberg lettuce production in California. Publ. 7215. Vegetable Research and Information Center, Agriculture and Natural Resources, University of California, Davis. http://anrcatalog.ucanr.edu/pdf/7215.pdf

(Prepared by E. T. Natwick and R. N. Raid)

Class: Insecta

Order: Hemiptera

Family: Aphididae

Aphids

Description and Life Cycle

Aphids are small (1–6 mm), soft-bodied, bulbous insects with needlelike piercing–sucking mouthparts (Figs. 127–128). Most have a pair of tubelike appendages on the distal, dorsal abdomen called "cornicles" or "siphunculi." The aphid uses these appendages to excrete excess water and sugars when it extracts nutrients from plant sap.

Aphids are phloem feeders and may be found on all the major plant parts. Their life cycles can be very complex, involving both sexual and asexual reproduction. In regions with cooler, temperate climates that experience hard freezes during the winter, aphids have cyclical parthenogenesis (asexual reproduction), and an alternate phase of sexual reproduction allows for overwintering in the egg stage. In regions with warmer Mediterranean and subtropical climates, only female aphids are produced by parthenogenetic reproduction.

When aphids are in the parthenogenetic reproduction phase, they do not produce eggs but rather give birth to live young called "nymphs." The neonates, or newly birthed nymphs, are born with their nymphal offspring already developing within them. Adult aphids are capable of 10–12 live nymph births per day. Nymphs can grow to be adults in as little as 2 weeks.

In lettuce production areas with favorable weather conditions, some aphid species may go through 20 or more generations per year. This rate of multiplication gives aphids a very high reproductive potential, allowing for rapid buildup if they are not kept in check by natural enemies or with chemical or cultural management.

There are two morphological types of adult aphids: alate (winged) and apterous (wingless). Alate adults develop from nymphs when the host plant is senescing or when there is a high density of aphids feeding on the host. Alate morphs allow adults to disperse over short or long distances rapidly to non-infested host plants. Apterous adults are most frequently involved in rapid reproduction.

In addition to new colony establishment, alate aphids are responsible for the rapid spread of viruses in lettuce crops. Aphids feed with their piercing–sucking mouthparts injected into leaves, from which they extract plant sap. This feeding behavior plays a key role in the transmission of viruses, causing diseases in lettuce crops.

Another important characteristic of some aphid species, such as the lettuce root aphid (*Pemphigus bursarius*), is heteroecy, or the regular migration between two distantly related host plants. One plant species is the primary host, which is used for sexual reproduction, and the other is the secondary host, which is colonized only by parthenogenetic morphs.

Damage

Aphids are often the most important insect pests in lettuce production, and they can cause all three types of injury to lettuce plants. First, by removing plant sap and injecting salivary fluids while feeding, aphids can slow plant development, caus-ing stunting. They can also cause chlorosis, leaf distortion, and plant wilting. Second, aphids' removal of plant sap results in their excreting a sugary fluid called "honeydew." This sticky substance contaminates lettuce leaves and supports the growth of sooty mold, further degrading plant quality. Aphid body parts and exuviae can also contaminate lettuce heads. Whether dead or alive, aphids are undesirable contaminants that often lead to rejection of lettuce crops (Fig. 134). Lastly, many aphids—including some that feed but do not colonize lettuce—can vector viruses that are pathogenic to lettuce.

Two notable aphid pests of lettuce are the currant-lettuce aphid (*Nasonovia ribisnigri*) and the foxglove aphid (*Aulacorthum solani*). Both can vector viruses, but more importantly, they infest the inner leaves of lettuce heads, rendering the lettuce unmarketable. Because both the currant-lettuce aphid and foxglove aphid become protected within the lettuce head as more leaves develop, early detection and treatment of incipient populations is essential. Neither of these aphids is adequately controlled with neonicotinoid insecticide treatments via soil injection (i.e., imidacloprid) or foliar spraying (e.g., acetamiprid), but newer classes of foliar-applied insecticide (e.g., spirotetramat) serve as substitutes for neonicotinoid aphid control.

Two aphid species with worldwide distribution are the green peach aphid (*Myzus persicae*) and the potato aphid (*Macrosiphum euphorbiae*), and both can be significant lettuce pests. Populations of the green peach aphid and potato aphid first build up on the outer leaves of lettuce plants, where they are less likely to contaminate lettuce heads. Because of their limited distribution on the outer leaves, they are more susceptible to predation and easier to treat with foliar insecticides. However, both types of aphid are vectors of several lettuce-infecting viruses.

Another aphid introduced into North America from Europe is the shallot aphid (*Myzus ascalonicus*). Like other aphids, the shallot aphid secretes honeydew, which fouls lettuce leaves, and

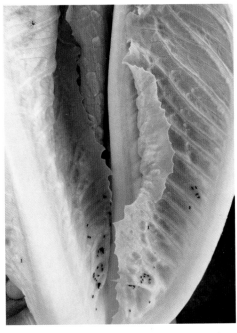

Fig. 134. Adult aphids (*Uroleucon pseudambrosia*) on the inner leaves of romaine lettuce. (Courtesy S. Glucksman—© APS)

its feeding can contribute to leaf curling and stunting. The shallot aphid is a vector of *Dandelion yellow mosaic virus,* which causes yellow mosaic, but it is not a vector of *Lettuce mosaic virus,* which causes lettuce mosaic.

The lettuce root aphid (*Pemphigus bursarius*) is one of the most important pests of lettuce in areas in which Lombardy poplar trees (*Populus nigra*) are grown. Even though the lettuce root aphid is not known to vector any viruses, heavy infestation by this aphid causes lettuce plants to wilt during the day, and developing heads remain soft and fail to develop properly. Root aphids are easily distinguished from other aphids found on lettuce by their undeveloped cornicles, their short antennae (less than one-third body length), and their clustering in white, powdery, wax-covered colonies on lettuce roots. Lettuce root aphids overwinter in the egg stage on the bark of Lombardy poplar trees in areas in which lettuce or related weeds are not available. The nymphs hatch in the spring and feed on poplar leaves before migrating to lettuce. They can be managed by removing Lombardy poplar trees. Additionally, some lettuce sources have root aphid resistance.

Management

Many aphid species can be managed effectively using insecticides such as pyrethroids and neonicotinoids, and some of the newer antifeedant (e.g., flonicamid) compounds and systemic foliar sprays (e.g., spirotetramat) are also efficacious. However, some aphid populations are becoming resistant to almost all the major classes of insecticides.

Fortunately, aphid pests of lettuce have many natural enemies, including fungal pathogens that commonly develop during cool, wet conditions. In addition, parasitic wasps can help suppress aphid species that colonize the outer leaves of lettuce. Syrphid fly larvae and other aphid predators (e.g., lady beetles) can help suppress aphid species that infest the inner leaves. Predation of the lettuce aphid by syrphid fly larvae is essential for the organic production of leaf lettuce.

Host plant resistance to aphids and/or the diseases caused by the viruses they transmit can also be useful in integrated pest management (IPM). A variety of *Nasonovia*-resistant romaine lettuce called "Nirvanus" is available, but it is not resistant to all species of aphids. Management practices such as eliminating favored host crops (i.e., Lombardy poplar, which hosts the root aphid), controlling weeds along ditch banks, and fallowing can likewise be useful in reducing aphid–virus damage.

(Prepared by E. T. Natwick and R. N. Raid)

Family: Aleyrodidae

Whiteflies

The most economically important whitefly pest of lettuce is the sweetpotato whitefly (*Bemisia tabaci*) (Fig. 130). In 1986, an infestation of sweetpotato whitefly occurred in the poinsettia crops of south-central Florida, and it was followed by heavy infestations in vegetable crops the next year. Similar infestations occurred in south Texas during 1989 and 1990, and they were followed by infestations in vegetable crops in southern California (including lettuce) in 1991.

The new whitefly was described as a new species (*B. argentifolii*), and it was referred to as the "silverleaf whitefly" by some entomologists because of the previously undescribed symptoms it caused. Later, it was determined to be an invasive cryptic species within the *B. tabaci* species complex called "Middle East–Asia Minor 1 (MEAM1)," also known as "sweetpotato whitefly biotype B." This biotype infests crops worldwide in the tropics and subtropics, in Mediterranean-type climates, and within greenhouses in temperate climates. MEAM1 causes slow growth and delayed maturity of the lettuce crop, and it is the vector of *Lettuce chlorosis virus* (LCV).

Description and Life Cycle

Whiteflies are small insects (0.8–1.2 mm long) and have white-scaled, covered wings that are held tentlike over a yellow body. Females lay yellow, oblong eggs, each of which has a short, pointed pedicle at its base. The pedicle is inserted into leaf tissue so that the egg stands perpendicular to the leaf surface. Nearly all the 50–400 eggs produced by a single female are inserted into the abaxial leaf surface. Each egg turns brown at the tip just prior to hatching.

Nymphs hatch from the eggs and pass through four instars prior to emerging as adults. Among the nymphal instars, only the neonates, or first instar nymphs (0.03–0.60 mm long), are mobile; they are called "crawlers." Crawlers are oval and flat, have six legs, and are pale yellow. Within 1–24 h of hatching, they move about to find a feeding site; at the site, they insert their piercing–sucking mouthparts to feed and do not move again. The second and third instar nymphs are scalelike, and they feed and molt in place. The fourth instar nymph is also called the "pupal" stage, and the red eye of the developing adult can be clearly seen through the dorsal cuticle. The adult emerges through two sutures that form a T-shape in the dorsal cuticle of the fourth instar. Females that mate with males produce diploid female offspring, whereas nonfertilized eggs produce haploid male offspring.

The entire life cycle can be completed in as little as 2–3 weeks under warm conditions. Under such conditions and in the absence of predators and parasites, huge numbers of sweetpotato whitefly are produced within a few months. One female can produce 1 million offspring in just three generations (assuming no mortality).

Damage

The sweetpotato whitefly causes injury similar to that caused by aphids, and it is an important vector of viruses that infect lettuce crops. Feeding by nymphs and adults can cause direct feeding injury to lettuce by removing plant sap and injecting salivary fluids with piercing–sucking mouthparts. A large sweetpotato whitefly population, particularly during the early stages of the lettuce crop, can potentially slow growth, delay crop maturity, and cause significant stunting and yellowing.

Also, like aphids, whiteflies produce honeydew, which may contaminate the lettuce crop directly or incite the development of sooty mold. Sooty-mold-blackened leaves can contribute to plant injury by interfering with transmission of light to chloroplasts, and they cause cosmetic damage, which may downgrade product acceptability.

The sweetpotato whitefly adult can also introduce viral pathogens while feeding, including *Lettuce infectious yellows virus* and LCV.

Management

Direct feeding injury is managed at planting with the injection of systemic insecticides and during the growing season with the spraying of foliar insecticides. These applications do little to prevent virus transmission, however.

Honeydew can be washed from the outer lettuce leaves, and sooty-mold-blackened wrapper leaves can be removed prior to packing lettuce in boxes. Even so, preventing accumulation is the key to honeydew management, because washing is cost prohibitive and not compatible with field packing.

Although whiteflies can be controlled with insecticides, they may become resistant if one chemical class is used too heavily. Insecticides with different modes of action should be rotated regularly.

(Prepared by E. T. Natwick and R. N. Raid)

Family: Cicadellidae

Leafhoppers

Description and Life Cycle

Leafhoppers are small, wedge-shaped insects that vary in color, color pattern, and size (Fig. 129). They feed by removing plant sap with their piercing–sucking mouthparts.

Female leafhoppers insert eggs into the tissues of their plant hosts, and the eggs hatch into nymphs, which resemble adults without wings. Nymphs usually pass through five instars before becoming adults.

Damage

'*Candidatus* Phytoplasma asteri,' or Aster yellows phytoplasma (AYP), causes lettuce yellows (formerly "aster yellows") disease in lettuce, and it is vectored primarily by the aster leafhopper (*Macrosteles quadrilineatus*). The development of lettuce yellows is the main concern for damage to lettuce crops caused by leafhoppers.

Three other leafhopper species are found on lettuce in the western United States: the potato leafhopper (*Empoasca fabae*); the bean or southern garden leafhopper (*E. solana*); and the Mexican leafhopper (*E. mexara*). These species are nearly identical morphologically and can be distinguished only by close examination. Although these three leafhopper species are occasionally found as adults on lettuce crops, they pose little threat to crop health. However, when large numbers of adults migrate from nearby crops, their physical presence within lettuce heads represents a serious form of contamination. A significant migration typically follows the cutting of alfalfa to make hay. Contamination can reduce the marketability of lettuce crops.

Management

Leafhoppers seldom require management on lettuce, but large populations can be reduced using insecticides, such as pyrethroids. In areas in which lettuce fields are near alfalfa fields that are heavily infested with leafhoppers, applying an insecticide to alfalfa before cutting the hay crop can prevent the mass migration of leafhoppers to lettuce.

(Prepared by E. T. Natwick and R. N. Raid)

Family: Membracidae

Treehoppers

Description and Life Cycle

The three-cornered alfalfa hopper (*Spissistilus festinus*) is a treehopper that prefers to live and feed on legume plants (Fig. 135). The adult is a medium-sized insect approximately 16 mm long. It is green to yellowish-green and wedge shaped, and it has clear wings.

Although treehoppers prefer to feed on leguminous plants, including alfalfa, they will feed on many different species, including lettuce. When the treehopper population builds up in alfalfa and the crop is cut or when a bean crop dries down near harvest, the adults will fly to other crops in the vicinity, such as lettuce.

Damage

The three-cornered alfalfa hopper becomes an occasional pest of lettuce crops when adults fly from their legume host plants (e.g., alfalfa and bean) and become trapped within let-

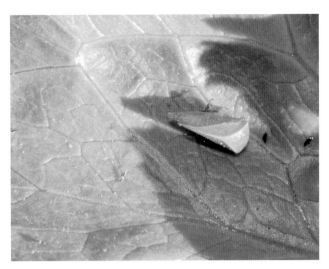

Fig. 135. Adult three-cornered alfalfa hopper (*Spissistilus festinus*) on crisphead lettuce. (Courtesy E. T. Natwick—© APS)

tuce heads. Adults feed by inserting their mouthparts into plant stems to extract plant sap and may cause injury in lettuce similar to that caused by plant bugs (*Lygus* spp.) (see later section). Even so, treehoppers are mainly a contamination problem, as their physical presence inside lettuce heads reduces the marketability of the crop.

Management

Control of treehoppers is seldom warranted, but insecticides (pyrethroids) can be used to reduce the treehopper population in areas in which lettuce is grown close to alfalfa or other legumes.

(Prepared by E. T. Natwick and R. N. Raid)

Family: Lygaeidae

Seed Bugs

Description and Life Cycle

The false chinch bug (*Nysius raphanus*) is an occasional pest of lettuce. The adult's body is elongate, approximately 3 mm long, and only about one-third to one-fourth as wide. Adults are gray-brown but can have a silvery appearance in bright sunlight. The nymphs are gray and have red and white markings.

During hot conditions, false chinch bugs typically seek shelter under plants, in leaf litter, and in soil cracks during the heat of the day. Both adults and nymphs migrate from brassica crops and weeds to lettuce crops. This is especially true following wet winters in low-desert lettuce production areas, when fallow fields and noncultivated areas are commonly populated with mustard weed species. When the weeds dry down, the bugs migrate to adjacent crops, such as lettuce.

False chinch bugs are often confused with the beneficial insect predator bigeyed bugs (*Geocoris* spp.). Bigeyed bugs have broader heads and much larger eyes than false chinch bugs.

Damage

Feeding by migrating false chinch bug adults and nymphs can kill lettuce seedlings and even mature plants within hours. However, the primary damage concern among lettuce growers is the contamination of the crop, caused by the physical presence of insect bodies within tightly closed lettuce heads.

Management

Treatment with an insecticide will kill adults and nymphs, but their bodies will remain in the lettuce heads, rendering the crop unmarketable. If the false chinch bugs are detected early, the damage can be confined to a few border rows, preserving the rest of the field.

A ditch filled with water can prevent the invasion of migrating nymphs from adjacent fields but not winged adult bugs.

(Prepared by E. T. Natwick and R. N. Raid)

Family: Miridae

Plant Bugs

Description and Life Cycle

Plant bugs in the genus *Lygus*—such as the western tarnished plant bug (*L. hesperus*) and the tarnished plant bug (*L. lineolaris*)—are occasional pests of lettuce crops. As adults, most are 5–6 mm long and about half as wide. Their body colors range from tan or light green to dark brown, depending on the species (Fig. 136). Plant bugs have piercing–sucking mouthparts, which they use to extract plant sap from near the bases of the midribs of lettuce leaves.

The host range of *Lygus* spp. is very broad, so plant bug populations can become large in crops such as alfalfa and on weeds. Adults may migrate to lettuce crops from alfalfa when it is cut and from weeds when they senesce and dry down.

Damage

Damage to lettuce is caused when *Lygus* spp. insert their piercing–sucking mouthparts in the midribs of lettuce leaves and extract plant sap, which contains nutrients needed for normal plant development. However, more serious damage results when the salivary fluids injected at the feeding site begin to break down plant cells, causing sunken, brown lesions.

Further degradation of lettuce quality is caused by fecal excrement and from bugs that die and remain within the lettuce heads.

Management

Treatment with an insecticide will kill plant bug adults and nymphs, but their bodies will remain in the lettuce heads, rendering them unmarketable. If the plant bugs are detected early, the damage can be confined to a few border rows, preserving the rest of the field. The timely application of an insecticide (pyrethroids) may reduce the number of pests on lettuce grown near alfalfa and other infested crops.

(Prepared by E. T. Natwick and R. N. Raid)

Order: Diptera

Family: Agromyzidae

Leafminers

Description and Life Cycle

Dipterous leafminers are highly polyphagous insect pests; larvae feed on the leaf mesophyll layer, creating visible "mines" between epidermal layers (Fig. 132). The few leafminer species known to injure lettuce are the pea leafminer (*Liriomyza langei*), the serpentine leafminer (*L. trifolii*), and the vegetable leafminer (*L. sativae*).

An adult fly is black to gray with yellow markings and approximately 6–7 mm long (Fig. 137). An adult female feeds on plant sap that oozes from the punctures it makes in a leaf with its ovipositor—an appendage used to insert eggs into leaf tissue. The female fly also deposits single eggs in a few of these punctures.

Larvae, or maggots, hatch within leaf tissues 2–4 days following oviposition, and they feed between the upper and lower surfaces of leaves. As their feeding progresses, larvae create whitish, serpentine tunnels or mines (from which the name "leafminer" is derived). Just before pupation, larvae cut holes in the leaf surfaces and emerge. Larvae may pupate on leaves or drop to the soil to pupate.

Several generations of leafminers develop each year on lettuce, as well as on alternative host crops or weeds. Under warm conditions, the entire life cycle may be completed in 3 weeks or less.

Damage

Leafminer damage is caused primarily by larval feeding on the mesophyll tissue between the upper and lower leaf surfaces, which forms tunnels or mines. The presence of tunnels degrades the quality of lettuce, making it unmarketable if the damaged leaves cannot be removed.

Fig. 136. Adult plant bug (*Lygus* sp.) on alfalfa. (Courtesy E. T. Natwick—© APS)

Fig. 137. Adult agromyzid leafminer (*Liriomyza* sp.). (Courtesy E. T. Natwick—© APS)

Additionally, adult female flies cause stippling damage by puncturing leaf surfaces with their ovipositors to extract fluid on which to feed. Stippling also degrades the quality of lettuce, and the open wounds can serve as infection courts for secondary pathogens, particularly bacteria.

Management

Liriomyza spp. larvae are highly susceptible to parasitism by minute, endoparasitic *Hymenoptera* spp. wasps, especially those in the genus *Diglyphus*. The natural level of parasitism normally maintains leafminer populations below the numbers that can cause economically significant injury, unless insecticide applications interfere with parasitic wasp activity. *Liriomyza* spp. leafminers often become pests of lettuce because of the use of broad-spectrum insecticides, which destroy the leafminers' numerous natural enemies. When an insecticide applied to control another pest disrupts the balance between the wasp parasites and the leafminers, an additional insecticide may be required to control leafminer populations. Insecticides are applied to manage larvae, rather than the more mobile, insecticide-resistant adults.

Liriomyza spp. leafminers may attack various vegetable crops grown in close proximity. For this reason, lettuce should not be planted next to a leafminer-infested vegetable field, especially one near harvest.

(Prepared by E. T. Natwick and R. N. Raid)

Family: Anthomyiidae

Seedcorn Maggot

Description and Life Cycle

The seedcorn maggot (*Delia platura*) can be a serious pest of lettuce crops during stand establishment. The legless larval stage is a white maggot that lacks a distinctive head with eyes; it has only two curved hooks for mouthparts. The adult is a slender, light-gray fly and approximately 0.5 cm long.

After mating, gravid female flies are attracted to residue from a previous crop or manure. They deposit white, slightly curved, posteriorly rounded eggs in nondecomposed organic matter in cool, moist soils. The eggs hatch into larvae called "maggots." When mature, the white to light-yellow, cylindrical, anteriorly tapered maggots measure 0.5–0.6 cm long.

Maggots feed for 1–3 weeks on organic matter, seeds, and germinating seedlings. Mature maggots burrow into the soil to pupate, and pupae resemble small, brown gel capsules.

Seedcorn maggots are usually most abundant during the spring, when soils are wet and cool. Under favorable conditions, several generations can be produced per year.

Damage

Seedcorn maggots damage lettuce stands by burrowing into germinating seeds and preventing germination. Maggots also feed on and can kill lettuce seedlings. Slow emergence and poor stand establishment are signs of seedcorn maggot activity. Where emergence is slow or spotty, growers should dig up seeds and inspect them for maggot feeding.

For most lettuce crops, damage does not extend beyond the seedling establishment stage.

Management

Damage from seedcorn maggots can be prevented by not planting lettuce in cool, wet soils with nondecomposed organic matter from a previous crop, such as green manure or animal manure. Before planting lettuce, growers should allow time for previous crop residues to decompose.

(Prepared by E. T. Natwick and R. N. Raid)

Order: Coleoptera

Family: Chrysomelidae, Subfamily: Alticinae

Flea Beetles

Description and Life Cycle

Flea beetles are small insects and characterized by greatly enlarged hind legs, which enable them to jump when disturbed. The jumping behavior resembles that of fleas—thus, the name "flea beetles."

Several species of flea beetle adults attack lettuce crops, including the palestriped flea beetle (*Systena blanda*) (Fig. 138), the striped flea beetle (*Phyllotreta striolata*), the western black flea beetle (*P. pusilla*), and the western striped flea beetle (*P. ramose*) (Fig. 139).

After mating, adult female flea beetles deposit eggs in the soil. After hatching, larvae live in the soil and feed on root hairs, but this does not cause serious injury to lettuce crops.

Adult flea beetles vary in size and markings, depending on the species. However, all are small (1–3 mm long) and shiny and have enlarged hind legs that propel them though the air to escape danger.

Damage

Flea beetles are mostly pests of lettuce crops during stand establishment. Adult flea beetles chew many round or irregularly shaped holes as they feed on the undersides of leaves. Heavy feeding damage can retard plant growth, and in severe cases, it may kill seedling lettuce plants. Flea beetles rarely cause economically significant damage to older plants, because the lower leaves damaged early in plant development are gone long before harvest.

Damage is more likely to occur in lettuce fields that are weedy, surrounded by weeds, or adjacent to an alternative host, such as alfalfa.

Management

Damage can be avoided by removing weeds along field margins, by planting away from flea-beetle-infested alternative

Fig. 138. Adult palestriped flea beetle (*Systena blanda*) on crisphead lettuce. (Courtesy E. T. Natwick—© APS)

Fig. 139. Adult flea beetle (*Phyllotreta* sp.) on crisp-head lettuce. (Courtesy E. T. Natwick—© APS)

Fig. 140. Damage on romaine lettuce caused by adult banded cucumber beetles (*Diabrotica balteata*). (Courtesy S. Glucksman—© APS)

host crops, by deeply incorporating plant residue in infested fields after harvest, and by applying pyrethroid insecticides.

(Prepared by E. T. Natwick and R. N. Raid)

Family: Chrysomelidae, Subfamily: Chrysomelinae

Leaf Beetles

Description and Life Cycle

Leaf beetles are a large subfamily, Chrysomelinae, within the family Chrysomelidae. Most species are less than 12 mm long, and many are brightly colored. Adult leaf beetles feed primarily on foliage and flowers, as do larvae.

Numerous members of this family are economically important pests, including the western spotted cucumber beetle (*Diabrotica undecimpunctata undecimpunctata*) and the banded cucumber beetle (*Diabrotica balteata*). Although known as "cucumber beetles," these pests are polyphagous and feed on a wide range of plant hosts, including lettuce, melons, beans, some grasses, and various weed species.

Cucumber beetles are approximately 9–12 mm long. They have greenish-yellow bodies with black spots or yellow bands on the outer wings.

Cucumber beetles can overwinter as adults and are active throughout the growing season. Adult females lay eggs at the bases of host plants, and after the larvae hatch, they feed on plant roots. Following pupation, adults emerge to feed on foliage. Cucumber beetles may produce up to three generations a year.

Damage

Cucumber beetles damage lettuce by directly feeding on the foliage, chewing irregularly shaped holes on the leaves at any

Fig. 141. Damage along the midrib of romaine lettuce caused by adult banded cucumber beetles (*Diabrotica balteata*). (Courtesy S. Glucksman—© APS)

stage of development (Figs. 140 and 141). However, when lettuce seedlings are very small, cucumber beetles may cause a significant level of defoliation, slowing plant growth and even killing the seedlings (Fig. 142).

Management

The adult stage is most injurious to lettuce; thus, cucumber beetles are typically controlled with pyrethroids or other insecticides applied through sprinkler irrigation or aerial spraying. Because cucumber beetles may also feed on numerous weed hosts, good weed management in both the field and surrounding areas may keep populations at levels that will not cause economically significant damage.

(Prepared by E. T. Natwick and R. N. Raid)

Fig. 142. Heavy feeding damage on young crisphead lettuce caused by adult banded cucumber beetles (*Diabrotica balteata*). (Courtesy S. Glucksman—© APS)

Family: Elateridae

Wireworms

Description and Life Cycle

Wireworms are the larvae of click beetles and pests of a number of vegetable crops. The larval forms are generally elongated and cylindrical, and they vary in color from tan to copper. Wireworms are soil inhabitants and have hard bodies, unlike the larval stages of other soil pest insects (maggots and grubs). Wireworms range in length from 1 to 4 cm.

Adult click beetles are typically elongated and tapered at both ends; most are 1.2–3.0 cm long. They can be easily identified by the characteristic "clicking" or snapping behavior they use to right themselves when placed on their backs.

There are numerous wireworm pest species, but the corn wireworm (*Melanotus communis*) is by far the most damaging to lettuce crops in Florida (United States), where it is considered a serious pest (Fig. 143). In the western United States, the Pacific Coast wireworm (*Limonius canus*) is perhaps the most widely distributed wireworm pest. The life cycle of these coleopteran pests may range from 2 to 6 years, depending on the species. In most infested fields, multiple larval stages can

be observed. Larvae move up and down in the soil profile in response to temperature, crop presence, and moisture, and they feed on the roots of plants. The larval stage is definitely the most prolonged and damaging stage of the life cycle. Foliar feeding by adults is usually insignificant.

Because wireworms have such a long life cycle, they usually emerge as a lettuce pest in fields following rotation with a perennial crop, such as sugarcane in Florida.

Damage

Wireworms feed on the roots of lettuce and other host plants, frequently burrowing into the cortical region (Fig. 144). Where

Fig. 144. Crisphead lettuce dying from feeding of corn wireworm (*Melanotus communis*) larvae in the stem. (Courtesy R. N. Raid—© APS)

Fig. 145. Internal cavity created in crisphead lettuce by feeding of corn wireworm (*Melanotus communis*) larvae. (Courtesy R. N. Raid—© APS)

Fig. 143. Corn wireworm (*Melanotus communis*). (Courtesy R. N. Raid—© APS)

Fig. 146. Lettuce stand reductions caused by feeding of corn wireworm (*Melanotus communis*) larvae. (Courtesy S. Glucksman—© APS)

Fig. 147. Adult darkling beetle (*Blapstinus* sp.) on crisphead lettuce. (Courtesy E. T. Natwick—© APS)

internal feeding is extensive, the core of the plant may be hollowed out, killing it (Fig. 145). Damaged plants may first appear stunted and wilted, and a heavy infestation can cause significant stand reduction (Fig. 146).

After killing a plant, wireworms will move through the soil to a neighboring plant if not controlled.

Management

Wireworms are not usually a serious lettuce pest in the western lettuce-producing states of California and Arizona. However, they can be a serious problem in the eastern United States, particularly when lettuce follows a perennial crop, such as sugarcane or alfalfa. Their presence can be detected using grains or potatoes as baits in freshly prepared fields prior to planting.

Where warranted, wireworms are most often controlled using a diazinon or other insecticide bait at planting. In Florida, fallow flooding and rotating lettuce with rice have also proven effective in managing wireworm pests. (Soil larvae are killed by the long-term floods.) Rotation with other crops is usually not as successful, as wireworms feed on the roots of a broad range of plants.

(Prepared by E. T. Natwick and R. N. Raid)

Family: Tenebrionidae

Darkling Beetles

Description and Life Cycle

Darkling beetles (*Blapstinus* spp., *Caelus* spp., and others) are dusty bluish-black or black beetles in the coleopteran family Tenebrionidae (Fig. 147). They range in length from 3 to 6 mm and are approximately half as wide as they are long. The adults are occasional pests of lettuce crops.

Like other so-called trash pests, darkling beetles are most active at night and usually invade from adjacent weedy areas or adjacent crops. The adults of some species are strong flyers and attracted to lights at night.

The larvae live in the soil and resemble wireworms; they are often referred to as "false wireworms."

Damage

Damage often begins on the edges of lettuce fields, where darkling beetles chew off seedlings near the soil surface or feed on foliage. Once a lettuce crop stand is well established, dark-

ling beetles no longer cause economically significant damage. Adult beetles occasionally migrate from adjacent fields, such as alfalfa and grain fields, or from weedy areas.

Management

In some areas, chemigation (i.e., applying a chemical through irrigation water) with a pyrethroid insecticide is a standard treatment for preventing damage from beetles.

(Prepared by E. T. Natwick and R. N. Raid)

Order: Lepidoptera

Family: Noctuidae

Caterpillars

Description and Life Cycle

Caterpillars (frequently referred to as "worm pests") are the larval stage of pests in the insect order Lepidoptera, and a number of species feed on lettuce crops. Many but not all of the caterpillars that attack lettuce crops are in the insect family Noctuidae, which includes armyworms and cutworms. Noctuids, as their name implies, are nocturnal insects, so most if not all of their feeding activity is done from late afternoon until sunrise.

Some of the most common noctuid worm pests of lettuce include the beet armyworm (*Spodoptera exigua*), cabbage looper (*Trichoplusia ni*) (Fig. 148), alfalfa looper (*Autographa californica*) (Fig. 149), armyworm (*Mythimna unipuncta*), black cutworm (*Agrotis ipsilon*) (Fig. 150), variegated cutworm (*Peridroma saucia*), granulate cutworm (*Feltia subterranea*), corn earworm (*Helicoverpa zea*) (Fig. 151), and tobacco budworm (*Heliothis virescens*). The saltmarsh caterpillar (*Estigmene acrea*) and the omnivorous leafroller (*Platynota stultana*) are not noctuids but belong to the Lepidoptera families Arctiidae and Tortricidae, respectively. (Given the sheer importance of these pests, some of them are described in separate sections later in Part II.)

Adult noctuid moths fly, feed, and mate at night. The mouthparts of a moth form a long tube, from which the moth sucks nectar from flowers and water. Female moths emit a sex or mating pheromone to attract male moths of the same species for

Fig. 148. Cabbage looper (*Trichoplusia ni*) larva on crisphead lettuce. (Courtesy E. T. Natwick—© APS)

Fig. 150. Black cutworm (*Agrotis ipsilon*) larva. (Courtesy E. T. Natwick—© APS)

Fig. 149. Alfalfa looper (*Autographa californica*) larva. (Courtesy E. T. Natwick—© APS)

Fig. 151. Corn earworm (*Helicoverpa zea*) larvae. (Courtesy E. T. Natwick—© APS)

mating. A single female may mate with one of several male moths.

Following mating, the female moth lays eggs singly or in clusters, depending on the pest species. Larvae hatch from eggs within a few days and begin to feed on the lettuce plant in which the eggs were laid. Cutworm eggs are laid near the base of the plant, and the larvae hide in soil cracks or beneath leaf litter during the day, feeding at night. Other noctuid caterpillars remain on the plant to feed but may move down rows of plants during stand establishment and during seedling growth.

After passing through five larval instars (i.e., the periods between molting), larvae drop to the soil, where they pupate within cracks or under litter. Moths emerge from pupae in approximately 1–2 weeks during the spring through autumn, but most will overwinter as pupae.

Damage

Caterpillars cause sporadic problems throughout lettuce-growing regions of the world. They damage crops by clipping off seedling lettuce plants during stand establishment, by consuming leaf tissue between stand establishment and head development, by boring into lettuce heads during development, and by contaminating lettuce with their feces and body parts.

The two critical periods during the lettuce production cycle when damage from caterpillars cannot be tolerated are stand establishment (when emerged seedlings can be quickly lost) and head development (because some larvae will bore into the heads and fecal contamination can be trapped within developing lettuce heads). Lettuce plants can tolerate low to moderate feeding damage from caterpillars during the period between stand establishment and head development. Nonetheless, severe feeding damage during this period can stunt plants or render them unmarketable if the growing point is damaged.

Management

Management is achieved mostly through the use of insecticides. However, caterpillars are susceptible to several natural enemies, including fungal pathogens, viral pathogens, entomopathogenic nematodes, and several species of insect predators. Dipterous and hymenopterous parasitoids, spiders, and birds all prey on worm pests. Caterpillars should be treated with selective insecticides when infestation levels reach established treatment thresholds for specific worm pests or when there is an imminent threat of economically significant injury to the lettuce crop. Selective insecticides that specifically target members of the order Lepidoptera are preferable for management of beet armyworm, loopers, cutworms, saltmarsh caterpillar, and other caterpillars to preserve natural enemies and prevent secondary infestations of other pests, such as leafminers.

Synthetic pheromones are used to monitor the activity of male moths, but the data collected should not be used in making treatment decisions. Some noctuid moths can be managed by releasing overwhelming quantities of a synthetic pheromone that is very similar to the natural pheromone unique to each species of noctuid. The massive release of synthetic pheromones confuses male moths. Because they can no longer follow a natural pheromone plume in the breeze to find a female of the same species, their mating is disrupted, and eggs laid by nonmated female moths will not be fertile.

(Prepared by E. T. Natwick and R. N. Raid)

Armyworm

The armyworm (*Mythimna unipuncta*) is also called the "true armyworm" to distinguish it from other caterpillar species that include "armyworm" in their common names. It is a worldwide pest that mostly infests grain and grass forage crops but occasionally attacks lettuce crops.

The adult is a nocturnal moth with a wingspan of approximately 4 cm. The pointed forewings are light reddish-brown, and each has a transverse line of small, black spots that terminates in a black line at the anterior wing tip. The hind wings are grayish and have lighter gray or whitish margins.

Mating occurs at night approximately 3 days after puparia emerge from the soil. Following mating, gravid females feed on nectar before depositing eggs singly or in small clusters of up to 10 eggs. The oviposition period normally lasts 4–5 days but may last up to 10 days. A single female may deposit from 500 to 1,500 eggs. The spherical eggs are creamy white or yellowish but turn gray just before hatching.

Neonate larvae hatch from the eggs in 3–6 days during warm conditions but may take as long as 24 days to hatch during cooler conditions. Each larva is grayish green or grayish brown and has a broad, dark stripe dorsally and along each side; a light, subspiracular stripe often runs laterally beneath the dark stripe. The larva has a yellowish-brown head capsule with dark, netlike markings.

Larvae grow to approximately 35 mm and normally pass through six instars before pupating, but seven to nine instars have been observed. Larvae drop from the plant to pupate in the soil or beneath leaf litter. The pupal stage lasts 7–14 days during warm conditions but sometimes lasts 40 days during cooler conditions. The generation time is 30–50 days, depending on temperature. Two generations are produced per year in the colder northern regions of North America, but five or more generations are produced in the warmer regions.

(Prepared by E. T. Natwick and R. N. Raid)

Beet Armyworm

The activity of the beet armyworm (*Spodoptera exigua*) varies according to climatic conditions, but in locations with warm weather—such as southern California, southwestern Arizona, and Florida (United States)—all the life stages can be found throughout the year. The life cycle can be completed in as few as 24 days, and six or more generations can be produced per year in locations with warm climates.

A female beet armyworm moth lays clusters of 50–150 eggs per mass on lettuce leaves, including cotyledons. The female covers the egg masses with fine, hairlike wing scales to protect them from predation and parasitism, giving the egg mass a distinctive fuzzy, grayish-tan appearance. Newly hatched beet armyworms are small, green larvae and often feed in groups (Fig. 152). Neonate beet armyworms feed aggregately throughout

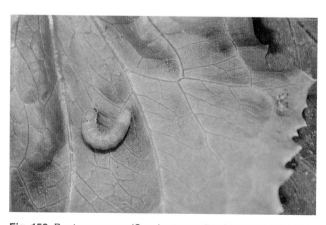

Fig. 152. Beet armyworm (*Spodoptera exigua*) larva on crisphead lettuce. (Courtesy E. T. Natwick—© APS)

their first instar but soon disperse down lettuce rows as second instar larvae. After passing through five instars, larvae drop from the plants to pupate in the soil or under leaf litter.

Management of the beet armyworm is critical during stand establishment, when larvae feed in plant crowns and can severely stunt or kill seedlings. Some feeding damage can be tolerated between thinning and head formation, but after lettuce heads form, serious injury can occur when larvae bore into the heads from the bottoms. Because the damage cannot be seen from above without close monitoring, it goes undetected until harvest, when damaged heads must be culled.

Beet armyworms are attacked by several natural enemies, such as parasitic wasps (*Hyposoter exiguae* and *Chelonus insularis*) and the tachinid fly parasite (*Lespesia archippivora*). Larvae can also be killed by natural epizootic events and introduced viral pathogens.

(Prepared by E. T. Natwick and R. N. Raid)

Loopers

Larvae of the cabbage looper (*Trichoplusia ni*) and alfalfa looper (*Autographa californica*) arch their backs when they crawl, distinguishing them from other lettuce worm pests (Figs. 148 and 149). A female looper moth lays single dome-shaped eggs on the upper or lower surface of the leaf, but clusters of six to seven eggs are occasionally found. Two or three generations are produced per year in regions with cooler climates, and up to seven generations are produced per year in regions with warmer climates.

Neonate and early instar loopers are mostly found skeletonizing the undersides of lower leaves as they feed. High levels of looper larvae can damage lettuce seedlings severely enough to kill them or slow their growth enough to inhibit uniform crop maturation. During lettuce head formation, late instar larvae may burrow into the heads from the tops.

Natural enemies often keep looper populations low enough to prevent economically significant damage. Those enemies include egg parasites such as parasitic wasps (*Trichogramma pretiosum, Hyposoter exiguae, Copidosoma truncatellum,* and *Microplitis brassicae*) and larval parasites such as tachinid flies (*Voria ruralis*).

Loopers are also killed by infections with *Nuclear polyhedrosis virus* (NPV). Some NPV is endemic and can naturally cause an epizootic event, greatly reducing looper populations, but more commonly, NPV is formulated for spray application for augmentative management of looper larvae.

Insecticides made from crystalline parasporal bodies isolated from *Bacillus thuringiensis* (commonly referred to as "Bt insecticides") also provide excellent control of loopers, as do the spinosad insecticides derived from the actinomycete *Saccharopolyspora spinosa* and several selective synthetically derived insecticides.

(Prepared by E. T. Natwick and R. N. Raid)

Cutworms

Many species of cutworms attack lettuce. Common species include the black cutworm (*Agrotis ipsilon*) (Fig. 150), variegated cutworm (*Peridroma saucia*), and granulate cutworm (*Feltia subterranea*). Cutworms are nocturnal and thus found on plants mostly at night; they hide in loose soil or leaf litter during the day. Larvae of most species curl into a characteristic C-shape when disturbed.

Cutworm larvae often migrate into lettuce fields from weedy areas. The most serious injury they cause occurs during stand establishment, when they cut off seedlings at or just below the soil line. Later in the season, cutworms may bore into lettuce heads, and some species may damage leaves. In some areas, the granulate cutworm population can build to a high level in alfalfa and will occasionally migrate in massive numbers to adjacent crops such as lettuce, destroying a large area of a field in only a few hours.

Management is most effective when initiated before planting by checking for cutworm larvae around the weeds that border fields and by eliminating weedy areas near lettuce fields. During stand establishment, growers should look for wilted plants and plants with severed stems. Larvae can be revealed by digging around the bases of injured plants and sifting the soil.

Some insecticidal baits have been used successfully for cutworm management and may prevent migrating cutworm larvae from moving into a lettuce field when applied outside the field as a barrier. Some insect-growth-regulator, crop-protection products (e.g., methoxyfenozide) control cutworms without causing secondary pest infestations. A water-filled ditch can also prevent mass migrations from an adjacent field by acting as a barrier.

(Prepared by E. T. Natwick and R. N. Raid)

Corn Earworm
and Tobacco Budworm

The corn earworm (*Helicoverpa zea*) (Fig. 151) and tobacco budworm (*Heliothis virescens*) are two closely related worm pests. The moths lay eggs singly on lettuce plants.

The caterpillars can migrate from weeds and other crops to lettuce fields. Severe stand losses can occur when these caterpillars move down rows of seedlings, clipping them off. The caterpillars can also cause serious damage by feeding on plant crowns, destroying the growing points of developing lettuce plants. Because the caterpillars bore into lettuce heads, there is no tolerance for these worm pests during head development.

(Prepared by E. T. Natwick and R. N. Raid)

Family: Arctiidae

Saltmarsh Caterpillar

The saltmarsh caterpillar (*Estigmene acrea*) is a native insect of the Americas. The adult is a fairly large moth with a wingspan of 3.5–4.5 cm. Its forewings are mostly white but have numerous small, irregularly shaped, black spots. Male moths have yellow hind wings, whereas those of female moths are white. Most of the moths' abdominal segments are yellow and marked with a series of large, black dorsal spots.

The moths are nocturnal and thus mate during the evening following emergence from puparia; egg deposition occurs the following evening. A female lives for only 4–5 days but may produce several egg masses of a few hundred to more than 1,000 eggs per cluster on the undersides of leaves—often on weeds or crops adjacent to lettuce fields. Neonate larvae hatch from within an egg mass on a leaf in 4–5 days and initially feed in aggregate on that leaf or on adjacent leaves. Later instars migrate singly to other plants to feed.

When the food source adjacent to a lettuce field is exhausted, the caterpillars will migrate in mass to lettuce, quickly destroying seedlings or severely damaging plants further along in de-

velopment. A ditch filled with water can serve as a barrier to mass migrations from an adjacent field, preventing damage to lettuce plants.

(Prepared by E. T. Natwick and R. N. Raid)

Order: Thysanoptera

Family: Thripidae

Thrips

Description and Life Cycle

Thrips are minute, slender-bodied insects that have two pairs of long, narrow wings—the margins of which are fringed with long hairs. Thrips are somewhat unique in having rasping mouthparts, in contrast to the chewing mouthparts of beetles and caterpillars and the piercing–sucking mouthparts of aphids and leafhoppers. Four thrips species of primary importance that may cause injury or contamination to lettuce are the western flower thrips (*Frankliniella occidentalis*) (Fig. 131), tobacco thrips (*F. fusca*), onion thrips (*Thrips tabaci*), and less frequently, bean thrips (*Caliothrips fasciatus*) (Fig. 153).

Adult thrips typically range from 1.3 to 1.5 mm in length. The immature stages have the same general body shape as the adult but are usually lighter colored and wingless. Thrips pass through six developmental stages: an egg, two larval stages, a prepupal stage, a pupal stage, and an adult. The time between generations varies with the thrips species and the temperature but generally takes approximately 1 month. Most species insert eggs into plant tissue and pupate in or on the soil. Only first instar larvae acquire the tospoviruses that are commonly transmitted by adult thrips to lettuce plants.

Adult western flower thrips (~1.5 mm in length) have eight segmented antennae and vary greatly in body color; there are light, dark, and intermediate morphological types in yellow, orange, brown, and black. When the adult is at rest, thick, bristle-like hairs at the tip of the abdomen extend beyond the wing tips. Nymphs and larvae are white, yellow, or orange and have small, dark eyes. The western flower thrips population can build on weeds and other vegetation during the spring and migrate to lettuce, where adults mate, reproduce, and rapidly colonize into a large population.

Adult onion thrips are similar to adult western flower thrips in size and coloration. The body of the adult onion thrips is

Fig. 153. Adult bean thrips (*Caliothrips fasciatus*) on crisphead lettuce. (Courtesy E. T. Natwick—© APS)

yellow with brown blotches on the thorax and abdominal terga, and the legs are yellowish-brown. The adult onion thrips has seven segmented antennae. Segment one and the bases of segments three, four, and five are brownish-white, and the rest of the antennae are brown.

The body of the adult bean thrips is rust to brown in color. The appendages, legs, and antennae have light and dark bands, and the forewings have two dark and two pale bands.

Thrips species identification is important because some species are entomophagous (feeding on insects, including pests) and therefore beneficial, whereas others are phytophagous (feeding on plants). Unfortunately, the populations of predaceous thrips rarely remain below economically significant levels of injury.

Damage

Only 1% of the nearly 5,000 known species of thrips are pests. These thrips pierce the epidermal leaf cells and then suck out the plant sap. Their feeding causes cosmetic injury to lettuce leaves when the plant develops scars (Fig. 154). Damaged areas initially have a silvery appearance that eventually turns brown, resembling damage caused by windblown sand (Fig. 155). Further cosmetic damage is caused by the deposit of dark-brown to black fecal specks on leaves. Lettuce heads are also degraded from the presence of bodies of live and dead thrips.

Fig. 154. Leaf scarring caused by adult thrips (*Frankliniella* sp.) feeding on romaine lettuce. (Courtesy S. Glucksman—© APS)

Fig. 155. Thrips (*Frankliniella* sp.) feeding damage on romaine lettuce that looks like wind damage. (Courtesy S. Glucksman—© APS)

Some thrips species are important vectors of plant viruses. Of those species commonly found on lettuce, all but the bean thrips are vectors of *Tomato spotted wilt virus* and *Impatiens necrotic spot virus*.

On lettuce, the western flower thrips is the most important species, not only because of virus transmission but also because of significant direct-feeding injury, which produces cosmetic damage on the leaf margins and midribs. The bean thrips is problematic in the interior low-desert growing areas of Arizona and southern California (United States). The bean thrips migrates into lettuce fields during the fall in years in which the population builds in alfalfa fields. Large numbers of migrating bean thrips can contaminate lettuce heads with their bodies, degrading the quality of the lettuce crop. Even low numbers of bean thrips can cause concern for lettuce to be exported to certain countries.

Management

The first step in any pest management program is to accurately identify the pest. Identification of thrips species is particularly important for biological control, because natural enemies are often specific to a single pest or group of pests. Additionally, some thrips are entomophagous predators, which prey on phytophagous thrips and other lettuce arthropod pests.

Identifying thrips can be difficult because of their small size and the similarities in color among some species. To prepare for identification, an adult thrips specimen must be chemically cleared and mounted on a microscope slide with the appendages (wings, antennae, and legs) spread apart. The specimen is then examined under a microscope to observe the distinguishing morphological characteristic provided in an identification key.

Pest species of thrips have several key natural enemies, including green lacewings (*Chrysopa* spp. and *Chrysoperla* spp.), minute pirate bugs (*Orius* spp.), predatory mites, many species of parasitic wasps, and entomopathogenic fungi (*Beauveria* spp., *Lecanicillium* spp., *Metarhizium* spp., *Paecilomyces* spp., and others). Cultural control measures for preventing thrips damage to lettuce crops include using overhead irrigation to wash off some exposed thrips, avoiding planting downwind from crops that harbor thrips (e.g., small-grain crops), and practicing crop sanitation (quickly destroying plant residues from harvested crops before thrips migrate to later lettuce plantings).

Applying insecticides is often necessary to prevent thrips damage to lettuce crops, and the timing of spray applications is critical to success. During hot conditions, insecticides should be applied in the early morning or the evening, when temperatures are cooler and thrips are more active. The use of a spreading surfactant helps insecticides reach the areas in which larvae are hidden near the bases of leaves. Growers should rotate products with different modes of action to help prevent the development of insecticide resistance in populations of western flower thrips and other pest thrips species.

(Prepared by E. T. Natwick and R. N. Raid)

Order: Orthoptera

Family: Gryllidae

Field Crickets

Description and Life Cycle

Several species of field crickets (*Teleogryllus* spp.) are occasional pests in sprinkler-irrigated fields in the low desert region

Fig. 156. Adult field cricket (*Teleogryllus* sp.). (Courtesy E. T. Natwick—© APS)

Fig. 157. Adult earwig (*Forficula* sp.). (Courtesy E. T. Natwick—© APS)

of the southwestern United States. Adults are 10–25 mm long, are shiny black or brown, and have long antennae and wings (Fig. 156).

Both wingless nymphs (which resemble adults) and adults hide under dead or live weeds or plant debris during the day. At night, they move from these uncultivated areas, which provide shelter, into lettuce fields. Crickets also move into lettuce fields from other crops, such as cotton, alfalfa, and grass.

Damage

Crickets are pests primarily during stand establishment, when they eat emerging lettuce seedlings; they can move quickly down rows and damage large areas of a field. Crickets occasionally enter lettuce fields from adjacent weedy areas or crops, such as alfalfa, cotton, and grass. Crickets are a more significant pest in low desert lettuce production areas than in coastal lettuce production areas.

Management

Crickets seldom cause damage of economic importance. Even so, they can be managed by applying insecticides and by minimizing crop debris. Growers should avoid planting lettuce next to crops that tend to be infested with crickets, such as alfalfa and cotton.

(Prepared by E. T. Natwick and R. N. Raid)

Order: Dermaptera

Family: Forficulidae

Earwigs

Description and Life Cycle

The most common and widespread earwig pest of lettuce is the European earwig (*Forficula auricularia*), which is native to Europe (Fig. 157). It was first reported in the United States in 1970 in the state of Washington, and it has since spread throughout the United States and southern Canada.

Damage

The most economically important damage from earwigs occurs during stand establishment, when they clip off lettuce seedlings. Earwigs may occasionally chew holes in leaves and seek shelter in the crowns of lettuce plants, where they may become a contaminant.

Management

Because earwigs rarely fly, a ditch filled with water can create a barrier and prevent invasions from adjacent fields.

(Prepared by E. T. Natwick and R. N. Raid)

Order: Collembola

Springtails

Description and Life Cycle

Springtails are minute (less than 3 mm long), wingless insects that have a forked appendage (called a "furcula") at the tip of the abdomen. This appendage is used to propel the insect into the air to escape threat when it is disturbed. Springtails dwell primarily on or near the soil surface.

Damage

Springtails feed on emerging lettuce seedlings and young lettuce transplants, attacking the tender parts of plants close to the ground. Springtails are also occasionally seen on foliage.

Management

To prevent damage to lettuce crops from springtails, growers should avoid planting in fields with nondecomposed organic matter, such as added compost, residue from a previous crop, and residue from incorporation of a cover crop. Waiting a short period (5–6 weeks) until the organic materials have degraded will dramatically reduce the springtail population during stand establishment.

(Prepared by E. T. Natwick and R. N. Raid)

Class: Symphyla

Order: Symphyla

Family: Scutigerellidae

Garden Symphylan

Description and Life Cycle

The garden symphylan (*Scutigerella immaculata*) is a soil-dwelling arthropod pest of lettuce. It resembles a centipede but is much smaller. The garden symphylan is slender and elongated but not more than 0.85 cm long as an adult. In addition, it is translucent white and has prominent antennae but no eyes.

Adult females lay eggs in the soil, and the eggs hatch into juveniles. Juveniles resemble adults but have fewer segments and legs. Neonates have only six pairs of legs, but they add a body segment and a pair of legs with each molt, so that adults have 15 body segments and 11–12 pairs of legs. Adults may live several years.

Garden symphylans can move rapidly through the soil between soil particles. They may be found from the soil surface down to a depth of nearly 50 cm.

Damage

Garden symphylans help to recycle nutrients in the soil by consuming decaying vegetation, but they can harm lettuce crops by consuming sprouting seeds, by feeding on seedlings before or after emergence, and by feeding on the roots and root hairs of older plants. They are particularly damaging to lettuce seedlings during stand establishment.

Symphylans can also cause stunting of transplants by feeding on the new root shoots growing out of transplant plugs. Feeding on older roots causes pitting, which may create points of entry for microbial pathogens.

Management

Applying soil insecticides may protect a zone of soil, providing a chance for germinating seeds, seedlings, or transplant plugs to become established. However, the efficacy of soil insecticides is limited because of the garden symphylan's ability to migrate through the soil.

Damage from garden symphylans may also be reduced through careful soil tillage and moisture management.

(Prepared by E. T. Natwick and R. N. Raid)

Class: Arachnida

Order: Acari

Family: Acaridae

Bulb Mites

Description and Life Cycle

Bulb mites (*Rhizoglyphus* spp. and *Tyrophagus* spp.) range in length from 0.5 to 0.9 mm and have four pairs of legs. They are creamy white, shiny, and bulbous, resembling tiny pearls when magnified.

Bulb mite eggs are translucent white, ellipsoidal, and 0.12 mm long. Neonate larvae are white, oval, and 0.15–0.20 mm long when they hatch from eggs, and they eventually grow to 0.25 mm and have three pairs of legs. The next stage of development, the protonymph, is oval and approximately 0.4 mm long; it has four pairs of legs. The protonymph stage can be distinguished from the subsequent stage, the tritonymph, by the number of genital suckers: The protonymph has two compared with three or four for the tritonymph. The deutonymph or hypopus is a quiescent stage and lacks mouthparts. It is convex on top, flat below, brown, and 0.2–0.3 mm long; its back-lower side has a conspicuous sucker plate. The tritonymph grows to a length of 0.5 mm but does not possess the distinct genital aperture found in the adult.

Bulb mites help decompose organic matter in the soil, and their populations increase to extremely high levels when crop residues of plant mulches are incorporated into cool, moist soils. At large populations, the mites appear as a creamy, boiling mass on plant residue. After organic materials such as plant mulch, crop residues, and manures decompose, bulb mite populations decline rapidly to nearly undetectable levels, and the mites no longer pose a threat to lettuce crops.

Damage

Bulb mites damage lettuce only when there are large populations at germination. The mites can penetrate the seed coat of a germinating seed and consume all but the seed coat. They can also damage or kill emerging seedlings. The most severe damage occurs when seedling emergence is slowed by cool, wet conditions. Therefore, this pest is usually not a problem in the low desert lettuce production regions of Arizona and California (United States), but it can cause severe injury to lettuce in coastal lettuce production areas and areas with temperate climates.

Large bulb mite populations are particularly likely to develop when cole crop residues are disked into cool, wet soils.

Management

Growers can prevent damage from bulb mites by not planting lettuce in cool, wet soils with nondecomposed organic matter. Before planting lettuce, growers should allow time for the previous crop residues to fully decompose.

(Prepared by E. T. Natwick and R. N. Raid)

Spider Mites

Description and Life Cycle

Two spider mite species that commonly colonize lettuce are the vegetable mite (*Tetranychus neocaledonicus*) and the Carmine spider mite (*T. cinnabarinus*). Spider mites are pests of lettuce crops in regions with arid climates, but infestations may occur on lettuce grown in regions with wetter climates, especially during hot, dry conditions. Spider mites are found in or under the fine silk webbing they spin on the undersides of leaves.

Fertilized spider mite eggs produce diploid females, and nonfertilized eggs hatch into haploid males. An adult female is capable of laying up to 20 eggs per day, totaling several hundred eggs during her life of 2–4 weeks. Although spider mite species vary in development, their typical life cycle is composed of the egg, the larva, two nymphal stages (protonymph and deutonymph), and the adult. Eggs are attached to silk webbing on the undersides of leaves, and larvae hatch from eggs in approximately 3–5 days. A larva molts first to become a protonymph, again to become a deutonymph, and once more to become an adult. Completion of the life cycle varies depending on temperature, but under optimum conditions (~26–32°C), spider mites complete their development in 5–8 days.

Spider mite populations can build rapidly in the absence of predators, and many overlapping generations can be produced per year.

Damage

Spider mites feed by sucking the cell contents from lettuce leaves. The initial damage appears as a stippling of light dots on leaves, which does not usually cause concern. However, feeding by large mite populations can cause a bronze, greasy appearance on infested stems and leaves. The damage is usually limited to the older leaves, which are removed during harvest.

Management

Mites seldom warrant chemical control, but sulfur and conventional miticides can be effective in reducing populations.

(Prepared by E. T. Natwick and R. N. Raid)

Class: Malacostraca

Order: Isopoda

Sowbugs and Pillbugs

Sowbugs (*Oniscus aséllus*) and pillbugs inhabit areas in fields littered with crop debris, and they can also be found in soil cracks and under leaf litter in the margins of lettuce fields (Fig. 158). They are most active at night and feed mostly on decaying plant materials.

Sowbugs and pillbugs are stand-establishment pests and clip off lettuce seedlings. Although these pests seldom warrant control, they are best managed by planting in fields free of crop debris.

(Prepared by E. T. Natwick and R. N. Raid)

Fig. 158. Sowbug (class: Crustacea). (Courtesy E. T. Natwick— © APS)

Part III. Injuries and Abiotic and Noninfectious Diseases and Disorders

Mineral Deficiencies and Toxicities

Nutrient deficiencies and toxicities are caused by inadequate or excessive levels of nutrients in the soil and by environmental factors that limit the availability of nutrients to plant roots. Lettuce has a shallow root system and is particularly responsive to nutrient content in the surface layer of the soil. Growth and yield can be impaired by short-lived periods of nutrient deficiencies.

When attempting to diagnose nutrient problems, growers should focus on soil factors that affect nutrient retention and availability, such as soil texture and pH, soil moisture content, and the balance among mineral elements in the soil. Having information on soil nutrient levels will make diagnosis more accurate and nutrient management more efficient. In a field in which symptoms suggest a nutrient disorder, it can be useful to search for patterns of distribution of affected plants in relation to localized topography, soil characteristics, and previous site management. Nutrient deficiencies cannot be diagnosed solely based on visual symptoms, because a particular symptom may be caused by a number of other factors, including nutrient toxicity, salinity, poor irrigation management, and infectious disease.

When a nutrient deficiency is suspected, the location on the plant at which the symptom is expressed is a clue to which nutrient might be involved. Some elements are mobile in plants and can be remobilized from older tissue to newly forming leaves; examples include nitrogen and potassium and, to a lesser extent, phosphorus and magnesium. Therefore, deficiencies of these nutrients tend to be expressed on lower (older) parts of the plant. Conversely, other nutrients are quite immobile in plants, and their deficiency tends to be expressed in the youngest leaves; examples include calcium, sulfur, and most micronutrients.

Macronutrients and Micronutrients

The nutrients essential for plant growth are often divided into categories based on the amounts of the nutrients required. Macronutrients are required in large quantities (leaf tissue concentrations are measured in percentages of dry matter), whereas micronutrients are present in leaves in a parts-per-million range. Macronutrients are further divided as follows:

- *Primary nutrients:* nitrogen, phosphorus, and potassium, for which fertilization is often required for peak production
- *Secondary nutrients:* calcium, magnesium, and sulfur, which are generally abundant in soil and for which fertilization is less commonly required

Micronutrient fertilization is less frequently required because of the much lower requirements for plant uptake.

A growth-limiting nutrient deficiency is uncommon in commercial lettuce production. When field symptoms are encountered that might be caused by a nutrient deficiency or toxicity, leaf tissue analysis is critical for accurate diagnosis. Table 3 provides lettuce macronutrient and micronutrient leaf nutrient sufficiency thresholds; these values are from a number of studies in different parts of the United States and should be broadly applicable. The further below these thresholds a diagnostic sample falls, the more likely the symptoms observed are caused at least in part by a nutrient deficiency.

Nitrogen

An insufficient soil nitrogen supply slows lettuce plant growth and causes a pronounced yellowing of lower leaves (Fig. 159). New leaves are smaller than normal and may also be pale yellowish-green. The basal leaves senesce much earlier in nitrogen-deficient plants. Nitrogen-deficient lettuce may fail to form tight heads. Environmental conditions that promote nitrogen deficiency are leaching rains and overirrigation, especially in coarse, sandy soil. Additional factors may be soil with a low level of organic matter (low nitrogen mineralization potential) and waterlogged, poorly drained soil (enhanced denitrification).

TABLE 3. Lettuce Nutrient Sufficiency Thresholds[a]

Nutrient	Early Heading[b]	Preharvest[c]
Nitrogen (N)[d]	3.00	3.00
Potassium (P)[d]	0.35	0.30
Phosphorus (K)[d]	3.00	3.00
Calcium (Ca)[d]	1.00	1.00
Magnesium (Mg)[d]	0.25	0.25
Sulfur (S)[d]	0.25	0.25
Iron (Fe)[e]	50.00	50.00
Manganese (Mn)[e]	20.00	20.00
Zinc (Zn)[e]	20.00	20.00
Boron (B)[e]	20.00	20.00

[a] Courtesy T. K. Hartz—© APS.
[b] In recently mature leaf.
[c] In youngest wrapper leaf.
[d] Measured in percentage of dry matter.
[e] Measured in parts per million (ppm) of dry tissue.

Ammonium toxicity can be a serious problem in lettuce, causing root damage, plant stunting, and even death. The root hairs and lateral roots die, and the taproot shows a reddish-brown internal discoloration (Fig. 160). The root core may be hollowed out in extreme cases. The internal root discoloration may be confused with that caused by a *Verticillium* or *Fusarium* infection. The exterior tissues of the larger roots may crack and have a corky appearance, which may be confused with symptoms of corky root disease. Aboveground symptoms include plant stunting, dark-green or gray-green leaves, and a temporary wilt. Eventually, leaf margins may turn brown and plants may die.

Ammonium toxicity is most commonly associated with the use of ammonium or urea (ammonium-forming) fertilizer, particularly if banded at a high application rate close to developing seedlings. The disorder is usually associated with conditions that slow the conversion of ammonium to nitrate, such as cool soil temperatures and waterlogged or compacted soil.

(See also the section "Ammonium Toxicity" later in Part III.)

Phosphorus

The initial response to a phosphorus deficiency is reduced growth with few other notable symptoms (Fig. 161). As the deficiency progresses, lettuce leaves may become a dull green and sometimes develop a bronze or purplish color. Lettuce with a severe phosphorus deficiency maintains a rosette form, and the heads develop late or fail to form. However, such a severe deficiency is seldom observed under commercial cultivation.

Compared with most other crops, lettuce requires a higher soil phosphorus availability to achieve maximum production; to avoid deficiency, the preplant soil phosphorus level must be determined. Low soil temperatures and extremes of soil pH (both high and low) reduce soil phosphorus availability. Phosphorus deficiency is most likely to occur at the early growth stages, before an extensive root system has developed.

Potassium

Because potassium is highly mobile in plants, potassium deficiency is initially observed on the oldest leaves. Leaf tips and margins develop chlorotic blotches, which become purplish-brown and then necrotic, and interveinal scorching may also occur. The rest of the leaf remains dark or mottled green. Leaf blades are smaller than normal, and their edges may curl down. Growth is reduced, and heads are small and loose.

Lettuce may take up more potassium than any other element, including nitrogen; therefore, a relatively high soil potassium availability must be maintained. Coarse, sandy soil with a low cation exchange capacity (CEC) is likely to have limited soil potassium availability and may allow the leaching of fertilizer potassium with rain or excessive irrigation. Conversely, soil with high organic matter content or a high percentage of vermiculitic clay has a high CEC, but potassium may constitute only a small fraction of it (sometimes, <2%). In such a situation, the potassium uptake may be reduced by competi-

tive ion effects, particularly if the soil is high in exchangeable magnesium.

Calcium

Calcium deficiency is expressed in young, actively growing tissue. The most common symptom is tipburn—a disorder characterized by browning of the margins of young, maturing leaves. The brown area may be limited to a few small spots at or near the leaf margins, or all the edges of the leaf may be affected.

The expression of tipburn is nearly independent of the soil calcium status; instead, the controlling factors are environmental. Factors that limit leaf transpiration induce tipburn, because transpiration is the mechanism by which calcium is provided to young leaves. Thus, tipburn develops most commonly on the interior leaves of lettuce heads, usually during conditions of low transpiration (fog, high humidity, soil water stress). In hydroponic experiments, other symptoms (including chlorosis or necrosis of exposed leaf margins, death of growing points) can be induced by calcium deficiency. Such symptoms are seldom observed in the field, however, because soil calcium deficiency is rare.

(See also the section "Tipburn" later in Part III.)

Magnesium

Magnesium deficiency in lettuce mimics potassium deficiency and initially appears as chlorotic marbling on older leaves. As the deficiency progresses, interveinal necrosis occurs, and the leaves curl down.

Because these symptoms are similar to those induced by some virus infections, tissue testing is needed to confirm the

Fig. 160. Discoloration and death of crisphead lettuce roots caused by excess ammonia. (Courtesy R. F. Smith—© APS)

Fig. 161. Response of crisphead lettuce plants to varying levels of phosphorus. (Courtesy E. A. Kurtz and L. J. Wyland—© APS)

Fig. 159. Response of crisphead lettuce plants to varying levels of nitrogen. (Courtesy E. A. Kurtz and L. J. Wyland—© APS)

diagnosis. Although rare, magnesium deficiency can occur in coarse, acidic soil with a low CEC or in soil that has been heavily limed.

Sulfur

Sulfur deficiency is characterized by the development of a general chlorosis of lettuce leaves; younger leaves are usually more affected than older leaves. In the case of a severe sulfur deficiency, leaves may be small and stiff and plants may be stunted.

Sulfur deficiency is rare, because substantial quantities of sulfur are applied to fields in macronutrient fertilizers, as sulfate in irrigation water, and as fungicides. The field conditions under which sulfur deficiency may occur include coarse, low-organic-matter soil and a high level of precipitation. Historically, the emission of sulfur dioxide from fossil fuel combustion was a significant source of sulfur on agricultural fields, and in regions close to industrial centers, sulfur toxicity in lettuce occasionally occurred. However, improvements in pollution control have drastically reduced sulfur deposition from this source.

Iron

The characteristic symptom of iron deficiency in lettuce is interveinal chlorosis of young leaves. Although soil iron availability is significantly reduced at high soil pH levels, iron deficiency is rare at the pH range typically maintained in commercial fields (5.5–8.0). However, heavy irrigation or rainfall on slow-draining soil (which creates waterlogging and impairs root function) can induce transient symptoms similar to those associated with iron deficiency. When soil aeration returns to normal, leaf chlorosis usually subsides within a few days.

Manganese

Manganese deficiency induces a general chlorosis on young leaves, which is more pronounced in interveinal areas. In the case of a severe deficiency, affected areas may turn brown or necrotic. Deficiency is most likely to develop in high pH, calcareous soil. Although rare, manganese toxicity can occur in strongly acidic soil, but it can be reversed by liming.

Zinc

Zinc deficiency first appears as interveinal chlorosis on young leaves, similar to iron deficiency. Severe zinc deficiency can result in stunted, rosette-formed plants with small leaves that have a scorched appearance. Zinc deficiency occurs in soil that has low zinc content in the parent material, high organic matter, or high pH.

Boron

Boron deficiency in lettuce produces symptoms similar to those caused by calcium deficiency, except that necrosis is worse near growing points, which become black and fail to produce new leaves. With boron deficiency, young leaves are also more deformed, thickened, and brittle. Boron deficiency is more common in regions with high levels of precipitation and in coarse-textured soil derived from parent material with little naturally occurring boron.

Plant toxicity can develop in lettuce when soil in unusually high in boron, irrigation water contains substantial boron, or boron fertilization is excessive. Boron accumulates in leaves and is not mobile in phloem; thus, older leaves are most seriously affected, developing edge burns and necrosis.

Selected References

Hartz, T. K., Johnstone, P. R., Williams, E., and Smith, R. F. 2007. Establishing lettuce leaf nutrient optimum ranges through DRIS analysis. HortScience 42:143-146.

Hochmuth, G., Maynard, D., Vavrina, C., Hanlon, E., and Simonne, E. 2012. Plant Tissue Analysis and Interpretation for Vegetable Crops in Florida. Pub. No. HS964. University of Florida, Institute of Food and Agricultural Sciences (IFAS) Extension, Gainesville. http://edis.ifas.ufl.edu/ep081

Jones, J. B., Wolf, B., and Mills, H. A. 1991. Plant Analysis Handbook. Micro-Macro, Athens, GA.

(Prepared by L. E. Jackson; revised by T. K. Hartz and S. Castro Bustamante)

Noninfectious Physiological Disorders

Tipburn

Symptoms

Tipburn is a physiological disorder of lettuce characterized by "burned" or necrotic tissue on the edges of the leaf blade. Tipburn can occur under a range of production conditions, although it is most common in spring- and summer-harvested, field-grown lettuce and lettuce grown under protected culture. Tipburn occurs on all types of lettuce and typically on the younger, inner leaves. In field-grown lettuce, the symptoms often develop within weeks or days preceding harvest maturity. Symptoms may occur sooner and be more severe for lettuce grown under protected culture.

In most occurrences, the damaged area is typically a small portion of the plant's leaves. Initial symptoms include darkening of the veins near the leaf margins (Fig. 162); in addition, the area surrounding the affected veins may appear flaccid. The darkening of the veins is thought to indicate rupture of a latificer (i.e., a cell, tissue, or vessel that contains latex), which causes latex to be released into the surrounding tissue and results in coagulation of the latex within the latificer system. The surrounding tissue collapses until the entire area becomes necrotic (Figs. 163 and 164).

These symptoms are unsightly, objectionable to consumers, and may predispose lettuce to rot. Packaged salad-cut lettuce with tipburn symptoms is often rejected at retail distribution centers, resulting in a complete loss for the processor. For crisphead and some types of romaine lettuce, symptoms that develop on the inner leaves cannot be seen at harvest. Packing companies typically scout fields prior to harvest to look for tipburn and may reject an entire field when even a small percentage of plants have symptoms.

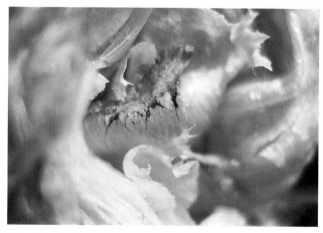

Fig. 162. Darkening of veins near leaf margins of crisphead lettuce, caused by tipburn. (Courtesy R. J. Hayes)

Causal Factors

A localized calcium deficiency in the leaf margin is widely regarded as the cause of tipburn. The role of calcium in the manifestation of the symptoms is not well explained but may be related to the loss of membrane function or integrity.

Most agricultural soils have adequate calcium fertility, but tipburn may still occur. Under most soil conditions, calcium transport occurs passively and is related to water uptake. The transport of calcium to the root surface and through the plant (which occurs through the xylem) depends on the plant's transpiration rate. Consequently, tipburn may result from insufficient water movement to low-transpiring tissue, such as during periods of low air movement and high daytime relative humidity. This insufficiency is often used to explain why tipburn increases after the tops of lettuce heads close. After closure, the transpiration of younger leaves inside the heads decreases relative to the transpiration of outer leaves.

Disruptions of root pressure flow may increase the incidence of tipburn. During the night, the continued uptake of water when stomata are closed may create root pressure flow, moving calcium to all the plant tissues. Conditions that decrease the transpiration of outer leaves at night, such as high relative humidity, may also promote root pressure flow. Conversely, during dry, windy nights, root pressure flow may decrease, and the incident of tipburn may increase. Other conditions that may disrupt root pressure flow include excessively dry soil, saline soil, and poor root health.

The incidence of tipburn often increases under production conditions that promote rapid growth, such as high light intensity, long photoperiods, warm temperatures, and high fertilization rates.

Management

No method of cultural control guarantees the prevention of tipburn. Usual crop inputs should be appropriate for the type of lettuce and the time of year of production. Growers should maintain soil conditions that are favorable for root pressure flow.

Applying foliar calcium sprays is generally of little use for most lettuce cultivars, because these products are effective only if applied to leaves that will develop symptoms. In an especially conducive environment, early harvest before symptoms appear might be appropriate. When lettuce is bulk harvested for salad processing, tipburn symptoms can sometimes be trimmed off plants. Indoor growers should avoid excessive light intensity and provide air movement over plants. Other methods—such as misting plants at night (thereby reducing transpiration of outer leaves) to promote root pressure flow and applying growth regulators—have shown inconsistent results.

The primary and easiest management strategy is to grow resistant cultivars—that is, cultivars that regularly have a low incidence of tipburn when grown under conducive conditions. Although no cultivar is completely resistant to tipburn (as of early 2017), there is considerable variation for resistance within each lettuce type. Most open-top leaf cultivars experience minimal tipburn under normal production conditions, although exceptions are known. Numerous crisphead cultivars with generally adequate levels of resistance have been developed for most of the planting areas in California and Arizona (United States). Tipburn resistance in romaine needs further improvement, although some cultivars appear to be superior to others.

Breeding cultivars for resistance is difficult compared with breeding them for other traits. Resistance is conditioned by a combination of major and minor quantitative trait loci and is subject to pronounced genotype–environment interactions. Selection for resistance in early generations, especially among individual plants, is ineffective. Consequently, extensive field testing is needed to accurately identify resistant breeding lines and cultivars.

Fig. 163. Tissue collapse and necrosis of romaine lettuce, caused by tipburn. (Courtesy R. J. Hayes)

Fig. 164. Tissue collapse and necrosis of leaf lettuce, caused by tipburn. (Courtesy R. J. Hayes)

Selected References

Barta, D. J., and Tibbitts, T. W. 1986. Effects of artificial enclosure of young lettuce leaves on tipburn incidence and leaf calcium concentration. J. Am. Soc. Hortic. Sci. 111:413-416.

Collier, G. F., and Tibbits, T. W. 1982. Tipburn of lettuce. Hortic. Rev. 4:49-65.

Corriveau, J., Gaudreau, L., Caron, J., Jenni, S., and Gosselin, A. 2012. Testing irrigation, day/night foliar spraying, foliar calcium and growth inhibitor as possible cultural practices to reduce tipburn in lettuce. Can. J. Plant Sci. 92:889-899.

Jenni, S., and Hayes, R. J. 2010. Genetic variation, genotype × environment interaction, and selection for tipburn resistance in lettuce in multi-environments. Euphytica 171:427-439.

Jenni, S., Truco, M. J., and Michelmore, R. W. 2013. Quantitative trait loci associated with tipburn, heat stress-induced physiological disorders, and maturity traits in crisphead lettuce. Theor. Appl. Genet. 126:3065-3079.

Thibodeau, P. O., and Minotti, P. L. 1969. The influence of calcium on the development of lettuce tipburn. J. Am. Soc. Hortic. Sci. 94:372-376.

(Prepared by R. J. Hayes)

Bolting

Symptoms

Lettuce is an annual plant that is harvested as a vegetative rosette. However, depending on the environment and plant genotype, the stem may elongate, or bolt, at a given time, and the life cycle of the plant will conclude with flowering and seed set (i.e., little or no leaf production).

Latex content increases with the onset of bolting, which causes leaves to have a bitter flavor. In addition, the leaf color often develops a slight bluish or grayish tint—a quality referred to as "glaucous."

Causal Factors

The photoperiod is a critical factor in promoting bolting. There is considerable genetic variation across lettuce cultivars regarding the time at which bolting is initiated, but the genetic basis is not fully understood.

Cultivars have traditionally been categorized as "long-day" or "day-neutral." A single gene (labeled T) controls the difference, although this genetic model may be an oversimplification. Cultivars used for winter production are generally considered to be day-length sensitive. For lettuce grown during the winter, the critical photoperiod to promote bolting does not occur prior to harvest. Cultivars adapted for summer production are generally considered to be day-neutral, and they may bolt at a genetically determined time or in response to other factors. In addition to gene T, numerous other major and minor genetic loci are known to control bolting. Still other loci likely exist in lettuce but have yet to be identified. Using this genetic variation, it is possible to breed slow-bolting cultivars.

Periods of prolonged high temperatures (35/25°C, day/night) may mediate or accelerate the bolting process, possibly through the accumulation of gibberellins. This can result in premature bolting—a condition in which plants begin to bolt before attaining the size and shape needed to be marketable (Fig. 165). Premature bolting may disrupt the normal rosette architecture of the cultivar or prevent head formation in crisphead and hearting romaine.

Yield losses can be severe when premature bolting occurs (Fig. 166). Lettuce crops grown in northern regions and in the

Fig. 165. Premature bolting of romaine lettuce. (Courtesy R. J. Hayes)

Fig. 166. Premature bolting of romaine lettuce plants in a production field. (Courtesy R. J. Hayes)

Salinas Valley (California, United States) occasionally experience premature bolting following periods of unusually high temperatures. In the low deserts of California and Arizona (United States), fall-planted crops may also experience premature bolting when seedlings are exposed to higher than normal temperatures. Low desert crops grown for spring harvest are vulnerable to high temperatures as they approach maturity. A group of interrelated cultivars bred for resistance to premature bolting are commonly grown in the low desert during these seasons.

Management

Bolted lettuce is unmarketable. The presence of an elongated stem reduces the quality of the lettuce head. In addition, plants with long cores are not useful for salad processing, because the cores are difficult to remove. Therefore, it is important to harvest plants before bolting begins.

Bolting can be managed by growing well-adapted cultivars that are selected to be slow bolting. Generally, lettuce cultivars bred for adaptation to a specific environment or planting slot will be sufficiently slow bolting for commercial production. The genes that regulate bolting can interact strongly with the environment. Consequently, growing plants outside the environment for which they were bred may result in bolting before harvest.

Selected References

Amasino, R. 2010. Seasonal and developmental timing of flowering. Plant J. 61:1001-1013.

Fukuda, M., Matsuo, S., Kikuchi, K., Mitsuhashi, W., Toyomasu, T., and Honda, I. 2009. The endogenous level of GA1 is upregulated by high temperature during stem elongation in lettuce through *LsGA3ox1* expression. J. Plant Physiol. 166:2077-2084.

Ryder, E. J., and Milligan, D. C. 2005. Additional genes controlling flowering time in *Lactuca sativa* and *L. serriola*. J. Am. Soc. Hortic. Sci. 130:448-453.

Waycott, W. W. 1995. Photoperiodic response of genetically diverse lettuce accessions. J. Am. Soc. Hortic. Sci. 120:460-467.

(Prepared by R. J. Hayes)

Rib Discoloration

Rib discoloration is a heat-related physiological disorder of crisphead lettuce; it is also known as "rib breakdown," "brown rib," "red rib," and "rib blight." This disorder was first noted after the release and widespread production of Great Lakes cultivars, which are more susceptible than other groups of cultivars.

Symptoms

Symptoms begin as a light-brownish discoloration of the midrib, which turns brown or black as the disorder advances. The interveinal tissue may eventually become discolored. Symptoms are typically found on the first few leaves underneath the cap leaf and localized to the midribs, where they broaden into the leaf blades. Wrapper leaves are less likely to be affected. The discoloration is most intense on the inner (adaxial) surface of the leaf. When the leaf is viewed from the abaxial side, the symptoms may look roughly like internal rib necrosis.

Symptoms appear as the head matures and may develop more frequently in overly mature lettuce. The symptomatic tissue may become infected with soft-rot-causing bacteria.

Causal Factors

Rib discoloration is prevalent when periods of high temperatures occur after the onset of heading. Consequently, rib discoloration has been observed in a range of locations in which crisphead lettuce is periodically exposed to high temperatures.

Management

The best management approach is to grow resistant cultivars during times of the year in which high temperatures may occur. Crisphead cultivars Summertime, Estival, Hochelaga, and Shawnee were selected for resistance under conditions in Oregon (United States), Quebec (Canada—cultivars Estival and Hochelaga), and Florida (United States), respectively. Other resistant cultivars probably exist, and breeding additional resistant cultivars is likely feasible. The resistance appears to be heritable, but the level of resistance expressed is dependent on the production environment.

Multilocation field experiments are needed to accurately determine a cultivar's level of resistance. The symptoms can be induced in a growth chamber as a method of selecting for resistance.

Selected References

Baggett, J. R., Mansour, N. S., and Kean, D. 1990. 'Summertime' crisphead lettuce. HortScience 25:1453-1454.

Jenni, S. 2005. Rib discoloration: A physiological disorder induced by heat stress in crisphead lettuce. HortScience 40:2031-2035.

Jenni, S., and Yan, W. S. 2009. Genotype by environment interactions of heat stress disorder resistance in crisphead lettuce. Plant Breed. 128:374-380.

Jenni, S., de Koeyer, D. D., and Emery, G. C. 2008. Rib discoloration in F_2 populations of crisphead lettuce in relation to head maturity. J. Am. Soc. Hortic. Sci. 133:249-254.

Lipton, W. J., Stewart, J. K., and Whitaker, T. W. 1972. An Illustrated Guide to the Identification of Some Market Disorders of Lettuce. Marketing Res. Rept. No. 950. U.S. Department of Agriculture, Agricultural Research Service, Washington, DC.

Raleigh, G. L., and Guzman, V. L. 1980. Shawnee a Crisphead Lettuce Adapted to Organic Soils of Florida. Univ. Fla. Agric. Exp. Stn. Circ. S269:6.

(Prepared by R. J. Hayes)

Weather-Related Injury

Injury to lettuce from weather-related causes occurs in all production areas on a sporadic basis. In many instances, the weather itself may cause significant losses, or weather-related damage may be compounded by various pathogens, particularly bacteria and fungi. Weather-related injuries frequently create avenues for pathogen entry (e.g., wounds), and environmental conditions may be conducive to infection and/or pathogen reproduction and spread (Fig. 167).

Cold Injury

Although lettuce is quite tolerant of frost and freezing temperatures, low temperatures can cause injuries to lettuce foliage. Low early morning temperatures in the range of –1 to 0°C may cause ice to form under the epidermal cells. Water vapor forms as the ice melts, and sunlight heats the trapped moisture. The resulting pressure causes the epidermis to separate from the mesophyll, giving leaves a silvery or blistered appearance (Figs. 168 and 169). In some instances, exposed tissue turns brown or appears bronzed (Fig. 170).

Prolonged periods of temperatures in the range of –2 to 1°C often cause tissue breakdown in outer lettuce leaves. These leaves must be removed before harvest to avoid decay during transit.

Lower temperatures in the range of –2 to 1°C for any extended period (2–3 days) may result in individual heads being unsuitable for harvest because of cold injury.

Heat Injury

Lettuce seeds may germinate at temperatures as low as 4°C, but the optimal temperature range for germination is 15–21°C.

Fig. 167. Strong fronts with high winds, torrential rains, and blowing soil may severely wound lettuce plants, creating avenues for pathogen entry. (Courtesy R. N. Raid—© APS)

Fig. 168. Water vapor frequently forms when crisphead lettuce leaf tissue is frozen, causing epidermal separation. (Courtesy S. Glucksman—© APS)

Lettuce is subject to thermal dormancy at temperatures above 27°C; seed may not germinate at all or will germinate erratically. As a result, stands will not be uniform, resulting in losses at harvest.

Exposure of young plants to high temperatures (>32°C) may injure emerging seedlings (Fig. 171) or individual lettuce leaves, even if the soil moisture level is sufficient. High temperatures may also cause leaf scorch (Fig. 172), tipburn (Fig. 173), puffiness, and, on occasion, sunscald (Fig. 174) and rib-related disorders. Heat combined with a water deficit may cause an entire lettuce field to exhibit wilt symptoms (Fig. 175), and an extended period of heat may cause total crop failure (Fig. 176). Abnormally high temperatures may also result in premature bolting, foliar cracking (Fig. 177), and unwanted development of seed stalks (Fig. 178).

Hail Injury

Hail and even torrential rain may cause leaf tearing or splitting (Fig. 179). In terms of lettuce plant development, the most serious injuries from hail occur either during the early seedling stage or just before harvest. During the early seedling stage, sections of fields may be lost or stands may be reduced. Hail damage near harvest may injure individual outer leaves, which may require removal before harvest. A severe hailstorm near harvest can result in the complete loss of the crop (Fig. 180) or cause open wounds, allowing the entry of bacteria and secondary pathogens.

Lightning Injury

In production areas in which thunderstorms frequently occur, lettuce plants may be injured by lightning. Areas of lightning damage in fields are usually circular, and the most severely damaged lettuce plants are in the center. The damage typically decreases in a uniform gradient outward from the center of the strike. Plants in the most severely affected areas may appear "cooked" and are soft to the touch (Fig. 181).

The sudden collapse of wrapper leaves and heads may resemble the symptoms of lettuce drop and soft rot (Fig. 182). However, unlike plants with these biotic disorders, plants struck by lightning display symptoms within 24–48 h after the thunderstorm, and the damaged area does not expand. Lightning-damaged areas may range from several meters to more than 30 m in diameter.

Fig. 170. Crisphead lettuce leaf with bronzing, a common symptom of cold damage. (Courtesy S. Glucksman—© APS)

Fig. 169. Silvering and blistering on cold-damaged wrapper leaves of crisphead lettuce. (Courtesy S. Glucksman—© APS)

Fig. 171. Dehydrated radicle of a germinated lettuce seed, caused by high temperatures. (Courtesy G. J. Holmes—© APS)

Fig. 172. Marginal leaf scorch on crisphead lettuce, caused by excessively high temperatures. (Courtesy S. Glucksman—© APS)

Fig. 173. High temperatures for an extended period may result in accelerated growth and tipburn, as shown on crisphead lettuce. (Courtesy S. Glucksman—© APS)

Fig. 174. High temperatures may cause sunscald, or the collapse of wrapper leaf tissue, as shown on crisphead lettuce. (Courtesy R. N. Raid—© APS)

Fig. 175. Severe wilt and plant death of crisphead lettuce, caused by a water deficit and high temperatures. (Courtesy S. Glucksman—© APS)

Fig. 176. Total crop failure of crisphead lettuce, caused by an extended period of heat. (Courtesy S. Glucksman—© APS)

Fig. 177. Crisphead lettuce with foliar cracking, which commonly results from accelerated growth associated with excessively warm temperatures. (Courtesy S. Glucksman—© APS)

Fig. 178. Premature bolting, the undesired development of seed stalks, of romaine lettuce, caused by warm temperatures. (Courtesy R. N. Raid—© APS)

Fig. 179. Torn crisphead lettuce leaves, caused by hail. (Courtesy R. N. Raid—© APS)

Fig. 180. Hail-injured romaine lettuce. Hail at or near harvest may cause the loss of the entire crop. (Courtesy R. N. Raid—© APS)

Water Injury

Excessive amounts of water usually result from abnormally high levels of precipitation. Heavy rain results in soil deposition on leaf surfaces and wilting of lettuce foliage caused by depletion of soil oxygen levels (Fig. 183). If the water recedes within 2–3 days, plants may recover and produce a normal crop. Soil particles on leaf surfaces may be removed by sprinkler irrigation.

During a prolonged period of excessive soil moisture, there may be a significant increase in the incidence of bacterial soft rot and/or bottom rot. Entire heads may become rotted, starting at their bases.

Wind Injury

Damage from wind and windblown soil is most severe during the early seedling stage, immediately following thinning, and/or just before harvest. During the early seedling stage (i.e., cotyledon to first true leaf), individual plants may be lost and stands may be reduced.

Fig. 181. Lightning damage of crisphead lettuce, showing rapid tissue collapse. (Courtesy R. N. Raid—© APS)

Fig. 182. Lightning damage of crisphead lettuce, showing collapsed wrapper leaves and heads. (Courtesy R. N. Raid—© APS)

Fig. 183. Severe wilting of a field of crisphead lettuce, caused by saturation from heavy rain. Such a field frequently becomes filled with soft rot. (Courtesy R. N. Raid—© APS)

Fig. 184. Wind whipping of small lettuce plants at thinning may cause them to break off at the soil line. (Courtesy R. N. Raid—© APS)

Fig. 185. Severely depleted crisphead lettuce stands, caused by strong winds breaking off seedlings following thinning. (Courtesy R. N. Raid—© APS)

Fig. 186. Wind damage is frequently unidirectional. One side of a romaine lettuce plant is dehydrated and exhibiting necrosis. (Courtesy R. N. Raid—© APS)

At the thinning stage, wind whipping often causes damage, which girdles the stem at the soil line (Fig. 184). Weeding, thinning, and mechanical cultivation often remove soil from the base of the plant, making it more susceptible to wind whipping (Fig. 185).

Strong winds near harvest may damage the outer leaves, which will need to be removed at harvest. Wind damage is frequently unidirectional, causing damage to one side of the plant more than the other (Fig. 186). Strong winds close to harvest may also lodge soil particles inside the heads of nearly mature lettuce, resulting in losses. In some cases, yields can be salvaged by removing the outer leaves at harvest.

Damage from wind-driven soil particles can be reduced by watering the dirt roads adjacent to lettuce fields.

Selected References

Bardin, R. 1912. Disease of Lettuce in the Salinas–Watsonville Area of California. Agricultural Commissioner's Office, Salinas, CA.

Flint, M. L., and Clark, J. K., eds. 1987. Integrated Pest Management for Cole Crops and Lettuce. Pub. 3307. Division of Agriculture and Natural Resources, University of California, Oakland.

Whitaker, T. W., Ryder, E. J., Rubatsky, V. E., and Vail, P. V. 1974. Lettuce Production in the United States (Rev.). U.S. Dep. Agric. Res. Serv. Agric. Handb. 221.

(Prepared by E. A. Kurtz, G. J. Holmes, K. S. Mayberry, and R. N. Raid; revised by R. N. Raid)

Ammonium Toxicity

Symptoms

Excess ammonium in the soil is toxic to the roots of lettuce plants. The core of the root of an affected plant turns reddish-brown to black. In addition, the tissue becomes soft (necrotic), and the root becomes hollow as the plant ages (Fig. 160). Damaged plants wilt and become dark green. Plants may remain alive, but they will be behind in development and ultimately

Fig. 187. Romaine lettuce plant with stunted growth, caused by ammonium toxicity (left), compared with a healthy plant (right). (Courtesy R. F. Smith—© APS)

stunted (Fig. 187). If the damage is severe and/or the plants are small, affected plants may die.

Causal Factors

Ammonium toxicity on lettuce commonly occurs in the early spring, when soil temperatures are below 10–15°C. Ammonium levels can become elevated under cool soil conditions, because the bacteria that convert ammonium to nitrate are less active. As a result, toxic levels of ammonium build up. When the soil warms later in the spring, ammonium is quickly converted to nitrate by soil bacteria, and the risk of ammonium toxicity decreases.

Management

Careful placement of side-dress fertilizer applications sufficiently away from the roots of lettuce plants can help reduce the severity of ammonium toxicity in a field. The use of nitrate forms of nitrogen, rather than urea and ammonium, can also be helpful.

Selected References

Hoque, M. M., Ajwa, A. A., and Smith, R. 2008. Nitrite and ammonium toxicity on lettuce grown under hydroponics. Commun. Soil Sci. Plant Anal. 39:207-216.

van Bruggen, A. H. C., Brown, P. R., and Greathead, A. 1990. Distinction between infectious and noninfectious corky root of lettuce in relation to nitrogen fertilizer. J. Am. Soc. Hortic. Sci. 115:762-770.

(Prepared by R. F. Smith)

Soil pH and Salinity

Soil pH

The optimum pH for lettuce is generally 6.0–6.5 for muck soils and 6.5–7.0 for mineral soils. Nevertheless, with appropriate management, lettuce is successfully grown in soils ranging in pH from 5.0 to 8.5.

Lettuce is only slightly tolerant of soil acidity and metal toxicities. Reductions in lettuce growth, yield, and quality are frequently associated with acidity or toxicities from aluminum, iron, and manganese. Manganese toxicity causes the formation of irregularly shaped, yellow blotches on leaves (Fig. 188). Symptoms of excess acidity include the development of dull-gray roots and reduction or cessation of plant growth. Calcium,

phosphorus, magnesium, and molybdenum are the nutrients most deficient in acidic soils. Mineral soils should be limed if the soil pH is less than 5.5. Muck soils should be limed if the pH is less than 5.2 and the potential for aluminum (or iron) toxicity exists.

Few agricultural soils are too alkaline for lettuce. As the soil pH increases above 6.5 for muck soils and 7.5 for mineral soils, free carbonates often limit the availability of phosphorus, iron, zinc, and manganese. Foliar applications of micronutrients may be required for some alkaline soils, particularly muck soils. Soil pH can be reduced by adding acid or acid-forming materials, such as sulfur and sulfuric acid. However, because pH reduction for such soils is usually temporary, the economics of acidifying soil should be carefully considered.

Soil pH values approaching 9 and greater are typically associated with high soil sodium. Such soil is not suitable for lettuce production, unless an aggressive reclamation effort is undertaken.

Salinity

Lettuce is moderately sensitive to salt. Symptoms of excess salt include heads that are less compact and slow to form and outer leaves that are thick and leathery and have bitter flavor. A sudden increase in salinity causes the development of necrosis along leaf margins and the browning of veins.

The maximum soil salinity (saturated extract) tolerated by lettuce without yield loss is 1.3 deci-Siemens per meter (dS/m) (1 dS/m = ~640 mg of salt per L). For every dS/m above this threshold, the lettuce yield decreases by approximately 13%. Excess salt can also delay germination. At a salinity level between 4 and 12 dS/m, germination can be delayed by as much as 8 days without significantly affecting the final level of germination. As the salt level increases beyond 12 dS/m, germination is both delayed and greatly reduced.

High salinity may reduce yield without causing visual injury. As the soil salinity increases, the ability of lettuce roots to extract water decreases because of the movement of water from low to high salt concentration (i.e., osmotic effect). Over-fertilization can have a similar effect by causing a high osmotic potential in the soil solution. A high level of salt reduces the movement of calcium to developing leaves (see the section "Tipburn") and reduces the availability of potassium, iron, manganese, and zinc.

Seedlings are more sensitive to salt than mature plants; thus, it is important to maintain the salinity level as low as possible in the seed bed. One way to manage the salt level is by leaching. In the California (United States) low desert production fields, tile drains buried 1.5–2.0 m in the soil improve leaching. Plant placement is another means of management. Planting in two rows per bed or near the shoulders of a sloped bed keeps the

Fig. 188. Leaf lettuce leaves with yellow, irregularly formed blotches, caused by manganese toxicity. (Courtesy R. F. Smith—© APS)

roots away from areas in which salts accumulate (i.e., the center and peak of the bed).

Water management can also be used to manage salinity. Drip irrigation reduces the effects of high salinity by continuously supplying moisture to lettuce plants. Irrigating with sprinklers until the crop is established keeps the soil in the upper root zone low in salt. Once the crop is established, furrow irrigation can be used through the remainder of the season.

Selected References

Lorenz, O. A., and Maynard, D. N. 1988. Knott's Handbook for Vegetable Growers. 3rd ed. John Wiley & Sons, New York.

Maas, E. V., and Hoffman, G. J. 1977. Crop salt tolerance—Current assessment. J. Irrig. Drain. Div. Am. Soc. Civ. Eng. 103(IR2):115-134.

Marlatt, R. B. 1974. Nonpathogenic Diseases of Lettuce: Their Identification and Control. 2nd ed. Tech. Bull. 721A. Institute of Food and Agricultural Sciences, University of Florida, Gainesville.

(Prepared by G. J. Holmes, K. S. Mayberry, and C. A. Sanchez; revised by R. F. Smith)

Bird Damage

Bird damage can be a severe problem in the lettuce production areas of California and Arizona (United States). In California, the primary damage-causing bird is the horned lark, which uproots seedlings, grazes on seedling leaves (i.e., cotyledons), and eats seeds. Other species of birds—including crowned sparrows, starlings, blackbirds, mourning doves, and house finches—may also cause significant yield losses. In southwestern Arizona, the major bird species of concern are the red-winged blackbird, brown-headed cowbird, and great-tailed grackle. Starlings and Eurasian collared doves also occasionally cause significant damage.

Although millions of dollars are believed to be lost annually from bird depredation of lettuce at various stages of development, statistics on the extent of bird damage are scarce. In some cases, growers have reported entire crops destroyed by horned larks.

Symptoms

Damage caused by horned larks usually begins in the center of a field. If the number of birds is large, the damage spreads rapidly until only narrow fringes of undamaged plants remain near the field borders. Horned larks begin feeding soon after a lettuce field is planted by excavating seeds, and they may continue to feed on lettuce plants until the seedlings are approximately 8 cm in height. Although the most severe attacks are usually on seedlings, horned larks may also damage the outer leaves of crisphead lettuce (Fig. 189).

Feeding along the edges of a field is usually attributed to crowned sparrows and house finches. Crowned sparrows feed on seedlings and mature plants, whereas house finches feed mostly on seeds and seedlings. The damage caused by red-winged blackbirds, brown-headed cowbirds, great-tailed grackles, starlings, and Eurasian collared doves is caused primarily by feeding on seeds and seedlings.

Causal Species

As noted earlier, the primary bird pest in California lettuce fields is the horned lark (*Eremophila alpestris*). The horned lark is approximately 15–18 cm long, or slightly larger than a sparrow. Its body is brown, and its face has patterns of yellow and white; it also has black bands on the face and throat. Small, black tufts of erect feathers above the eyes of a mature male give the species its common name. The female is duller colored than the male and does not have "horns," but it displays the black, yellow, and white face patterns. Horned larks prefer dry ground and areas with short, sparse vegetation. They avoid habitats in which the grass is more than a few centimeters high, instead frequenting cleared areas, such as plowed fields and mowed expanses around airstrips.

The white-crowned sparrow (*Zonotrichia leucophrys*) is a migratory bird and found in the lettuce-growing areas of California during the fall, winter, and early spring. The adult bird is plain gray in color and has black and white stripes on its head (hence, the name "crowned"). An immature white-crowned sparrow has a brown stripe on its head. Crowned sparrows naturally inhabit brushy areas with nearby open ground for foraging.

The house finch (*Haemorhous mexicanus*) is brown and has streaks of dark brown to nearly black on its body. Its beak is rather robust and used for crushing seeds. The male has a distinctive red-colored head and breast. House finches are commonly found in urban areas, but their native habitats include desert, grassland, chaparral, and open woods.

The red-winged blackbird (*Agelaius phoeniceus*) is approximately 22 cm long. The male has a glossy-black body and red shoulder patches broadly tipped with yellow. The female's body is dark brown above and heavily streaked below. Red-winged blackbirds are often found in large flocks during the winter.

The brown-headed cowbird (*Molothrus ater*) is 19 cm long and commonly found in farmlands and suburbs. The male has a brown head and a metallic green-black body, whereas the female is gray-brown above and paler below.

The great-tailed grackle (*Quiscalus mexicanus*) has a very long, keel-shaped tail and golden-yellow eyes. The male can be up to 46 cm in length; it is an iridescent black and has a purple sheen on its head, back, and underparts. The female is about 38 cm in length; it is less iridescent than the male and has brown upperparts, a cinnamon-buff breast, and a grayish-brown belly.

Epidemiology

The severity of crop damage caused by birds varies with season, field topography, production and irrigation methods, availability of natural foods, and densities of bird populations. Most bird damage to lettuce occurs between September and March, when natural seed production in surrounding areas is scarce and bird populations (especially for the horned lark and crowned sparrow) have peaked. In desert lettuce-growing regions, lettuce seedlings may be the only food source available. In certain areas, vegetation such as lettuce, beet, wheat, and oats sometimes represents approximately 91% of birds' diet.

Food Safety

Birds are not only notorious for destroying lettuce seeds, seedlings, and full-grown crops, but they also deposit fecal material in lettuce fields. Various bird species that frequent agricultural

Fig. 189. Adult male horned lark. (Courtesy J. L. Cummings— © APS)

fields are known to carry non-O157 Shiga toxin-producing *Escherichia coli* and *Salmonella* spp.—zoonotic enteric pathogens that can contaminate fresh produce and potentially cause human illness. Whereas less than 4% of individual birds carry these pathogens, birds sometimes flock in large numbers, increasing the potential risk to produce. Once the pathogens have been deposited in fields through birds' feces, a number of variables determine the risk to humans, including irrigation method (furrow versus overhead) and weather (wind, precipitation, solar radiation).

If fecal contamination is identified in a lettuce field, guidelines state that a grower cannot harvest any product within 5 feet of the fecal matter. In the case of a large flock flying overhead and dropping fecal material across a large area, a grower may have to sacrifice several rows or even an entire field of lettuce to meet the strict guidelines of this food safety protocol.

Thus, birds can have a significant economic impact on growers not only by destroying crops but by potentially making them unfit for harvest.

Management

Several management methods can be used to reduce bird damage to lettuce, but applying methods during the seedling stage is most critical in terms of the time frame. Control of bird damage involves combining several methods, such as habitat removal, scare tactics, trapping, and using lettuce transplants where possible.

Habitat removal is effective in disrupting foraging by crowned sparrows and house finches. Removing brush and weeds, stacked boxes, and other protective covers/shelters discourages sparrows and finches from feeding in a given area.

Scare tactics, such as firing a gas cannon, are effective for crowned sparrows but not for horned larks and house finches, because these species are not timid and do not scare easily. The timing and location of the gas cannon should be changed frequently so birds do not become accustomed to its firing. Gun noises such as shell crackers can be effective, but in a large field, the birds may simply move to another area. Combining a gas cannon with a loud noise maker is more effective than using either alone. Other scare tactics—such as helium balloons and kites with images of predators—can be used, but their effectiveness is questionable. Amplification of recorded tapes of distress and alarm calls of horned larks, calls of their natural enemies (falcons), and electronically generated sounds have been used but without much success. The equipment used to broadcast calls is expensive, and several units may be required per acre. Mylar flags and plastic strips of tape positioned over lettuce rows can be effective when coupled with hazing. Ultimately, scare tactics work best when used before damage occurs; once birds have established a feeding pattern, changing it is difficult.

Trapping finches and sparrows is possible with lily pad and cloverleaf traps using milo or fine-cracked corn as bait. Both species, however, are federally protected migratory birds, so getting a trapping permit from the county agriculture commissioner is required. It is important to note that trapping is not an effective method of control for horned larks.

A subspecies of the horned lark called the "streaked horned lark" (*Eremophila alpestris strigata*) was listed as "threatened" in the Endangered Species Act in 2013. A special permit is required to haze or kill this subspecies.

The use of lettuce transplants is perhaps the most effective method of bird management. Transplants quickly grow to a size that the birds cannot damage, unlike seeds and seedlings, which must endure a long period of susceptibility.

Some growers use natural methods of control that involve territorial predatory birds, such as hawks and falcons. Once the predatory bird establishes its home range near the lettuce field, it will hunt nuisance birds and deter them from landing in the field. Predatory birds will also provide rodent control. Once established in an area, a predatory bird will mate, producing offspring that will potentially establish a home range near lettuce fields. Research is currently being conducted to determine if this is a feasible and economical management option.

Selected References

Cornell University. 2015. All about Birds. Cornell Lab of Ornithology. www.allaboutbirds.org/guide/search

DeHaven, R. W. 1974. Bird Damage to Seeds and Seedling Crops in California—A Questionnaire Survey. Tech. Rept. No. 11, Work Unit DF-102.3. Denver Wildlife Research Center, U.S. Department of the Interior, Fish & Wildlife Service, Denver, CO.

Dunn, J. L., and Alderfer, J. 2011. National Geographic Field Guide to the Birds of North America. National Geographic Society, Washington, DC.

National Audubon Society. 2016. Guide to North American Birds. National Audubon Society, New York. www.audubon.org/bird-guide

University of California, Statewide Integrated Pest Management Program (UCIPM). 2009. UC Pest Management Guidelines: Lettuce—Birds. UC ANR Pub. 3450R. Agriculture and Natural Resources, University of California, Parlier.

(Prepared by J. L. Cummings; revised by J. Nunez, P. Kahn-Rivadeneira, and M. E. Matheron)

Herbicide Injury

Adverse responses to herbicides may result from misapplication, excessive levels of chemical residues in the soil, and movement of phytotoxic pesticides through the soil into the root zone. Forms of misapplication include drift from an adjacent field or noncrop area, use of incompatible products, contamination of application equipment, and exceeding label-recommended rates. Injury to lettuce can be temporary or permanent; the amount of damage and the potential for recovery depend on the herbicide involved and the growth stage of the crop.

Table 4 identifies and describes foliar symptoms of herbicide injury according to herbicide family, mode of action, and chemical. Figures 190–204 provide illustrations of specific symptoms.

(Prepared by K. M. Jennings and S. Chaudhari)

Fig. 190. Chlorosis of romaine lettuce seedlings, caused by glyphosate injury. (Courtesy K. M. Jennings—© APS)

Fig. 191. Growth malformation of romaine lettuce, caused by glyphosate injury. (Courtesy K. M. Jennings—© APS)

Fig. 194. Chlorosis and necrosis of romaine lettuce, caused by diuron injury. (Courtesy K. M. Jennings—© APS)

Fig. 192. Romaine lettuce with interveinal chlorosis and necrosis, caused by metribuzin injury. (Courtesy K. M. Jennings—© APS)

Fig. 195. Stunting and general yellowing of romaine lettuce, caused by foliar contact with rimsulfuron. (Courtesy K. M. Jennings—© APS)

Fig. 193. Distorted growth of romaine lettuce, caused by metribuzin injury. (Courtesy K. M. Jennings—© APS)

TABLE 4. Foliar Symptoms of Herbicide Injury to Lettuce (by Herbicide Family, Mode of Action, and Chemical Name) and Notes about Related Factors and Prevention[a]

Symptom(s)	Herbicide Family: Mode of Action	Herbicide(s)	Description of Symptom(s)	Probable Causes of Injury	Related Factors and Prevention
Chlorosis (yellowing)	**Amino acid derivatives:** Glyphosate inhibits 5-enolpyruvyl-shikimate-3-phosphate (EPSP) synthase enzyme Glufosinate inhibits glutamine synthetase enzyme	glyphosate glufosinate	Growth is inhibited soon after application, followed by chlorosis in the youngest leaves and at growing points and sometimes, crop death (Figs. 190 and 191). New growth may be malformed.	Foliar contact or drift. Spray tank contamination.	Avoid applying amino acid herbicides to adjacent areas under windy conditions. Glyphosate can be used in a "stale bed" situation for lettuce but must be applied to emerged weeds before seeding or emergence of the lettuce crop.
	Triazines: Photosystem II inhibitors	atrazine simazine metribuzin	Symptoms begin with interveinal chlorosis (yellowing) of foliage followed by necrosis (browning) and eventually death of the plant (Figs. 192 and 193); generally, older leaves show injury first. Metribuzin from soil uptake may cause lettuce plants to have an overall yellow appearance, with no chlorosis or necrosis.	Carryover in soil from previous crops. Spray drift. Spray tank contamination.	Most members of the triazine family have long half-lives (average 90 days). Persistence in the soil may increase with higher soil pH and with cool, dry soil conditions. Carryover of these herbicides is likely if label-recommended amounts are not adhered to.
	Substituted ureas: Photosystem II inhibitors	diuron linuron fluometuron	With soil application, plants develop chlorosis followed by necrosis (Fig. 194); older leaves are damaged more than new growth. With foliar application, plants initially develop veinal chlorosis of the leaves and yellowing of leaf margins; further chlorosis and necrosis follow.	Carryover in soil from previous crops. Spray tank contamination.	Average half-life is 60 days but ranges from 2 to 5 months.
	Substituted uracils: Photosystem II inhibitors	bromacil terbacil	Growth slows; plants appear stunted. With foliar application, new growth develops yellowing and distortion. With soil uptake, plants develop a general yellowing.	Carryover in soil from previous crops. Spray tank contamination.	Potential for a long half-life in the soil.
	Sulfonylureas, Imidazolinones, Sulfonanilides: Acetolactate synthase (ALS) enzyme inhibitors; inhibit synthesis of branched-chain amino acids	chlorimuron chlorsulfuron foramsulfuron halosulfuron iodosulfuron mesosulfuron metsulfuron nicosulfuron primisulfuron prosulfuron rimsulfuron sulfometuron thifensulfuron tribenuron trifloxysulfuron imazaquin imazapyr imazethapyr imazapic cloransulam-methyl	Absorption from the soil causes plant stunting and general yellowing. Foliar contact causes yellowing and distortion of new growth, cessation of terminal growth, shortening of internodes, reddening of veins, and dwarfing (Figs. 195 and 196). Symptoms usually begin to appear 10–14 days after application; may appear sooner under certain conditions.	Foliar application. Carryover in soil from previous crops.	Rotational restrictions must be observed in fields in which these herbicides are applied; rotational restrictions tend to be long. High soil pH increases the persistence of sulfonylureas in the soil. Dry, cool environment; high percentage of organic matter; and possibly low soil pH increase the persistence of imidazolinones.

Symptom	Mode of action	Active ingredient	Symptoms	Source of injury	Comments
Bleaching (whitening)	**Isoxazolidinones, Pyridazinones, Benzoylcyclohexanediones:** Pigment inhibitors	clomazone fluridone norflurazon mesotrione tembotrione topramezone	Root uptake can cause complete bleaching of foliage (Fig. 197). Foliar contact with clomazone causes chlorosis and bleaching. Foliar contact or root uptake of norflurazon may cause veinal chlorosis.	Spray drift. Carryover in soil from previous crops.	Injury is generally cosmetic and transient.
Necrosis (browning)	**Miscellaneous:** Photosystem II inhibitor	bentazon	Foliar bronzing and speckling generally occur on leaves.	Spray drift.	Adjacent crops should not be sprayed under windy conditions.
	Bipyridyliums: Cell membrane disruptor and Photosystem I inhibitor	paraquat diquat	When the entire plant is sprayed, rapid wilting and desiccation occur within a few hours (Fig. 198). Droplet drift will cause some distinct necrotic circular spots, outlined in red.	Spray drift.	Tightly adsorbed to soil particles; completely inactive in soil. Paraquat can be used in a "stale seed bed" situation but will cause injury if the application coincides with crop cracking and emergence. Hot, humid conditions enhance the activity of these herbicides.
	Diphenyl ethers: Inhibit protoporphyrinogen oxidase, an enzyme of chlorophyll biosynthesis	acifluorfen oxyfluorfen fomesafen lactofen	Foliar contact can cause speckling on leaves (bronzing), followed by rapid desiccation and necrosis (Fig. 199).	Spray drift. Misapplication. Spray tank contamination.	Hot, humid conditions enhance the activity of these herbicides.
	N-Phenylphthalimide: Inhibits protoporphyrinogen oxidase, an enzyme of chlorophyll biosynthesis	flumioxazin	Foliar contact can cause speckling on leaves, as well as chlorosis and/or necrosis (Fig. 200).	Spray drift. Spray tank contamination.	
	Aryloxyphenoxypropionate, Cyclohexanedione: Inhibit membrane synthesis	quizlaofop-P fluazifop-P clethodim sethoxydim	Broadleaf plants, such as lettuce, are tolerant of these herbicides. Injury sometimes occurs (likely related to use of an adjuvant); symptoms include general yellowing of young leaves, followed by bronzing.	Injury may occur if applied with a crop oil concentrate under high heat and humid conditions.	Injury is generally temporary.
	Triazolinone: Inhibit protoporphyrinogen oxidase, an enzyme of chlorophyll biosynthesis	sulfentrazone carfentrazone	Foliar contact causes rapid desiccation and necrosis. Root uptake of sulfentrazone may result in necrosis and plant death (Fig. 201).	Spray drift. Carryover in soil from previous crops.	Sulfentrazone rotation restrictions are long for some vegetable crops.

(continued)

134

TABLE 4. *Continued*

Symptom(s)	Herbicide Family: Mode of Action	Herbicide(s)	Description of Symptom(s)	Probable Causes of Injury	Related Factors and Prevention
Leaf cupping and "feathering," petiole and stem twisting, misshapen fruit	**Synthetic auxins:** Phenoxy Benzoic acid Pyridines Growth regulator-type activity	2,4-D; 2,4-DB[b] dicamba picloram triclopyr aminopyralid clopyralid	Growth regulator-type activity from foliar contact is epinastic. Initial symptoms are twisting of petioles, bending and enlarging of stems, "feathering" and cupping of leaves, and in some instances, plant death (Figs. 202 and 203). Root uptake of phenoxy (2,4-D) herbicides usually produces mild symptoms. Root uptake of dicamba and pyridines may cause symptoms similar to those caused by foliar contact. Responses likely to occur at very low rates; order of sensitivity (most to least) is pyridines, dicamba, and 2,4-D. High rates may result in plant death.	Spray or vapor drift. Contamination of sprayers and measuring cups. Carryover from previous crops.	These herbicides should not be applied to adjacent fields under windy or extremely hot conditions. Salt or amine formulations of 2,4-D are essentially nonvolatile and the safest to use in adjacent row crops.
Stunting	**Chloroacetamide:** Inhibits the biosynthesis of several plant components, such as fatty acids, lipids, proteins, isoprenoids, and flavonoids.	alachlor metolachlor S-metolachlor dimethenamid-P	Can cause stunting, crinkled or rough leaves, yellowing of leaves, and in severe cases, crop death (Fig. 204).	Spray drift.	
	Dinitroanilines: Cell division inhibitors	ethalfluralin oryzalin pendimethalin trifluralin	Primary symptoms are cessation of root growth. Roots may be swollen at the tips or club shaped.	Carryover from previous crops. Inaccurate sprayer calibration and/or herbicide rate application.	Cool, wet conditions are conducive to injury by these herbicides.

[a] Courtesy K. M. Jennings and S. Chaudhari, North Carolina State University—© APS.
[b] 2,4-Dichlorophenoxyacetic acid; 4-(2,4-Dichlorophenoxy)butyric acid.

Fig. 196. Romaine lettuce with distortion of new growth, cessation of terminal growth, shortening of internodes, and reddening of veins, caused by halosulfuron injury. (Courtesy K. M. Jennings—© APS)

Fig. 197. Bleaching of romaine lettuce foliage, caused by root uptake of clomazone. (Courtesy K. M. Jennings—© APS)

Fig. 198. Desiccation and wilting of romaine lettuce, caused by paraquat spray injury. (Courtesy K. M. Jennings—© APS)

Fig. 199. Speckling on romaine lettuce leaves (bronzing) was followed by rapid desiccation and necrosis, caused by fomesafen injury. (Courtesy K. M. Jennings—© APS)

Fig. 202. Petiole twisting and stem bending of romaine lettuce leaves, caused by 2,4-Dichlorophenoxyacetic acid (2,4-D) injury. (Courtesy K. M. Jennings—© APS)

Fig. 200. Speckling, chlorosis, and necrosis on romaine lettuce leaves, caused by flumioxazin injury. (Courtesy K. M. Jennings—© APS)

Fig. 203. Feathering and cupping of romaine lettuce leaves, caused by dicamba injury. (Courtesy K. M. Jennings—© APS)

Fig. 201. Tissue necrosis and death of a romaine lettuce plant, caused by sulfentrazone injury. (Courtesy K. M. Jennings—© APS)

Fig. 204. Romaine lettuce plant with stunted growth and crinkled leaves, caused by S-metolachlor injury. (Courtesy K. M. Jennings—© APS)

135

Part IV. Postharvest Diseases and Disorders

Harvested lettuce is susceptible to a variety of postharvest diseases. Tissue susceptibility depends on many factors, including postharvest storage conditions, lettuce type and variety, and the physiological state of the lettuce. Harvested lettuce is sensitive to temperature, relative humidity, and carbon dioxide. After harvest, lettuce should be immediately vacuum-cooled to remove field heat and then stored at 1.1–2.2°C in 98–100% relative humidity for maximum storage life.

Different lettuce types and cultivars vary in their risks to postharvest diseases. Maturity and health status also affect the susceptibility of lettuce to postharvest diseases. For example, overmature lettuce in general is more susceptible to postharvest disorders. Postharvest diseases can also be influenced by lettuce diseases in the field. Although lettuce with obvious disease symptoms is not harvested, small or latent infections may predispose a crop to postharvest diseases and shorten postharvest shelf life. Harvesting and packing of lettuce may also cause physical injuries, increasing susceptibility to postharvest diseases.

Lettuce is affected by several postharvest diseases. The following sections address bacterial soft rot, russet spotting, gray mold, brown stain, pink rib, and other diseases and disorders.

Selected References

Brandl, M. T. 2008. Plant lesions promote the rapid multiplication of *Escherichia coli* O157:H7 on postharvest lettuce. Appl. Environ. Microbiol. 74:5285-5289.

Lipton, W. J., Stewart, J. K., and Whitaker, T. W. 1972. An Illustrated Guide to the Identification of Some Market Disorders of Head Lettuce. U.S. Dep. Agric. Mark. Res. Rep. 950.

Moline, H. E., and Lipton, W. J. 1987. Market Diseases of Beets, Chicory, Endive, Escarole, Globe Artichokes, Lettuce, Rhubarb, Spinach, and Sweet Potatoes. U.S. Dep. Agric. Agric. Handb. 155.

Snowdon, A. L. 2010. A Colour Atlas of Post-Harvest Diseases and Disorders of Fruits and Vegetables. Vol. 2: Vegetables. Manson, London.

(Prepared by Y.-B. Liu)

Bacterial Soft Rot

Bacterial soft rot is the most serious postharvest disease of vegetables, including lettuce. It may occur on any type of lettuce from any growing region, and although it can develop at any temperature, it usually develops faster at higher temperatures. Bacterial soft rot occurs more often on lettuce that has been damaged mechanically, exposed to freezing temperatures, infected by fungi, or stressed by physiological disorders.

(See also the section "Bacterial Soft Rot" in Part I, including Figures 74–80.)

Symptoms

Bacterial soft rot often occurs near decayed tissue, appearing as elongated, tan to brown spots. These symptoms can be confused with the irregularly shaped spots caused by russet spotting (see following section, "Russet Spotting"). With bacterial rot, the tissue becomes soft and slimy under high humidity. In severe cases, entire lettuce heads may become a slimy mass but not have a putrid odor.

Causal Organisms

Bacterial soft rot is caused by *Pectobacterium carotovorum* subsp. *carotovorum* (syn. *Erwinia carotovora* subsp. *carotovora*) and *Pseudomonas marginalis* pv. *marginalis*. Other bacteria may occasionally be involved.

Management

Effective management is based on maintaining good sanitation and optimal storage conditions. Bacterial soft rot can be minimized by careful handling of lettuce during harvest, rapid cooling of lettuce after harvest, storing lettuce at 1.1–2.2°C, and removing lettuce affected with any type of disease.

Selected References

Cho, J. J., and Talede, K. Y. 1976. Evaluation of lettuce varieties for resistance to bacterial soft rot. Hortic. Dig. 35:4-5.

Lipton, W. J., Stewart, J. K., and Whitaker, T. W. 1972. An Illustrated Guide to the Identification of Some Market Disorders of Head Lettuce. U.S. Dep. Agric. Mark. Res. Rep. 950.

Moline, H. E., and Lipton, W. J. 1987. Market Diseases of Beets, Chicory, Endive, Escarole, Globe Artichokes, Lettuce, Rhubarb, Spinach, and Sweet Potatoes. U.S. Dep. Agric. Agric. Handb. 155.

Silva, A. M. F., Oliverra, W. J., Mariano, R. L. R., and Barbosa, E. B. 2014. Lettuce genotype resistance to "soft rot" caused by *Pectobacterium carotovorum* subsp. *carotovorum*. Sci. Agric. 71:1-8.

Snowdon, A. L. 2010. A Colour Atlas of Post-Harvest Diseases and Disorders of Fruits and Vegetables. Vol. 2: Vegetables. Manson, London.

(Prepared by Y.-B. Liu)

Russet Spotting

Russet spotting occurs sporadically in lettuce from any growing region, but it is more common in desert-grown lettuce in March and in lettuce from coastal California (United States) in September and October. Both crisphead and romaine lettuce are susceptible to russet spotting, and cultivars may differ in susceptibility.

Symptoms

Russet spots are small, tan or russet-brown depressions on the midribs and other parts of lettuce (Fig. 205). The spots are usually longitudinal and pitlike on the midribs and shallow, roundish, and somewhat diffuse on the blades. In severe cases, the spots may coalesce to form irregularly shaped, discolored areas (Fig. 206).

Russet spotting can resemble brown stain and an early stage of bacterial soft rot.

Causal Factors

Exposure to ethylene is the main cause of russet spotting. Ethylene at a concentration as low as 0.1 parts per million (ppm) can cause russet spotting in lettuce. The occurrence and severity of russet spotting increase with increases of ethylene concentration up to 10 ppm.

Russet spotting may also develop in overmature heads without exposure to ethylene.

Management

Russet spotting can be minimized or prevented by creating lettuce storage and shipping environments that are essentially ethylene free—for instance, by storing or shipping lettuce separately from other products that emit substantial amounts of ethylene, by avoiding holding overmature and decayed products,

by maintaining cold temperatures (1.1–2.2°C), and by holding lettuce with a high risk of developing russet spotting in a low-oxygen controlled atmosphere.

Selected References

Ke, D., and Saltveit, M. E. 1988. Plant hormone interaction and phenolic metabolism in the regulation of russet spotting in iceberg lettuce. Plant Physiol. 88:1136-1140.

Lipton, W. J., Stewart, J. K., and Whitaker, T. W. 1972. An Illustrated Guide to the Identification of Some Market Disorders of Head Lettuce. U.S. Dep. Agric. Mark. Res. Rep. 950.

Moline, H. E., and Lipton, W. J. 1987. Market Diseases of Beets, Chicory, Endive, Escarole, Globe Artichokes, Lettuce, Rhubarb, Spinach, and Sweet Potatoes. U.S. Dep. Agric. Agric. Handb. 155.

Snowdon, A. L. 2010. A Colour Atlas of Post-Harvest Diseases and Disorders of Fruits and Vegetables. Vol. 2: Vegetables. Manson, London.

(Prepared by Y.-B. Liu)

Gray Mold

Gray mold is one of the most common postharvest diseases of lettuce, and it can cause significant reductions in quality during storage, shipping, and marketing. Gray mold can develop following many predisposing factors, including other diseases, disorders, and damage.

Symptoms

Infected lettuce tissue is initially water soaked and later turns various shades of gray-green to brown. The tissue surrounding a lesion may have an orange or red cast. Affected areas rapidly turn into a soft, watery rot.

Depending on the storage conditions, the characteristic fuzzy, gray to brown growth of the pathogen may or may not be present on harvested lettuce (Fig. 207). Instead, the gray mold pathogen, *Botrytis cinerea,* may manifest itself as nondescript, white mycelium.

Postharvest gray mold can develop on any lettuce tissue that is injured, including the following:

- Leaf lesions, caused by pathogens such as *Bremia lactucae* (downy mildew) and *Xanthomonas campestris* pv. *vitians* (bacterial leaf spot)
- Infected or decayed crown tissue, caused by *Sclerotinia* spp. (white mold or lettuce drop) and *Boeremia exigua* (syn. *Phoma exigua*) (Phoma basal rot)
- Physiological disorders, such as tipburn (calcium deficiency)

Fig. 205. Russet spotting on crisphead lettuce. (Courtesy E. J. Ryder)

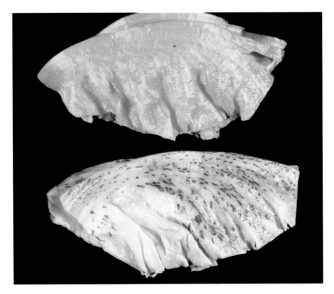

Fig. 206. Crisphead lettuce leaf with russet spotting (bottom) compared with a healthy leaf (top). (Courtesy M. E. Saltveit—© APS)

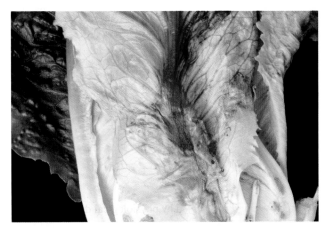

Fig. 207. Romaine lettuce with fuzzy, gray to brown growth of *Botrytis cinerea,* which causes gray mold. (Courtesy S. T. Koike—© APS)

(These diseases and disorders are discussed in earlier sections of the book: "Bacterial Leaf Spot," "Downy Mildew," "Lettuce Drop," and "Tipburn.")

Causal Organism

B. cinerea is widespread and survives both as a pathogen on many crops and as a saprophyte on organic substrates. The ellipsoidal or obovoid conidia are colorless to pale brown, exhibit a prominent hilum, and measure 4–11 × 6–18 μm. In mass, the conidia are gray to brown.

B. cinerea can develop over a wide temperature range, from –2 to 25°C; optimum growth occurs between 20 and 25°C. The fungus often produces black sclerotia that vary greatly in size and shape, although some isolates produce no sclerotia.

Because *B. cinerea* sporulates poorly in the absence of light, conidial growth may not be visible on diseased tissue of stored and transported lettuce. In such cases, only white mycelium and perhaps sclerotia will be present. Culturing or incubating affected lettuce tissues is necessary to confirm the presence of gray mold.

Disease Cycle and Epidemiology

Lettuce becomes exposed to *B. cinerea* conidia or saprophytic mycelia in the field and during handling. If rainfall occurs at or near harvest maturity, the pathogen can infect lettuce and produce serious yield losses.

If harvesting and handling procedures, diseases, physiological disorders, and other factors have injured the harvested product, then conidia can germinate and colonize the damaged tissue. In addition, latent infections in packed lettuce may continue to enlarge and develop during storage. A postharvest gray mold infection allows bacteria and other decay organisms to colonize lettuce, resulting in further breakdown of lettuce tissue.

Management

Losses from gray mold can be minimized by timely and rapid precooling (such as by vacuum cooling) of the harvested product and by storing and shipping lettuce at temperatures between 1.1 and 2.2°C. Increasing carbon dioxide (CO_2) levels can inhibit gray mold. Improved efficiency in shipment and marketing of lettuce may also reduce the opportunities for gray mold to grow.

In addition, it is essential to reduce damage to lettuce during harvest and shipping, because *B. cinerea* conidia readily colonize injured and compromised tissue. The use of film wraps can help limit the in-box spread of gray mold from one head to another. Modifying the atmospheres inside prewashed, bagged salad products likewise inhibit this postharvest problem.

Selected References

Ceponis, M. J., and Butterfield, J. E. 1982. Retail and consumer losses in the fall and winter crop of western head lettuce marketed in metropolitan New York. HortScience 17:258-259.

Ceponis, M. J., Cappellini, R. A., and Lightner, G. W. 1985. Disorders in crisphead lettuce shipments to the New York market, 1972–1984. Plant Dis. 69:1016-1020.

Coley-Smith, J. R., Verhoeff, K., and Jarvis, W. R., eds. 1980. The Biology of Botrytis. Academic Press, New York.

Delon, R., Kiffer, E., and Mangenot, F. 1977. Ultrastructural study of host-parasite interactions: II. Decay of lettuce caused by *Botrytis cinerea* and phyllosphere bacteria. Can. J. Bot. 55:2463-2470.

Moline, H. E., and Lipton, W. J. 1987. Market Diseases of Beets, Chicory, Endive, Escarole, Globe Artichokes, Lettuce, Rhubarb, Spinach, and Sweet Potatoes. U.S. Dep. Agric. Agric. Handb. 155.

Stewart, J. K. 1978. Influence of oxygen, carbon dioxide, and carbon monoxide levels on decay of head lettuce after harvest. Sci. Hortic. 9:207-213.

(Prepared by S. T. Koike)

Brown Stain

Brown stain is a common postharvest disorder of lettuce and is caused by elevated levels of carbon dioxide (CO_2). The use of controlled and modified atmospheres with reduced levels of oxygen (O_2) and elevated levels of CO_2 to extend the storage life of lettuce can result in development of this disorder.

Susceptibility of lettuce tissue to brown stain varies significantly among cultivars. Crisphead lettuce is most sensitive to brown stain, but romaine, leaf, and butterhead lettuce can also be affected. Visual symptoms of brown stain develop more rapidly on crisphead than on romaine and other types of leaf lettuce.

Area of production, plant maturity, and weather conditions also affect the susceptibility of lettuce to brown stain during storage and shipping. Brown stain is more severe under low-oxygen conditions, such as in modified-atmosphere storage and shipping.

Symptoms

Reddish to brown spots or stains develop on the midribs. These lesions are sunken areas of epidermal cells and can have various shapes (Fig. 208). Compared with russet spot lesions, brown stain lesions are larger and have darker-brown borders. In extreme cases, brown stain lesions extend onto leaf blade tissue, as well. The lesions are dry, and secondary infections are rare. Brown stain lesions typically measure approximately 0.5–1.0 cm, and they have distinct margins that are often darker than the slightly sunken centers. Brown stain occurs on both leaf surfaces—more often on or near the midrib and toward the base of the leaf.

At low storage temperatures, young lesions may be translucent. After they are exposed to higher temperatures, they develop a brownish color.

Brown stain most commonly develops on leaves just under the cap leaf, but it may also develop on heart leaves. Heart leaves may develop reddish-brown spots along the leaf margins, or entire leaves may be discolored.

Causal Factors

Exposure to elevated levels of CO_2 causes brown stain in harvested lettuce. The severity of brown stain increases in an atmosphere with more than 3% CO_2 and an O_2 level below 10% and as storage duration increases. Brown stain is more prevalent at the low temperatures maintained during storage and transport and less prevalent at higher temperatures. The incidence of the disorder is negligible above 10°C. This temperature effect can be explained by the fact that CO_2 has high water solubility at low temperatures, which results in more CO_2 being

Fig. 208. Brown stain lesions on pieces of crisphead lettuce. (Courtesy M. E. Saltveit—© APS)

trapped in leaf tissue and consequently causing brown stain. Overmature lettuce heads are compact and hinder CO_2 diffusion inside them, thereby increasing the risk for brown stain.

The use of controlled and modified atmospheres for long-term storage or transport of lettuce is often associated with the appearance of brown stain because of elevated CO_2 and reduced O_2 concentrations.

Management

Brown stain can be prevented by maintaining the CO_2 concentration in the storage atmosphere below 2% and the O_2 concentration above 10%. This can be achieved by reducing CO_2 production and removing CO_2. Lettuce should be stored in a controlled atmosphere with 2–5% O_2 and 0% CO_2. Increasing air exchange during storage and shipping can help to prevent CO_2 accumulation and brown stain. Scrubbing CO_2 using hydrated soda lime may also help to maintain a low CO_2 condition and prevent brown stain.

If elevated levels of CO_2 cannot be avoided, the severity of the disorder can be reduced by selecting resistant cultivars and by harvesting lettuce at the proper maturity. Although increasing the storage temperature to 5°C would significantly reduce brown stain susceptibility, it is not practical for long transit periods.

Selected References

Beaudry, R. M. 1999. Effect of O_2 and CO_2 partial pressure on selected phenomena affecting fruit and vegetable quality. Postharvest Biol. Technol. 15:293-303.

Brecht, P. E., Morris, L. L., Cheyney, C., and Janecke, D. 1973. Brown stain susceptibility of selected lettuce cultivars under controlled atmospheres and temperatures. J. Am. Soc. Hortic. Sci. 98:261-264.

Brecht, P. E., Kader, A. A., and Morris, L. L. 1973. The effect of composition of the atmosphere and duration of exposure on brown stain of lettuce. J. Am. Soc. Hortic. Sci. 98:536-538.

Brecht, P. E., Kader, A. A., and Morris, L. L. 1973. Influence of postharvest temperature on brown stain of lettuce. J. Am. Soc. Hortic. Sci. 98:399-402.

Kader, A. A., Brecht, P. E., Woodruff, R., and Morris, L. L. 1973. Influence of carbon monoxide, carbon dioxide, and oxygen levels on brown stain, respiration rate, and visual quality of lettuce. J. Am. Soc. Hortic. Sci. 98:485-488.

Ke, D., and Saltveit, M. E. 1989. Carbon dioxide-induced brown stain development as related to phenolic metabolism in iceberg lettuce. J. Am. Soc. Hortic. Sci. 114:789-794.

Liu, S. S., and Liu, Y.-B. 2014. Reducing CO_2 accumulation and its phytotoxicity to lettuce with absorbent in hermetic storage as a simulation of long-term fumigation. J. Asia-Pac. Entomol. 17:435-439.

Siriphanich, J., and Kader, A. A. 1985. Effects of CO_2 on total phenolics, phenylalanine ammonia lyase, and polyphenol oxidase in lettuce tissue. J. Am. Soc. Hortic. Sci. 110:249-253.

(Prepared by M. E. Saltveit; revised by R. F. Smith and Y.-B. Liu)

Pink Rib

Pink rib is a postharvest disorder of crisphead and romaine lettuce. Although it can develop in lightly processed crisphead lettuce, the stresses associated with processing do not appear to promote this disorder.

Symptoms

The most common symptom of pink rib is a diffuse, pink discoloration near the bases of the midribs of the outer head leaves. Other symptoms include a pink discoloration of the

Fig. 209. Pink discoloration of midribs on the outer leaves of crisphead lettuce, characteristic of pink rib. (Courtesy M. E. Saltveit—© APS)

normally milky-white latex in the tubules and walls of some water-conducting elements. Pink rib affects the chlorophyll-free midrib tissue at the bases of outer head leaves (Fig. 209). The pinkish color is seen most easily from the inner surfaces of detached leaves, but it can be seen from the outer surfaces of the leaves, as well. In severe cases, the pink discoloration may extend into the large veins of all but the youngest leaves.

Causal Factors

No specific cause of pink rib has been identified, but certain preharvest and postharvest factors affect its incidence and severity. Diffuse pink rib is often associated with disrupted cells; thus, it is likely that rapid growth favors its development. Also, because pink rib is more common on compact heads at harvest, senescence may be involved. Higher than optimal postharvest storage temperatures (1.1–2.2°C) also favor pink rib development.

Management

The incidence of pink rib can be minimized by avoiding the harvest of compact heads, by promptly precooling lettuce after harvest to 1.1–2.2°C, and by maintaining cool temperatures throughout marketing. Optimizing lettuce production management to avoid an excessive growth rate may also reduce the incidence of pink rib.

Storing lettuce under low oxygen (O_2) conditions can aggravate pink rib development. A 2% O_2 level increases the occurrence of pink rib during week 1 or storage at 10°C or week 4 at 2.5°C or 5°C.

Selected References

Lipton, W. J., Stewart, J. K., and Whitaker, T. W. 1972. An Illustrated Guide to the Identification of Some Market Disorders of Head Lettuce. U.S. Dep. Agric. Mark. Res. Rep. 950.

Marlatt, R. B., and Stewart, J. K. 1956. Pink rib of head lettuce. Plant Dis. Rep. 40:742-743.

Saltveit, M. 2004. Effect of 1-methylcyclopropene on phenylpropanoid metabolism, the accumulation of phenolic compounds, and browning of whole and fresh-cut 'iceberg' lettuce. Postharvest Biol. Tech. 34:75-80.

Snowdon, A. L. 2010. A Colour Atlas of Post-Harvest Diseases and Disorders of Fruits and Vegetables. Vol. 2: Vegetables. Manson, London.

(Prepared by M. E. Saltveit; revised by Y.-B. Liu and R. F. Smith)

Other Postharvest Diseases and Disorders

Other postharvest diseases and disorders are not common or occur only on specific cultivars or under certain conditions:

- Low-oxygen injury, which can occur on lettuce shipped under a low-oxygen atmosphere, is characterized by shiny to water-soaked gray, dead patches. Young head leaves may develop shallow, reddish-brown spots on the midribs.
- Internal rib necrosis and rusty-brown discoloration occur only on winter-harvested lettuce from the cultivar Climax and close relatives. Symptoms include diffuse, dark discoloration inside the midribs and on the leaf surfaces. Storage or shipping temperatures do not influence internal rib necrosis. Causal agents have not been confirmed.
- Rib discoloration occurs mainly during the warm season and appears as oblong, yellowish-tan to brown or black discoloration on the midribs. The causal agent has not been confirmed.
- Watery soft rot is caused by *Sclerotinia sclerotiorum*. Symptoms include water-soaked, light- or pinkish-brown tissue. In severe cases, a white, fuzzy mold may be observed on infected leaves. Watery rot can be found on lettuce in all growing regions.

Selected References

Beaudry, R. M. 1999. Effect of O_2 and CO_2 partial pressure on selected phenomena affecting fruit and vegetable quality. Postharvest Biol. Technol. 15:293-303.

Brandl, M. T. 2008. Plant lesions promote the rapid multiplication of *Escherichia coli* O157:H7 on postharvest lettuce. Appl. Environ. Microbiol. 74:5285-5289.

Lipton, W. J., Stewart, J. K., and Whitaker, T. W. 1972. An Illustrated Guide to the Identification of Some Market Disorders of Head Lettuce. U.S. Dep. Agric. Mark. Res. Rep. 950.

Liu, S. S., and Liu, Y.-B. 2014. Reducing CO_2 accumulation and its phytotoxicity to lettuce with absorbent in hermetic storage as a simulation of long-term fumigation. J. Asia-Pac. Entomol. 17:435-439.

Moline, H. E., and Lipton, W. J. 1987. Market Diseases of Beets, Chicory, Endive, Escarole, Globe Artichokes, Lettuce, Rhubarb, Spinach, and Sweet Potatoes. U.S. Dep. Agric. Agric. Handb. 155.

Snowdon, A. L. 2010. A Colour Atlas of Post-Harvest Diseases and Disorders of Fruits and Vegetables. Vol. 2: Vegetables. Manson, London.

(Prepared by Y.-B. Liu)

Appendix

Diseases of Lettuce
(*Lactuca sativa* L.)

The following content is also available on the website of The American Phytopathological Society in the section "Common Names of Plant Diseases." Any updates that are subsequently made to the taxonomy and nomenclature will be reflected on the website.

BACTERIAL DISEASES

Bacterial leaf spot (BLS)
　Xanthomonas campestris pv. *vitians* (Brown) Dye
Bacterial soft rot
　Pectobacterium carotovorum subsp. *carotovorum* (Jones)
　　Hauben et al.
　　(syn. *Erwinia carotovora* subsp. *carotovora* (Jones)
　　Bergey et al.)
Bacterial soft rot (Postharvest)
　Pectobacterium carotovorum subsp. *carotovorum* (Jones)
　　Hauben et al.
　　(syn. *Erwinia carotovora* subsp. *carotovora* (Jones)
　　Bergey et al.)
　Pseudomonas marginalis pv. *marginalis*
Corky root
　Rhizorhapis suberifaciens Francis et al.
Marginal leaf blight
　Pseudomonas marginalis pv. *marginalis* (Brown) Stevens
Varnish spot
　Pseudomonas cichorii (Swingle) Stapp

FUNGAL AND OOMYCETE DISEASES

Alternaria leaf spot
　Alternaria sonchi Davis
Anthracnose
　Microdochium panattonianum (Berl.) Sutton, Galea &
　　Price
　　(syn. *Marssonina panattoniana* (Berl.) Magnus)
Black rot
　Ceratocystis fimbriata Ellis & Halst.
Black root rot
　Thielaviopsis basicola (Berk. & Broome) Ferraris
　　(syn. *Chalara elegans* Nag Raj & W. B. Kendr.)
Bottom rot
　Rhizoctonia solani J. G. Kühn
　　(syn. *Thanatephorus cucumeris* (A. B. Frank) Donk)
Cercospora leaf spot
　Cercospora apii Fresen.
　C. lactucae-sativae Sawada
　　(syn. *C. longissima* Cugini ex Trav., illeg. hom.)
Damping-off, Pythium
　Pythium dissotocum Drechsler
　P. irregulare Buisman
　P. myriotylum Drechsler
　P. sylvaticum W. A. Campb. & F. F. Hendrix
　P. ultimum Trow

P. uncinulatum Plaats-Niterink & I. Blok
　P. violae Chesters & Hickman
Damping-off, Rhizoctonia
　Rhizoctonia solani J. G. Kühn
Downy mildew
　Bremia lactucae Regel
　Plasmopara lactucae-radicis Stangh. & Gilb.
Drop (Sclerotinia rot)
　Sclerotinia minor Jaggar
　S. sclerotiorum (Lib.) de Bary
Fusarium wilt (Fusarium root rot)
　Fusarium oxysporum f. sp. *lactucae* Matuo & Motohashi
Gray mold (Pre- and postharvest)
　Botrytis cinerea Pers.:Fr.
　　(syn. *Botryotinia fuckeliana* (de Bary) Whetzel)
Phoma leaf spot and basal rot
　Boeremia exigua (Desm.) Aveskamp, Gruyter & Verkley
　　(syn. *Phoma exigua* Desm.)
　P. tropica R. Schneid. & Boerema
Phytophthora stem and root rot
　Phytophthora cryptogea Pethybr. & Laff.
　P. drechsleri Tucker
　P. lactucae Bertier, H. Brouwer & DeCock
　P. pseudolactucae M. Z. Rahman et al.
Powdery mildew
　Golovinomyces cichoracearum (DC.) V. P. Heluta
　　(syn. *Erysiphe cichoracearum* DC.)
Pythium wilt and leaf blight
　Pythium aphanidermatum (Edson) Fitzp.
　P. megalacanthum de Bary
　P. polymastum Drechsler
　P. spinosum Sawada
　P. tracheiphilum Matta
　P. ultimum Trow
　P. uncinulatum Plaats-Niterink & I. Blok
Rust
　Puccinia dioicae Magnus
　　(syn. *P. extensicola* Plowr. var. *hieraciata* (Schwein.)
　　Arthur)
Septoria leaf spot
　Septoria birgitae Bedlan
　S. lactucae Pass.
Southern blight
　Athelia rolfsii (Curzi) C. C. Tu & Kimbr.
　　(syn. *Sclerotium rolfsii* Sacc.)

Stemphylium leaf spot
    Stemphylium botryosum f. sp. *lactucum* Padhi & Snyder
      (syn. *Pleospora tarda* E. G. Simmons)
    S. solani G. F. Weber
Texas root rot (Phymatotrichum root rot, Cotton root rot)
    Phymatotrichopsis omnivora (Shear) Hennebert
      (syn. *Phymatotrichum omnivorum* (Shear) Duggar)
Verticillium wilt
    Verticillium dahliae Kleb.
    V. isaacii Inderb. et al.
    V. klebahnii Inderb. et al.

NEMATODES, PARASITIC

False root-knot
    Nacobbus aberrans (Thorne) Thorne & Allen
Lesion
    Pratylenchus penetrans (Cobb) Filipjev & Schuurmans
      Stekhoven
Needle
    Longidorus africanus Merny
Root-knot
    Meloidogyne arenaria (Neal) Chitwood
    M. hapla Chitwood
    M. incognita (Kofoid & White) Chitwood
    M. javanica (Treub) Chitwood
Spiral
    Rotylenchus robustus (de Man) Filipjev
Stunt
    Tylenchorhynchus clarus Allen

NONINFECTIOUS DISEASES, DISORDERS, AND DAMAGE

Ammonium toxicity
    Physiological; excess ammonium levels during cool soil
      temperatures (<10–15°C)
Bird damage
    Brown-headed cowbird (*Molothrus ater* Boddaert)
    Great-tailed grackle (*Quiscalus mexicanus* Gmelin)
    Horned lark (*Eremophila alpestris* L.)
    House finch (*Carpodacus mexicanus* Statius Müller)
    Red-winged blackbird (*Agelaius phoeniceus* L.)
    White-crowned sparrow (*Zonotrichia leucophrys*
      J. R. Forster)
Bolting
    Physiological; prolonged high temperatures (35/25°C,
      day/night)
Brown stain
    Physiological; excess carbon dioxide; occurs postharvest
Cold injury
    Environmental; low temperatures (–2° to 1°C)
Hail injury
    Environmental; hail storm during the early seedling stage
      or just before harvest
Heat injury
    Environmental; high temperatures (>32°C) during seedling
      stages
Herbicide injury
    Chemical; various classes of herbicides used in excess or
      under adverse environmental conditions
Lightning injury
    Environmental; lightning strike at any crop stage
Pink rib
    Physiological; rapid growth and/or higher than optimal
      postharvest storage temperatures (1.1–2.2°C); occurs
      postharvest
Rib discoloration
    Physiological; high temperatures after the onset of heading
Russet spotting
    Physiological; excess ethylene; occurs postharvest

Tipburn
    Physiological; localized calcium deficiency and insufficient
      water uptake, high light intensity, warm tempera-
      tures, and high fertilization rates
Wind injury
    Environmental; wind whipping followed by girdling of
      seedlings or soil particles in the heads at harvest

PARASITIC HIGHER PLANT

Broomrape
    Orobanche cernua Loefl.
    O. crenata Forssk.
    O. minor Sm.
    O. palaestina Reut.
    Phelipanche aegyptiaca (Pers.) Pomel
      (syn. *O. aegyptiaca* Pers.)
    P. ramosa (L.) Pomel
      (syn. *O. ramosa* L.)

PHYTOPLASMA DISEASES

Australian lettuce phyllody
    Faba bean phyllody phytoplasma group
Lettuce phyllody
    Pigeon pea witches'-broom phytoplasma group
Lettuce yellows (Aster yellows)
    '*Candidatus* Phytoplasma asteri'
      (syn. Aster yellows phytoplasma)

VIRUS DISEASES

Alfalfa mosaic
    Genus *Alfamovirus*; *Alfalfa mosaic virus* (AMV)
Beet western yellows
    Genus *Polerovirus*; *Beet western yellows virus* (BWYV)
Beet yellow stunt
    Genus *Closterovirus*; *Beet yellow stunt virus* (BYSV)
Bidens mottle
    Genus *Potyvirus*; *Bidens mottle virus* (BiMoV)
Broad bean wilt
    Genus *Fabavirus*; *Broad bean wilt virus* (BBWV)
Cucumber mosaic
    Genus *Cucumovirus*; *Cucumber mosaic virus* (CMV)
Dandelion yellow mosaic
    Genus *Sequivirus*; *Dandelion yellow mosaic virus*
      (DaYMV)
Impatiens necrotic spot
    Genus *Tospovirus*; *Impatiens necrotic spot virus* (INSV)
Lettuce big vein
    Genus *Ophiovirus*; *Mirafiori lettuce big-vein virus*
      (MLBVV)
    Genus *Varicosavirus*; *Lettuce big-vein associated virus*
      (LBVaV)
Lettuce chlorosis
    Genus *Crinivirus*; *Lettuce chlorosis virus* (LCV)
Lettuce dieback
    Genus *Tombusvirus*; *Tomato bushy stunt virus* (TBSV),
      Moroccan pepper virus (MPV)
Lettuce mosaic
    Genus *Potyvirus*; *Lettuce mosaic virus* (LMV)
Lettuce mottle
    Genus *Sequivirus*; Lettuce mottle virus (LeMoV)
Lettuce necrotic yellows
    Genus *Cytorhabdovirus*; *Lettuce necrotic yellows virus*
      (LNYV)
Sonchus yellow net
    Genus *Nucleorhabdovirus*; *Sonchus yellow net virus*
      (SYNV)
Sowthistle yellow vein
    Genus *Nucleorhabdovirus*; *Sowthistle yellow vein virus*
      (SYVV)

Tobacco rattle
    Genus *Tobravirus; Tobacco rattle virus* (TRV)
Tobacco ringspot
    Genus *Nepovirus; Tobacco ringspot virus* (TRSV)
Tobacco streak
    Genus *Ilarvirus; Tobacco streak virus* (TSV)
Tomato spotted wilt
    Genus *Tospovirus; Tomato spotted wilt virus* (TSWV),
        Groundnut ringspot virus (GRSV), *Impatiens*

necrotic spot virus (INSV), *Tomato chlorotic spot virus* (TCSV)
Turnip mosaic
    Genus *Potyvirus; Turnip mosaic virus* (TuMV)

(Primary collators: K. V. Subbarao, R. M. Davis, R. L. Gilbertson, and R. N. Raid)

Glossary

A—acre

a.i.—active ingredient

C—Celsius or centigrade

cm—centimeter (1 cm = 0.01 m = 0.3937 in.)

F—Fahrenheit

ft-c—foot-candle

g—gram (1 g = 0.03527 oz)

gal—gallon (1 gal liquid (U.S.) = 3.785 L)

h—hour

ha—hectare (1 ha = 2.471 acres)

in.—inch (1 in. = 2.540 cm)

kb—kilobase pair

kg—kilogram (1 kg = 2.205 lb)

L—liter (1 L = 1.057 quarts liquid (U.S.))

lb—pound (1 lb = 453.59 g)

m—meter (1 m = 39.37 in.)

mg—milligram (1 mg = 0.001 g)

min—minute

ml—milliliter (1 ml = 0.001 L)

mm—millimeter (1 mm = 0.001 m = 0.03937 in.)

µg—microgram (1 µg = 10^{-6} g)

µm—micrometer (1 µm = 10^{-6} m)

nm—nanometer (1 nm = 10^{-9} m)

oz—ounce (1 oz = 28.35 g); fluid ounce (1 fl oz (U.S.) = 29.57 ml)

ppm—parts per million

sec—second

abaxial—directed away from the stem of a plant; pertaining to the lower surface of a leaf (*see* adaxial)

abiotic—pertaining to the absence of life, as diseases not caused by living organisms

abscise—to separate from a plant, as leaves, flowers, and fruits do when they fall

abscission—the shedding of leaves or other plant parts as the result of physical weakness in a specialized layer of cells (the abscission layer), which develops at the base of the structure

acervulus (pl. acervuli)—an erumpent, cushionlike fruiting body bearing conidiophores, conidia, and sometimes setae

acid—having a pH less than 7

acid precipitation—precipitation of low pH because of the presence of nitric and sulfuric acid formed by the combination of air pollutants (NO_x and SO_2) with water

acid rain—*see* acid precipitation

acropetal—upward from the base to the apex of a shoot of a plant (*see* basipetal); in fungi, producing spores in succession in the direction of the apex, so that the apical spore is the youngest

acute—with reference to symptoms, developing suddenly (*see* chronic)

adaxial—directed toward the stem of a plant; pertaining to the upper surface of a leaf (*see* abaxial)

adventitious—arising from other than the usual place, as roots from a stem rather than branches of a root

aeciospore—a dikaryotic spore produced in the aecium of a rust fungus; in heteroecious rust fungi, the spore stage that infects the alternate host

aecium (pl. aecia; adj. aecial)—the fruiting body of a rust fungus in which the first dikaryotic spores (aeciospores) are produced

aerial—occurring in air

aerobic—living only in the presence of oxygen

aflatoxin—a chemical by-product of *Aspergillus flavus* and *A. parasiticus* that is harmful to humans and other animals

agar—a jellylike material derived from algae and used to solidify liquid culture media; a medium containing agar

alate—winged (*see* apterous)

albino (n. albinism)—white or light colored; having a marked deficiency in pigmentation

alkaline—having basic (nonacidic) properties; having a pH greater than 7

alkaloid—any of various nitrogen-containing ring compounds produced by plants and having physiological effects on animals

allele—any of one or more alternative forms of a gene

allelopathy (adj. allelopathic)—the ability of one species to inhibit or prevent the growth of another species through the production of one or more toxic substances

alternate host—one of two kinds of plants on which a parasitic fungus (e.g., a rust fungus) must develop to complete its life cycle

alternative host—a plant other than the main host that can be colonized by a parasite but that is not required for completion of the developmental cycle of the parasite

anaerobic—living in the absence of oxygen

anamorph (adj. anamorphic)—the imperfect state or asexual form in the life cycle of certain fungi, producing asexual spores (e.g., conidia) or no spores (*see* holomorph; teleomorph)

anastomosis (pl. anastomoses)—the fusion of branches of the same or different structures (e.g., hyphae) to make a network

annual—a plant that completes its life cycle and dies within one year (*see* biennial; perennial)

antagonist—an organism or substance that counteracts or limits the action of another organism or substance

anterior—situated toward the front or head (*see* posterior)

anther—the pollen-bearing portion of a flower

antheridium (pl. antheridia)—the male sexual organ (male gametangium) of certain fungi

anthesis—the period of the opening of a flower, during which pollination can occur

anthracnose—disease caused by acervuli-forming fungi (order Melanconiales); characterized by sunken lesions and necrosis

antibiotic—any of various chemical compounds produced by microorganisms and killing or inhibiting the growth of other living organisms

antibody—a protein formed in the blood of warm-blooded animals in response to the presence of an antigen

antigen—any foreign chemical (normally, a protein) that induces antibody formation in warm-blooded animals

antiserum (pl. antisera)—blood serum containing an antibody

apex (pl. apices; adj. apical)—the tip of a root or shoot; contains the apical meristem

aphid—any of numerous species of small, sucking insects of the family Aphididae (order Hemiptera) that produce honeydew and injure plants when present in large populations

aplerotic—with reference to oospores, not filling the oogonium

apothecium (pl. apothecia)—open, cuplike or saucerlike, ascus-bearing fruiting body (ascocarp) of ascomycetous fungi; often supported on a stalk

appressed—closely flattened down or pressed against a surface (syn. adpressed)

appressorium (pl. appressoria)—a swollen, flattened portion of a fungal filament that adheres to the surface of a higher plant, providing anchorage for invasion by the fungus

apterous—wingless (*see* alate)

arbuscule (adj. arbuscular)—a branched haustorial structure of certain endomycorrhizal fungi; formed within living cells of the root

arthropod—any member of the phylum Arthropoda, which consists of animals with articulated bodies and limbs, including insects, arachnids, and crustaceans

ascocarp—a sexual fruiting body (e.g., apothecium, ascostroma, cleistothecium, perithecium, pseudothecium) of ascomycetous fungi, producing asci and ascospores (syn. ascoma)

ascogenous—pertaining to ascus-producing hyphae

ascogonium (pl. ascogonia)—a specialized cell that gives rise to hyphae that produce asci

ascoma (pl. ascomata)—*see* ascocarp

ascomycetes (adj. ascomycetous)—a group of fungi in the phylum Ascomycota (kingdom Fungi) characterized by the production of sexual spores (ascospores) within an ascus

ascospore—a sexual spore borne in an ascus

ascostroma (pl. ascostromata)—a fruiting body of ascomycetous fungi containing bitunicate (double-walled) asci in locules (cavities); usually dark and containing multiple locules but sometimes containing only a single locule (*see* pseudothecium)

ascus (pl. asci)—a saclike structure containing ascospores (typically eight) and usually borne in a fruiting body

aseptate—lacking cross-walls (septa); nonseptate; coenocytic

asexual—vegetative; lacking sex organs, gametes, or sexual spores (as in the imperfect or anamorphic stage of a fungus)

asexual reproduction—any type of reproduction not involving the union of gametes and meiosis

asexual stage—the imperfect (anamorphic) stage of certain fungi

attenuate—to narrow; to weaken; to decrease in virulence or pathogenicity

autoecious—with reference to rust fungi, producing all spore forms on one species of host plant (*see* heteroecious)

autotroph—any of various organisms (e.g., plants capable of photosynthesis) that synthesize their nutritive substances from inorganic molecules

avirulent—nonpathogenic; unable to cause disease (*see* virulent)

awn—a bristle-like structure at the apex of the outer bract of some cereal and grass flowers

axenic—culture in the absence of living bacteria or other organisms; pure culture

axil—the angle formed by a leaf petiole and the stem

axillary—pertaining to or placed within an axil

bacilliform—shaped like a short rod with rounded ends

backcross—to cross (mate) an offspring with one of its parents

bactericide—a chemical or physical agent that kills bacteria

bacterium (pl. bacteria)—a prokaryotic, microscopic, single-celled organism having a cell wall and increasing by binary fission

basidiocarp—the sexual fruiting body of fungi in the group basidiomycetes (syn. basidioma)

basidiomycetes (adj. basidiomycetous)—a group of fungi in the phylum Basidiomycota (kingdom Fungi) characterized by the formation of external basidiospores on basidia

basidiospore—a haploid (1n) sexual spore produced on a basidium

basidium (pl. basidia; adj. basidial)—a structure on which basidiospores are produced externally

basipetal—situated down from the apex toward the base of a shoot of a plant; developing in the direction of the base, so that the apical part is oldest (*see* acropetal)

bicellular—two-celled

biennial—a plant that produces seed and dies at the end of its second year of growth (*see* annual; perennial)

binary fission—a type of asexual reproduction in which two cells (usually of similar size and shape) are formed by the growth and division of one cell

binucleate—having two nuclei per cell (*see* multinucleate; uninucleate)

bioassay—any test (assay) using a living organism

biocide—a compound toxic to all forms of life

biological control—exploitation of the natural competition, parasitism, or antagonism of organisms for the management of pests and pathogens (syn. biocontrol)

biotic—pertaining to living organisms; with reference to disease, caused by a living organism

biotroph—an organism that can live and multiply only on another living organism (syn. obligate parasite) (*see* necrotroph)

biotype—a subdivision of a species, subspecies, or race based on some identifiable physiological trait, such as a particular virulence pattern

bitunicate—having two walls

blade—the flat portion of a grass leaf above the sheath

blight—the sudden, severe, and extensive spotting, discoloration, wilting, or destruction of leaves, flowers, stems, or entire plants

blotch—an irregularly shaped, usually superficial spot or blot

botryose—shaped like a bunch of grapes

bract—a reduced leaf associated with a flower or inflorescence; a modified leaf from the axil of which a flower arises

breeding line—a plant strain used in a plant breeding program and usually containing one or more desirable agronomic or breeding characteristics

broadcast application—application of fertilizer by spreading or scattering it on the soil surface

bursa—an extension or flap of cuticle at the side of the male nematode sex organ; used for orienting the body during mating

calcareous—rich in calcium carbonate (lime)

callus—specialized tissue that forms over a wound or cut in a plant (e.g., cork cambium may form, and the cells produced will gradually seal the wound)

canker—a plant disease characterized (in woody plants) by the death of cambium tissue and malformation or loss of bark and (in nonwoody plants) by the formation of sharply delineated, dry, necrotic, localized lesions on the stem; a lesion caused by such a disease, particularly in woody plants

canopy—the expanded leafy top of a plant or plants

capsid—the protective layer of protein surrounding the nucleic acid core of a virus; the protein molecules that make up this layer (syn. coat protein)

carbohydrate—any of various chemical compounds composed of carbon, hydrogen, and oxygen, such as sugars, starches, and cellulose

carpel—the ovule-bearing structure of a flower in angiosperms

catenulate—with reference to the spores of certain fungi, formed in a chain

causal agent—the organism or agent that produces a given disease

chimera, chimaera—a plant or organ consisting of two or more genetically different tissues

chlamydospore—a thick-walled or double-walled, asexual resting spore formed from hyphal cells (terminal or intercalary) or by transformation of conidial cells; functions as an overwintering stage

chlorophyll (adj. chlorophyllous)—any of a group of green pigments found in chloroplasts and critical to photosynthesis

chloroplast—a disk-like structure containing chlorophyll in which photosynthesis occurs in green plants

chlorosis (adj. chlorotic)—the failure of chlorophyll development, caused by disease or a nutritional disturbance; the fading of green plant parts to light green, yellow, or white

chromosome—the structure that contains the genes of an organism (in eukaryotes, chromosomes are in the nucleus and can be visualized with an optical microscope as threads or rods during meiosis and mitosis; in bacteria, the chromosome is usually a single circle of DNA and cannot be visualized with an optical microscope)

chronic—with reference to symptoms, slow-developing, persistent, or recurring (*see* acute)

circulative—with reference to viruses, passing through the gut and circulating in the body of an insect vector before being transmitted to a host

circulative transmission—virus transmission in which the virus must accumulate within or pass through the lymphatic system of an insect vector before it can be transmitted to a plant

cirrhus (pl. cirrhi), cirrus (pl. cirri)—a curled, tendril-like mass of exuded spores held together by a slimy matrix

clamp connection—a bridge- or buckle-like hyphal protrusion in basidiomycetous fungi, formed at cell division and connecting the newly divided cells

clavate—club shaped (syn. claviform)

cleistothecium (pl. cleistothecia)—a spherical ascocarp that is closed at maturity

coalesce—to grow together into one body, as enlarging lesions may join together to form a single spot

coenocytic—having multiple nuclei embedded in cytoplasm without cross-walls; nonseptate

colonize—with reference to plant pathogens, to infect and ramify through plant tissue

colony—a microorganism growing in mass, especially as a pure culture

conidiogenous—producing and bearing conidia

conidiophore—a simple or branched hypha on which conidia are produced

conidium (pl. conidia)—an asexual, nonmotile fungal spore that develops externally or is liberated from the cell that formed it

cortex (adj. cortical)—the region of parenchyma tissue between the epidermis and phloem in stems and roots; the region beneath the rind of a sclerotium

cotyledon—the primary embryonic leaf within the seed, in which nutrients for the new plant are stored (monocots have one cotyledon; dicots have two)

crown—the upper dome of a tree, bearing leaves, flowers, and fruits; the junction of the root and stem of a plant, usually at the soil line; in grafted woody plants, the rootstock portion of the plant near the soil surface

culm—the stem of grasses, cereals, and bamboos

cultivar (abbr. cv.)—a cultivated variety of a plant species, resulting from deliberate genetic manipulation and having recognizable characteristics, such as color; shape of flowers, fruits, and seeds; height; and form (syn. variety)

cultural practices—the methods by which plants are grown (e.g., application of nutrients, irrigation, cultivation, and so forth)

culture—the growth and propagation of microorganisms on nutrient media; the growth and propagation of living plants

cuticle (adj. cuticular)—the noncellular outer layer of an insect or nematode; the water-repellent, waxy layer of epidermal cells of plant parts, such as leaves, stems, and fruits

cyst—in fungi, a resting structure in a protective membrane or shell-like enclosure; in nematodes, the egg-laden carcass of a female nematode; in bacteria, a specialized cell enclosed in a thick wall; often dormant and resistant to environmental conditions

cytoplasm—the living protoplasm in a cell, not including the nucleus

damping-off—the death of a seedling before or shortly after emergence caused by decomposition of the root or lower stem (it is common to distinguish between preemergence and postemergence damping-off)

defoliation—the loss of leaves from a plant, whether normal or premature

dehiscent—opening by breaking into parts

demicyclic—pertaining to the life cycle of rust fungi (e.g., many species of *Gymnosporangium*) that lack the urediniospore (repeating) stage (see macrocyclic; microcyclic)

desiccate—to dry out

diagnostic (n. diagnosis)—pertaining to a distinguishing characteristic important for the identification of a disease or disorder

dichotomous—branching, often successively, into two more or less equal arms

dicot—a dicotyledon, or plant having two cotyledons (see monocot)

dieback (v. die back)—the progressive death of shoots, leaves, or roots, beginning at the tips

differential host—a plant host that develops disease symptoms that distinguish between strains or races of a plant pathogen (syn. differential cultivar)

digitate—having lobes radiating from a common center

dikaryon (adj. dikaryotic)—an organism having two sexually compatible haploid nuclei per cell that divide simultaneously in the reproductive phase called dikaryophase

dilution end point—the stage of a serial dilution of cells or preparations at which growth or infection from a standard sample of the suspension no longer occurs

dimorphic—having two distinct shapes or forms

diploid—having two complete sets of chromosomes (2*n* chromosomes) (see haploid; polyploid)

disease—the abnormal functioning of an organism

disease cycle—the succession of events and interactions among a host, a parasite, and the environment, from initial infection through pathogenesis to overseasoning, until another infection occurs

disinfest—to kill pathogens that have not yet initiated disease or other contaminating microorganisms that occur in or on inanimate objects (e.g., soil or tools) or on the surface of plant parts (e.g., seed)

dispersal—the spread of infectious material (inoculum) from diseased to healthy plants (syn. dissemination)

dissemination—see dispersal

distal—situated away from the point of attachment or origin or away from the main body (see proximal)

DNA—deoxyribonucleic acid; the double-stranded, helical molecule that contains genetic code information; consists of repeating units, or nucleotides, each of which is composed of deoxyribose (a sugar), a phosphate group, and a purine (adenine or guanine) or a pyrimidine (thymine or cytosine) base

dolipore septum—a type of cross-wall in fungi in the group basidiomycetes characterized by distinctive swellings and membranes in association with the septal pore

dominant—pertaining to a phenotypic trait that is expressed in hybrid progeny of diploid organisms even if contributed by only one of the parents (see recessive)

dormancy (adj. dormant)—a condition of suspended growth and reduced metabolism of an organism; generally induced by internal factors or environmental conditions as a mechanism of survival

dormant—resting; living in a state of reduced physiological activity

dorsal—situated toward the back or top of the body (ant. ventral)

dwarfing—underdevelopment of a plant or plant organs caused by disease, inadequate nutrition, or unfavorable environmental conditions

echinulate—having small spines projecting from the cell wall

ecology—the study of the interactions between individual organisms, groups of organisms, and organisms and their environments

ectoparasite—a parasite that feeds from the exterior of its host (see endoparasite)

ectotrophic—pertaining to fungal development primarily over the root surface

edema, oedema—blisters produced on leaves or other plant parts under conditions of high moisture and restricted transpiration (syn. intumescence)

effuse (adj.)—stretched out, especially with reference to a film-like growth

egg mass—a group of eggs held together by a gelatinous matrix

ELISA—enzyme-linked immunosorbent assay; a serological test in which the sensitivity of the reaction is increased by attaching an enzyme that produces a colored product in response to one of the reactants

ellipsoidal—elliptical in the plane section

embryo—an organism in the early stages of development, such as a young plant in the seed or a nematode before hatching from the egg

emergence—the growth of a seedling shoot through the surface of the soil

enation—an abnormal outgrowth from the surface of a stem or leaf

encapsidate—to enclose viral nucleic acid in a protein coat

encyst—to form a cyst or protective covering

endemic—native to a particular place; pertaining to a low and steady level of natural disease occurrence

endocarp—the inner layer of a fruit wall (see pericarp)

endoconidium (pl. endoconidia)—a conidium produced inside a hypha or conidiophore

endodermis—the layer of cells between the vascular tissue and the cortex of roots

endogenous—arising from inside (see exogenous)

endoparasite—a parasite that lives and feeds inside its host (see ectoparasite)

endophyte—a plant developing inside another organism; any of the various endoparasitic fungi associated with grass species

endosperm—the nutritive tissue formed within the embryo sac of seed plants

enzyme—a protein that catalyzes a specific biochemical reaction

enzyme-linked immunosorbent assay (ELISA)—a serological test in which the sensitivity of the reaction is increased by attaching an enzyme that produces a colored product in response to one of the reactants

epicotyl—the portion of the stem of a plant embryo or seedling above the node where the cotyledons are attached (see hypocotyl)

epidemic—an increase of disease in a population; a general and serious outbreak of disease (see epiphytotic)

epidemiology (adj. epidemiological)—the study of factors influencing the initiation, development, and spread of infectious disease; the study of disease in populations

epidermis (adj. epidermal)—the surface layer of cells of leaves and other plant parts

epinasty—the abnormal downward curling of a leaf, leaf part, or stem

epiphyllous—located on the upper surface of a leaf

epiphyte—an organism growing on a plant surface but not as a parasite

epiphytotic—pertaining to the widespread and destructive outbreak of a plant disease

eradicant—a chemical used to eliminate a pathogen from a host or environment

eradication—the control of plant disease by eliminating the pathogen after it has become established or by eliminating the plants that carry the pathogen

erumpent—bursting or erupting through the surface of a substrate

ethylene—a plant hormone influencing vegetative growth, fruit ripening, abscission of plant parts, and senescence of flowers

etiolation—the elongation of stems caused by low levels of light intensity

etiology—the study of the causes of diseases

eukaryote (adj. eukaryotic)—any of various organisms whose cells contain a membrane-bound nucleus and other organelles, including all higher plants, animals, fungi, and protists (*see* prokaryote)

exogenous—originating from the outside (*see* endogenous)

extracellular—not occurring or located within a cell

exudate—a liquid excreted by or discharged from diseased tissues, roots, leaves, and fungi

f. sp. (pl. ff. spp.)—*forma specialis* (pl. *formae speciales*); a taxonomic group within a pathogenic species, defined by its host range (members of different *formae speciales* infect different groups of plants)

facultative—capable of changing lifestyle (e.g., from saprophytic to parasitic or the reverse)

facultative parasite—an organism that is normally saprophytic but capable of living as a parasite

facultative saprophyte—an organism that is normally parasitic but capable of living as a saprophyte

fallow—pertaining to cultivated land kept free from a crop or weeds during the normal growing season

fasciation—the malformation of shoots or floral organs manifested as enlargement and flattening, as if several parts were fused

fascicle (adj. fasciculate)—a small group, bundle, or cluster

fastidious—with reference to prokaryotic organisms, having special requirements for growth and nutrition

feeder root—a fine root that absorbs water and dissolved nutrients

filament (adj. filamentous)—a thin, flexible, threadlike structure

filamentous—threadlike (syn. filiform)

filiform—long, needlelike (syn. filamentous)

flaccid—wilted; lacking turgor

flagellum (pl. flagella)—a hairlike, whiplike, or tinsel-like appendage of a motile cell, bacterium, or zoospore that provides locomotion

fleck—a minute, discolored spot in green tissue

flexuous—having turns or windings; capable of bending

focus (pl. foci)—a small area of diseased plants within a larger plot or field

foliar—pertaining to leaves

forma specialis (pl. *formae speciales*)—a taxonomic group within a pathogenic species, defined by its host range (members of different *formae speciales* infect different groups of plants); abbr. f. sp. (pl. ff. spp.)

fructification—any of the various spore-bearing organs formed by macro- and microfungi

fruiting body—any of the various complex, spore-bearing structures of fungi

fumigant (v. fumigate)—a gas or volatile substance used to kill or inhibit the growth of microorganisms or other pests

Fungi Imperfecti—a group of fungi lacking a sexual stage; a group comprising the asexual stages of fungi in the groups ascomycetes and basidiomycetes (syn. deuteromycetes)

fungicide (adj. fungicidal)—a chemical or physical agent that kills or inhibits the growth of fungi

fungistat (adj. fungistatic)—a compound that inhibits fungal growth or sporulation but does not kill fungi

fusiform—spindle shaped; tapering at each end

gall—an abnormal swelling or localized outgrowth, often roughly spherical, produced by a plant as a result of attack by a fungus, bacterium, nematode, insect, or other organism (syn. tumor)

gametangium (pl. gametangia)—a cell containing gametes or nuclei that act as gametes

gamete—sex cell

gelatinous—resembling gelatin or jelly

gene—a unit located on a chromosome and controlling the transmission of a heritable characteristic

genetic—pertaining to heredity or heritable characteristics

genetically modified organism (GMO)—an organism possessing a gene from another species; having been the subject of genetic engineering

geniculate—bent, like a knee

genome—the complete genetic information of an organism or virus

genotype—the genetic constitution of an individual or group; a class or group of individuals sharing a specific genetic makeup (*see* phenotype)

genus (pl. genera)—a taxonomic category that consists of species that are closely related structurally or phylogenetically (the genus or generic name is the first name in a Latin binomial)

germ tube—a hypha resulting from an outgrowth of the spore wall and cytoplasm after germination

germinate (n. germination)—to begin growth, as of a seed, spore, sclerotium, or other reproductive body

germplasm—the bearer of heredity material (often loosely applied to cultivars and breeding lines)

giant cell—an enlarged, multinucleate cell formed in a root by repeated nuclear division without cell division; induced by secretions of certain sedentary plant-parasitic nematodes

girdle—to circle and cut through a stem or the bark and outer few rings of wood, disrupting the phloem and xylem

globose—nearly spherical

graft transmission—the transmission of a pathogen from one host plant to another through fusion of living tissue from the diseased host with living tissue of a healthy host

gram-negative bacteria—bacteria that are stained red or pink after treatment with Gram's stain

gram-positive bacteria—bacteria that are stained violet or purple after treatment with Gram's stain

gravid—containing an egg or eggs; capable of depositing eggs

guttation—the exudation of watery, sticky liquid from hydathodes, especially along leaf margins

haploid—having a single complete set of chromosomes (*see* diploid; polyploid)

hardiness—the ability to withstand stress

haulm—stem or stalks, collectively

haustorium (pl. haustoria)—a specialized branch of a parasite formed inside a host cell to absorb nutrients

herbaceous—pertaining to primary, soft, nonwoody tissue of a plant or plant part; having the characteristics of an herb

herbicide—any of various chemicals that kill plants or inhibit their growth (e.g., a weed or grass killer)

hermaphrodite (adj. hermaphroditic)—having both male and female reproductive organs in a single individual

heteroecious—with reference to rust fungi, passing different stages of the life cycle on alternate hosts (*see* autoecious)

heterokaryon (adj. heterokaryotic)—a cell with genetically different nuclei

heterothallism (adj. heterothallic)—a fungal life cycle in which sexual reproduction can occur only in the presence of genetically different mycelia (*see* homothallism)

heterozygous—having the same form (allele) of a gene on different chromosomes (*see* homozygous)

holomorph—a fungus having sexual and asexual forms in its life cycle, considered in all its forms (*see* anamorph; teleomorph)

homothallism (adj. homothallic)—a fungal life cycle in which sexual reproduction occurs in a single, self-fertile thallus (*see* heterothallism)

homozygous—having the same form (allele) of a gene on homologous chromosomes (*see* heterozygous)

honeydew—a sugary ooze or exudate often secreted by aphids; a characteristic symptom of ergot

host plant—a living plant attacked by or harboring a parasite or pathogen, from which the invader obtains part or all of its nourishment

host range—the range of plants on which an organism (particularly a parasite) feeds

hull—the outer coat of a seed

hyaline—transparent or nearly so; translucent; colorless

hybrid (v. hybridize)—the offspring of two individuals of different genotypes

hydathode—an epidermal leaf structure specialized for the secretion or exudation of water; the opening at the terminus of a leaf vein

hymenium—the continuous, spore-bearing layer of a fungal fruiting body

hyperplasia (adj. hyperplastic)—an abnormal increase in the number of cells, often resulting in the formation of galls or tumors

hypersensitive—extremely or excessively sensitive, often with reference to an extreme reaction to a pathogen

hypertrophy (adj. hypertrophic)—an abnormal increase in the size of cells in a tissue or organ, often resulting in the formation of galls or tumors

hypha (pl. hyphae; adj. hyphal)—a tubular filament of a fungal thallus or mycelium; the basic structural unit of a fungus

hypocotyl—the portion of the stem below the cotyledons and above the root (*see* epicotyl)

icosahedral (n. icosahedron)—having 20 faces, like polyhedral virus particles (*see* isometric)

immune—not capable of being infected by a given pathogen

immunogenic—able to induce the production of antibodies

imperfect state—the anamorph, or asexual form in the life cycle of certain fungi, in which asexual spores (e.g., conidia) or no spores are produced (*see* perfect state)

in vitro—in glass, on an artificial medium, or in an artificial environment; not within a living host

in vivo—within a living organism

inclusion body—a structure developed within a plant cell as a result of infection by a virus; often useful in identifying the virus

indicator plant—a plant in which specific or distinctive symptoms develop in reaction to a pathogen or certain environmental conditions; used to detect or identify the pathogen or determine the effects of the environmental conditions

infection—the process in which an organism enters, invades, or penetrates and establishes a parasitic relationship with a host plant

infection court—a site in or on a host plant where infection can occur

infection cushion—an organized mass of hyphae formed on the surface of a plant and producing numerous infective hyphae

infection focus—the initial site of infection, generally with reference to a population of plants

infection peg—the specialized, narrow hyphal strand located on the underside of an appressorium and penetrating host cells (syn. penetration peg)

infectious—with reference to disease, capable of spreading from plant to plant

infective—able to attack a host and cause infection; with reference to vectors, carrying or containing a pathogen and able to transfer it to a host plant

infest (n. infestation)—to attack as a pest (used especially for insects and nematodes); to contaminate (as with microorganisms); to be present in large numbers

inflorescence—a flower or flower cluster

initial inoculum—inoculum (usually from an overwintering source) that initiates disease in the field, as opposed to inoculum that spreads disease during the growing season (syn. primary inoculum)

injury—damage caused by transitory interaction with an agent such as an insect, chemical, or unfavorable environmental condition

inoculate (n. inoculation)—to place inoculum in an infection court; to insert a pathogen into healthy tissue

inoculum (pl. inocula)—a pathogen or its parts capable of causing infection when transferred to a favorable location

inoculum density—a measure of the number of propagules of a pathogenic organism per unit of area or volume

intercalary—inserted within (e.g., located along a hypha, as opposed to located at the end of a hypha)

intercellular—between or among cells

intercrop—to grow two or more crops simultaneously on the same area of land

internode (adj. internodal)—the portion of a stem between two successive nodes

interveinal—between veins (of a leaf)

intracellular—through or within cells

intumescence—blisters produced on leaves or other plant parts under conditions of high moisture and restricted transpiration (syn. edema)

isolate—(n.) a culture or subpopulation of a microorganism separated from its parent population and maintained under controlled conditions; (v.) to remove from soil or host material and grow in pure culture

isometric—with reference to virus particles, having an icosahedral structure and thus appearing approximately round

juvenile—an immature form that appears similar to the adult stage but is usually smaller and is not sexually mature, as in nematodes or insect species that undergo gradual metamorphosis

knot—a gall or localized abnormal swelling

lamina—the expanded part of a leaf (*see* petiole)

land race—a locally developed strain of a plant

larva (pl. larvae)—the immature wormlike or caterpillar stage in the life cycle of an insect that undergoes complete metamorphosis

latent—present but not manifested or visible, as a symptomless infection

latent infection—an infection that does not have visible symptoms

latent period—the time elapsed between infection and the appearance of symptoms or production of new inoculum (sometimes synonymous with incubation period); the time elapsed after the acquisition of a pathogen by a vector but before the pathogen can be transmitted

leaf spot—a lesion typically restricted in development after reaching a characteristic size

leafhopper—any of various species of mobile insects with sucking mouthparts in the order Hemiptera

leaflet—one of the separate blades or divisions of a compound leaf

legume—a simple, dry, dehiscent fruit developing from a simple pistil and splitting at maturity along two seams; any plant in the family Fabaceae (formerly Leguminosae)

lenticel—a natural opening in the surface of a stem, tuber, fruit, or root, permitting gas exchange

lenticular—lens shaped (convex on both faces)

lesion—a localized diseased area or wound

life cycle—the cyclical stages in the growth and development of an organism

lignin—a complex organic substance or group of substances that impregnate the cell walls of xylem vessels and certain other plant cells; constituting wood

local lesion—a small, restricted lesion; often the characteristic reaction of a differential cultivar to a specific pathogen, especially in response to mechanical inoculation with a virus

lodge—with reference to hay or grain crops, to fall over

lumen (pl. lumina)—the central cavity of a cell or other structure

macerate—to cause disintegration of tissues by separation of cells; to soften by soaking

macroconidium (pl. macroconidia)—the larger of two kinds of conidia formed by certain fungi (*see* microconidium)

macrocyclic—pertaining to the life cycle of rust fungi that typically exhibit all five spore stages (pycniospores, aeciospores, urediniospores, teliospores, and basidiospores) in the course of their development (*see* demicyclic; microcyclic)

manual transmission—the spread or introduction of inoculum to an infection court by hand

mating types—compatible strains (usually designated + and − or A and B), both of which are necessary for sexual reproduction in heterothallic fungi

mechanical injury—injury of a plant part by abrasion, mutilation, or wounding

mechanical transmission—the spread or introduction of inoculum to an infection court by human manipulation, accompanied by physical disruption of host tissues (wounding)

medium (pl. media)—a mixture of organic or inorganic chemical compounds and water providing the nutrients needed for the growth of a microorganism in vitro; with reference to higher plants, a mixture of fertilizers and other components in which plants are grown

meiosis—nuclear division in which the number of chromosomes per nucleus is halved (i.e., the diploid state is converted to the haploid state) (*see* mitosis)

melanin (adj. melanoid)—a brown-black pigment

meristem (adj. meristematic)—plant tissue characterized by frequent cell division, producing cells that become differentiated into specialized tissues

meristem culture—an aseptic culture of a plant or plant part from a portion of the meristem

mesophyll—the central, internal, nonvascular tissue of leaves, consisting of the palisade and spongy mesophyll

messenger RNA (abbr. mRNA)—a form of RNA that carries information to direct the synthesis of protein

metabasidium—the part of the basidium in which meiosis occurs

metabolite—any chemical participating in metabolism; a nutrient

microclimate—weather conditions on a small scale, as at the surface of a plant or within a field

microconidium (pl. microconidia)—the smaller of two kinds of conidia formed by certain fungi (*see* macroconidium)

microcyclic—pertaining to the life cycle of rust fungi that produce only teliospores and basidiospores (*see* demicyclic; macrocyclic)

microflora—the combination of all of the microorganisms in a particular environment

microorganism—an organism small enough that it can be seen only with the aid of a microscope (syn. microbe)

microsclerotium (pl. microsclerotia)—a microscopic, dense aggregate of darkly pigmented, thick-walled hyphal cells

middle lamella—the layer between the walls of adjacent plant cells; consists largely of pectic substances

midrib—the central, thickened vein of a leaf

migratory—moving from place to place on a plant or from plant to plant when feeding (*see* sedentary)

mildew—a thin coating of mycelial growth and spores on the surfaces of infected plant parts

mitochondrion (pl. mitochondria)—a cellular organelle outside the nucleus; functions in respiration

mitosis—nuclear division in which the number of chromosomes per nucleus remains the same (*see* meiosis)

MLO—mycoplasmalike organism (*see* phytoplasma)

mold—any microfungus with conspicuous, profuse, or woolly superficial growth (mycelium or spore masses) on various substrates; commonly grow on damp or decaying matter and on the surfaces of plant tissues, especially with reference to economically important saprobes

mollicute—any of a group of prokaryotic organisms bounded by a flexuous membrane and lacking a cell wall (*see* phytoplasma; spiroplasma)

molt—to shed a cuticle or body encasement during a phase of growth

monocot—a monocotyledon, or a plant having only one cotyledon, such as species of grasses, including grain crops and corn (*see* dicot)

monoculture—the cultivation of plants of the same species in close proximity and with few or no other plant species present

monoecious—having male and female reproductive organs on a single individual

monogenic—determined by a single gene (*see* polygenic)

morphology (adj. morphological)—the study of the form of organisms; the form and structure of organisms

mosaic—a disease symptom characterized by nonuniform coloration, with intermingled normal, light-green and yellowish patches; usually caused by a virus (often used interchangeably with mottle)

motile—capable of self-propulsion by means of flagella, cilia, or amoeboid movement

mottle—a disease symptom characterized by light and dark areas in an irregular pattern; usually caused by a virus (often used interchangeably with mosaic)

mucilaginous—viscous; slimy

mulch—a layer of material, such as organic matter or plastic film, applied to the surface of the soil for purposes such as retention of water and inhibition of weeds

multinucleate—having more than one nucleus per cell (*see* binucleate; uninucleate)

multiseptate—having many septa (cross-walls)

muriform—having transverse and longitudinal septa

mutation—an abrupt heritable or genetic change in a gene or individual as a result of an alteration in a gene or chromosome or an increase in chromosome number

mycelium (pl. mycelia; adj. mycelial)—the mass of hyphae constituting the body (thallus) of a fungus

mycoparasite—a fungus that attacks another fungus

mycoplasmalike organism (abbr. MLO)—*see* phytoplasma

mycorrhiza (pl. mycorrhizae; adj. mycorrhizal)—a symbiotic association between a nonpathogenic or weakly pathogenic fungus and the roots of a plant

mycotoxin—any poisonous compound produced by a fungus

necrosis (adj. necrotic)—the death of cells or tissue; usually accompanied by blackening or browning

necrotroph—a parasite that typically kills and obtains its energy from dead host cells (*see* biotroph)

needle cast—a disease of conifers that causes the needles to fall

nematicide—an agent that kills nematodes; usually a chemical

nematode—any of various unsegmented roundworms (animals) that is parasitic on plants or animals or free living in soil or water

node (adj. nodal)—the enlarged portion of a shoot at which leaves or buds arise

nodule—a small knot or irregular, rounded lump; with reference to leguminous plants, a structure located on the root and containing nitrogen-fixing bacteria

noninfectious disease—a disease caused by an abiotic agent and not capable of being transmitted from plant to plant

nonpersistent transmission—virus transmission in which a virus is acquired and transmitted by a vector after a short feeding time and retained by the vector for only a short time (syn. stylet-borne transmission)

nonseptate—lacking cross-walls; coenocytic

nymph—the juvenile stage in the life cycle of an insect with incomplete metamorphosis; superficially resembles the adult

obclavate—shaped like an upside-down club

obligate parasite—an organism that can grow only as a parasite in association with its host plant and cannot be grown in artificial culture media (syn. biotroph)

obovoid—shaped like an upside-down egg

obtuse—rounded or blunt; pertaining to an angle greater than 90°

oedema—*see* edema

oogonium (pl. oogonia)—a female gametangium of fungi in the group oomycetes containing one or more gametes

oomycetes (adj. oomycetous)—a group of fungus-like organisms in the phylum Oomycota (kingdom Chromista); typically has nonseptate mycelium, asexual sporangia and zoospores, and sexual oospores

oospore—the thick-walled, sexually derived resting spore of organisms in the group oomycetes

ooze—a mass of bacterial cells mixed with host fluids

organelle—any of various membrane-bound structures contained within cells and having a specialized function (e.g., mitochondria and chloroplasts)

ostiole (adj. ostiolate)—a pore; the opening in the papilla or neck of a perithecium, pseudothecium, or pycnidium through which spores are released

ovary—the female reproductive structure of an organism; in plants, the enlarged basal portion of the pistil, containing the ovules and developing into the fruit

overseason—to survive or persist from one planting season to the next

oversummer—to survive or persist through the summer

overwinter—to survive or persist through the winter

oviposit—to deposit or lay eggs with an ovipositor

ovule—an enclosed structure that after fertilization becomes a seed; an egg contained within an ovary

ozone—a highly reactive form of oxygen (O_3) injurious to plants

palisade parenchyma—the tissue located beneath the upper epidermis of leaves; composed of elongate, tubular cells arranged upright in the manner of posts in a palisade fortification

papilla (pl. papillae; adj. papillate)—a small, blunt projection

paraphysis (pl. paraphyses)—a hairlike cell within a fungal fruiting structure

parasexual—pertaining to the recombination of genetic characters without a sexual process

parasite (adj. parasitic)—an organism that lives in intimate association with another organism, on which it depends for its nutrition; not necessarily a pathogen

parenchyma (adj. parenchymatous)—the soft tissue of living plant cells with undifferentiated, thin, cellulose walls

parthenogenesis (adj. parthenogenetic)—reproduction by the development of an unfertilized egg

pasteurization—the process by which a material (usually a liquid) is treated with heat to eliminate selected harmful microorganisms

pathogen (adj. pathogenic)—a disease-producing organism or agent

pathogenesis—the initiation and development of disease

pathogenicity—the ability to cause disease

pathology—the study of diseases

pathotype—a subdivision of a pathogenic species characterized by its pattern of virulence or avirulence to differential host varieties

pathovar (abbr. pv.)—a subdivision of a plant-pathogenic bacterial species, defined by its host range (a pathovar of a bacterial species is analogous to a *forma specialis* of a fungal species)

pedicel—a small, slender stalk; a stalk bearing an individual flower, inflorescence, or spore

peduncle—the stalk or main stem of an inflorescence; part of an inflorescence or fructification

penetration—the initial invasion of a host by a pathogen

penetration peg—the specialized, narrow hyphal strand located on the underside of an appressorium and penetrating host cells (syn. infection peg)

perennial—a plant that survives for several to many years (*see* annual; biennial)

perfect—sexual; capable of sexual reproduction

perfect flower—a flower possessing both stamens and pistils

perfect state—the teleomorph, or sexual form in the life cycle of certain fungi (*see* imperfect state)

pericarp—the outer layer of a seed or fruit (*see* endocarp)

perithecium (pl. perithecia)—the flask-shaped or subglobose, thin-walled fruiting body (ascocarp) of an ascomycetous fungus, containing asci and ascospores and having a pore (ostiole) at its apex, through which ascospores are expelled or released

peritrichous—having hairs or flagella distributed over the whole surface

persistent transmission—virus transmission in which a virus is acquired and transmitted by a vector after a relatively long feeding time and remains transmissible for a prolonged period while in association with the vector (syn. circulative transmission)

pest—any organism that damages plants or plant products

pesticide—any of various chemicals used to control pests

petiole—the stalk portion of a leaf (*see* lamina)

pH—the negative logarithm of the effective hydrogen ion concentration; a measure of acidity (pH 7 is neutral; values less than pH 7 are acidic, and values greater than pH 7 are alkaline)

phenotype—the composite of observable physical qualities of an organism produced by the interaction of its genotype with the environment

phialide—the end cell of a conidiophore with one or more open ends, through which a basipetal succession of conidia develops

phialospore—a conidium produced on a phialide

phloem—the food-conducting, food-storing tissue in the vascular system of roots, stems, and leaves

photochemical oxidant—any of various highly reactive compounds formed by the action of sunlight on less toxic precursors

photosynthate—a chemical product of photosynthesis

photosynthesis—the manufacture of carbohydrates from carbon dioxide and water in the presence of chlorophylls; uses light energy and releases oxygen

phycomycete—an obsolete term for any member of a group of fungi that lacks cross-walls (septa) in its mycelium

phyllody—a disorder in which floral organs are transformed into leaf-like structures

phyllotaxy—the arrangement of leaves on a stem in relation to one another

physiological race—a group of individuals belonging to the same species and differing from other members of the species in their behavior or other characteristics but not in morphology; a physiological form

phytoalexin—any of various substances produced by higher plants in response to chemical, physical, or biological stimuli and inhibiting the growth of certain microorganisms

phytopathology—the study of plant diseases (syn. plant pathology)

phytoplasma—any of various plant-parasitic pleomorphic mollicutes (prokaryotes lacking cell walls) found in phloem tissue and not capable of growth on artificial nutrient media (previously called mycoplasmalike organisms (MLOs))

phytotoxic—harmful to plants; usually with reference to chemicals

pigment—a colored compound, such as chlorophyll, in the cells of plants or fungi

pinnate—featherlike; having parts arranged along two sides of an axis

pistil—the ovule-bearing organ of a plant, consisting of the ovary and its appendages (e.g., the style and stigma)

pith—parenchymatous tissue occupying the center of a stem

plant pathology—the study of plant diseases (syn. phytopathology)

plasmodium (pl. plasmodia)—a naked multinucleate mass of protoplasm moving and feeding in amoeboid fashion

pleomorphic—able to assume various shapes and perhaps sizes; having a life cycle characterized by a succession of distinctly different forms

plumule—a rudimentary shoot of the plant embryo

polar—located at one end (pole) of the cell

pollen—male sex cells produced by the anthers of flowering plants or the cones of seed plants

pollination—the transfer of pollen from anther to stigma or from a staminate cone to an ovulate cone

polygenic—pertaining to or governed by many genes (*see* monogenic)

polyploid—having three or more complete sets of chromosomes (*see* haploid; diploid)

positive-sense RNA—RNA that can serve directly as messenger RNA

posterior—situated toward the back or tail (*see* anterior)

predispose (n. predisposition)—to make prone to infection and disease

primary inoculum—inoculum (usually from an overwintering source) that initiates disease in the field, as opposed to inoculum that spreads disease during the season (syn. initial inoculum)

primary leaf—the first true leaf that emerges from a plant following the cotyledons

primary root—a root that develops directly from the radicle of an embryo rather than from a crown or node

prokaryote (adj. prokaryotic)—any of various organisms lacking internal membrane-bound organelles and a distinct nucleus, such as bacteria and mollicutes (*see* eukaryote)

promycelium (pl. promycelia)—in rust and smut fungi, a germ tube issuing from a teliospore and bearing basidiospores

propagative virus—a virus that multiplies within its arthropod vector

propagule—any part of an organism capable of independent growth

protectant—an agent (usually a chemical) applied to a plant surface in advance of exposure to a pathogen for the purpose of preventing infection

protein—any of numerous nitrogen-containing organic compounds containing combinations of amino acids

protoplasm—the living contents of a cell

protoplast—the living contents of a cell, exclusive of the cell wall

proximal—situated toward or near the point of attachment or main body (*see* distal)

pseudothecium (pl. pseudothecia)—a perithecium-like fruiting body containing asci and ascospores dispersed rather than in an organized hymenium; an ascostroma with a single locule (cavity) containing bitunicate asci

pupa (pl. pupae; v. pupate)—the quiescent stage between the larval and adult stages of certain insects

pustule—a small, blister-like elevation of the plant epidermis that forms as spores emerge

pv.—pathovar; a subdivision of a plant-pathogenic bacterial species defined by its host range (a pathovar of a bacterial species is analogous to a *forma specialis* of a fungal species)

pycnidiospore—a spore (conidium) produced in a pycnidium

pycnidium (pl. pycnidia)—an asexual, globose or flask-shaped fruiting body of certain imperfect fungi, producing conidia

pycniospore—a haploid, sexually derived spore formed in the pycnium of a rust fungus (syn. spermatium)

pycnium (pl. pycnia)—the globose or flask-shaped haploid fruiting body of rust fungi, bearing receptive hyphae and pycniospores (syn. spermagonium)

pyriform—pear shaped

quarantine—an enforced isolation imposed to prevent the spread of disease; pertaining to plant disease, control of the transport of plants or plant parts to prevent the spread of pests or pathogens

quiescent—dormant; inactive

race—a subgroup or biotype within a species or variety that is distinguished from other races by virulence, symptom expression, or host range but not by morphology

rachis—the elongated main axis of an inflorescence

radicle—the part of the plant embryo that develops into the primary root

receptacle—the structure of a flower that bears the reproductive organs

receptive hypha—in rust fungi, the part of a pycnium (spermagonium) that receives the nucleus of a pycniospore (spermatium)

recessive—pertaining to a phenotypic trait that is expressed in the progeny of diploid organisms only if contributed by both parents (*see* dominant)

reniform—kidney shaped

resinosis—the exudation of resin

resistant (n. resistance)—possessing properties that prevent or impede disease development (*see* susceptible)

respiration—a series of chemical reactions that make energy available through oxidation of carbohydrates and fat

resting spore—a spore (often thick walled) that can remain alive in a dormant state for some time, germinating later and capable of initiating infection

reticulate—having netlike markings

Rhizobium—a genus of bacteria that live symbiotically with roots of leguminous plants, converting atmospheric nitrogen into a form useable by the plants

Rhizobium **nodules**—root galls caused by *Rhizobium* spp.

rhizome—a mostly horizontal, jointed, fleshy, often elongated, usually underground stem

rhizomorph—a macroscopic ropelike strand of compacted tissue formed by certain fungi

rhizosphere—the microenvironment in the soil immediately around a plant's roots

ribosome—a subcellular protoplasmic particle made up of one or more RNA molecules and several proteins; involved in protein synthesis

ring spot—a disease symptom characterized by yellowish or necrotic rings enclosing green tissue, as in some plant diseases caused by viruses

RNA—ribonucleic acid; any of several nucleic acids composed of repeating units of ribose (a sugar), a phosphate group, and a purine (adenine or guanine) or a pyrimidine (uracil or cytosine) base, transcribed from DNA and involved in translation to proteins

rogue—to remove and destroy individual plants that are diseased, infested by insects, or otherwise undesirable

root cap—a group of cells that protects the growing tip of a root

root hair—a threadlike, single-celled outgrowth from a root epidermal cell

rosette—a disease symptom characterized by short, bunchy growth habit caused by a shortening of internodes with no comparable reduction in leaf size

rot—softening, discoloration, and often disintegration of plant tissue as a result of fungal or bacterial infection

rotation—the practice of growing different kinds of crops in succession in the same field

rugose—wrinkled; roughened

runner—a slender, horizontal stem that grows close to the soil surface (syn. stolon)

runner plants—new plants produced asexually on a runner (stolon)

russet—a brownish, roughened area on the skin of fruit, resulting from cork formation

rust—any of several diseases caused by specialized fungi in the group basidiomycetes, some of the spores of which are a rusty color

sanitation—the destruction or removal of infected or infested plants or plant parts; the decontamination of tools, equipment, containers, work space, hands, and so on

saprobe—*see* saprophyte

saprophyte (adj. saprophytic)—an organism that obtains nourishment from nonliving organic matter (syn. saprobe)

satellite virus—a virus that accompanies another virus and depends on it for its multiplication

scab—a roughened, crust-like diseased area on the surface of a plant organ

scald—a necrotic condition in which tissue is usually bleached and has the appearance of having been exposed to high temperature

sclerenchyma (adj. sclerenchymatous)—tissue made up of thick-walled plant cells

sclerotium (pl. sclerotia)—a vegetative, resting body of a fungus composed of a compact mass of hyphae with or without included host tissue; usually has a darkened rind

scorch—a symptom that suggests the action of flame or fire on the affected tissue, often at the margins of leaves

scutellum (adj. scutellar)—the cotyledon of a grass embryo

secondary infection—an infection resulting from the spread of infectious material from a primary or secondary infection without an intervening inactive period

secondary inoculum—inoculum produced by an infection established earlier in the same growing season

secondary organism—an organism that multiplies in already diseased tissue but is not the primary pathogen

secondary root—a branch of a primary root

sedentary—remaining in a fixed location (*see* migratory)

seed—a ripened ovule consisting of an embryo and stored food enclosed by a seed coat

seed treatment—the application of a biological agent, chemical substance, or physical treatment to seed to protect the seed or resulting plant from pathogens or to stimulate germination or plant growth

seedborne—carried on or in seed

selective medium—a culture medium containing substances that inhibit or prevent the growth of certain species of microorganisms

senesce (adj. senescent; n. senescence)—to decline, as with maturation, age, or disease stress

sepal—one of the modified leaves composing a calyx

septate—having septa (cross-walls)

septum (pl. septa; adj. septate)—a dividing wall; in fungi, a cross-wall

serology (adj. serological)—a method using the specificity of the antigen–antibody reaction for the detection and identification of antigenic substances and the organisms that carry them

sessile—with reference to leaves, leaflets, flowers, florets, fruits, ascocarps, basidiocarps, and so on, lacking a stalk, petiole, pedicel, stipe, or stem; with reference to nematodes, permanently attached and not capable of moving about

seta (pl. setae)—a bristle- or hairlike structure, usually deep yellow or brown and thick walled

sexual spore—a spore produced during the sexual cycle of a fungus

sheath—the lower part of a grass leaf, which clasps the culm; a membranous cover

shot hole—a symptom in which small lesions on a leaf fall out, giving the leaf the appearance of being hit by buckshot

sieve element—a tube-shaped living cell in the phloem, functioning in the transport of dissolved organic substances in the plant (syn. sieve tube element)

sign—an indication of disease from direct observation of a pathogen or its parts on a host plant (*see* symptom)

sinuous—having curves, bends, or turns

slime molds—saprophytic organisms in the class Myxomycetes forming vegetative amoeboid plasmodia and spores

soft rot—a mushy disintegration of fleshy fruit or vegetables as a result of bacterial or fungal infection

soil drench—the application of a solution or suspension of a chemical to the soil, especially a pesticide to control soilborne pathogens

soilborne—carried on or beneath the soil surface

solarization—a disease management practice in which soil is covered with polyethylene sheeting to increase heating by sunlight and thus control soilborne plant pathogens

sooty mold—black, nonparasitic, superficial fungal growth; often develops on honeydew produced by aphids and other phloem-feeding insects

sorus (pl. sori)—a compact fruiting structure, especially with reference to spore masses of rust and smut fungi

sp. (pl. spp.)—species (the singular and plural abbreviations are used only after genus names; the singular form is used to refer to an undetermined species, and the plural form is used to refer to two or more species without naming them individually)

spermagonium (pl. spermagonia)—a structure in which male reproductive cells are produced; in rust fungi, the pycnium, a globose or flask-shaped haploid fruiting body composed of receptive hyphae and spermatia (pycniospores)

spermatium (pl. spermatia)—a male sex cell; a nonmotile male gamete; a haploid male gamete; in rust fungi, a pycniospore

spicule—the copulatory organ of a male nematode

spikelet—the spike-like appendage comprised of one or more reduced flowers and associated bracts; a unit of inflorescence in grasses; a small spike

spiroplasma—any of various spiral-shaped, plant-pathogenic mollicutes (prokaryotes lacking cell walls)

sporangiophore—the sporangium-bearing body of a fungus

sporangiospore—a nonmotile, asexual spore borne in a sporangium

sporangium (pl. sporangia)—a saclike fungal structure, the entire contents of which are converted into an indefinite number of asexual spores

spore—the reproductive structure of fungi and some other organisms, containing one or more cells; a bacterial cell modified to survive an adverse environment

sporidium (pl. sporidia)—the basidiospore of rust fungi, smut fungi, and other members of the group basidiomycetes

sporocarp—a spore-bearing fruiting body

sporodochium (pl. sporodochia)—a superficial, cushion-shaped, asexual fruiting body consisting of a cluster of conidiophores

sporulate—to produce spores

sporulating—producing and (often) liberating spores

spot—a small necrotic area occurring as a disease symptom on a leaf, flower, or stem

stamen (adj. staminal)—the male structure of a flower, composed of a pollen-bearing anther and a filament, or stalk

staminate flower—a male flower

stele—the central cylinder of vascular tissue, especially with reference to roots

stem pitting—a viral disease symptom characterized by depressions on the stem

sterigma (pl. sterigmata)—a small, usually pointed projection that supports a spore

sterile—unable to reproduce sexually; free of living microorganisms

sterile fungus—a fungus that is not known to produce any kind of spores

sterilization (adj. sterilized)—the total destruction of living organisms by various means, including heat, chemicals, and irradiation

stigma—the portion of a flower that receives pollen and on which pollen germinates

stipe—a stalk

stippling—a pattern of small dots or speckles on leaves where chlorophyll is absent

stipule—a small, leaflike appendage at the base of a leaf petiole; usually occurs as one of a pair

stolon—a slender, horizontal stem that grows close to the soil surface (syn. runner); in fungi, a hypha that grows horizontally along a surface

stoma, **stomate** (pl. stomata; adj. stomatal)—a structure composed of two guard cells and the opening between them in the epidermis of a leaf or stem; functions in gas exchange

strain—a distinct form of an organism within a species or virus, differing from other forms of the species biologically, physically, or chemically

striate (n. striations)—to mark with delicate lines, grooves, or ridges

stroma (pl. stromata)—a compact mass of mycelium (with or without host tissue) that supports fruiting bodies or in which fruiting bodies are embedded

stunting—a reduction in the height of plants resulting from a progressive reduction in the lengths of successive internodes or a decrease in their number

style—the slender part of many pistils, located between the stigma and the ovary and through which the pollen tube grows

stylet—the stiff, slender, hollow feeding organ of plant-parasitic nematodes or sap-sucking insects, such as aphids and leafhoppers

stylet-borne transmission—virus transmission in which a virus is acquired and transmitted by a vector after a short feeding time and is retained by the vector for only a short time (syn. nonpersistent transmission)

subepidermal—located or occurring just below the epidermis

subgenomic RNA—a piece of viral RNA, shorter than the entire genome of the virus, found in cells infected by the virus and sometimes encapsidated

substrate—the substance on which an organism lives or from which it obtains nutrients; a chemical substance acted upon, often by an enzyme

sunscald—the injury of plant tissues burned or scorched by direct sunlight

suscept—a susceptible plant

susceptible (n. susceptibility)—prone to develop disease when infected by a pathogen (*see* resistant)

symbiosis (adj. symbiotic)—a mutually beneficial association of two different kinds of organisms

symbiont—either of the organisms in a symbiotic association

symptom—an indication of disease by a reaction of the host (e.g., canker, leaf spot, wilt) (*see* sign)

symptomatology—the study of disease symptoms

symptomless carrier—a plant that is infected with a pathogen (usually a virus) but has no obvious symptoms

syncytium (pl. syncytia)—a multinucleate structure in root tissue formed by the dissolution of common cell walls induced by secretions of certain sedentary plant-parasitic nematodes (e.g., cyst nematodes)

synergism (adj. synergistic)—an interaction in which the total effect of the interacting factors is greater than the additive effects of the factors acting individually

synnema (pl. synnemata)—compact or fused, generally upright conidiophores, with branches and spores that form a head-like cluster (syn. coremium)

systemic—pertaining to a disease in which the pathogen (or a single infection) spreads generally throughout a plant; pertaining to chemicals that spread internally through a plant

taproot—a primary root that grows vertically downward and from which smaller lateral roots branch

taxonomy (adj. taxonomic)—the science of naming and classifying organisms

teleomorph—the perfect state, or sexual form in the life cycle of certain fungi (*see* anamorph; holomorph)

teliospore—a thick-walled resting spore produced by some fungi (notably rust and smut fungi) from which a basidium is produced

telium (pl. telia)—the fruiting body (sorus) that produces teliospores of a rust fungus

testa (pl. testae)—seed coat

thallus—the vegetative body of a fungus

thermal inactivation point—the lowest temperature at which heating for a limited period (usually 10 min) is sufficient to cause a virus to lose its infectivity or an enzyme to lose its activity

tiller—a lateral shoot, culm, or stalk arising from a crown bud; common in grasses

tissue—a group of cells, usually of similar structure, that perform the same or related functions

tissue culture—an in vitro method of propagating healthy cells from plant tissues

titer—a measure of the concentration of a substance in a solution

tolerance (adj. tolerant)—the ability of a plant to endure an infectious or noninfectious disease, adverse conditions, or chemical injury without serious damage or yield loss; with reference to pesticides, the amount of chemical residue legally permitted on an agricultural product entering commercial channels, usually measured in parts per million (ppm)

tomentose—covered with a dense mat of hair

toxicity—the capacity of a substance to interfere with the vital processes of an organism

toxin—any poisonous substance of biological origin

transgenic—possessing a gene from another species; having been the subject of genetic engineering

translocation—the movement of water, nutrients, chemicals, or food materials within a plant

translucent—clear enough to allow the transmission of light

transmit (n. transmission)—to spread or transfer, as in spreading an infectious pathogen from plant to plant or from one generation of plants to another

transovarial passage—the passage of a virus through the eggs or offspring of its vector and then to the next generation of host plants

transpiration—the loss of water by evaporation from leaf surfaces and through stomata

trichome—a plant epidermal hair, of which several types exist

triturate—to grind, as with a mortar and pestle

truncate—to end abruptly, as though an end has been cut off

tuber—an underground stem adapted for storage; typically produced at the end of a stolon

tumor—an abnormal swelling or localized outgrowth, often roughly spherical, produced by a plant as a result of attack by a fungus, bacterium, nematode, insect, or other organism (syn. gall)

turgid—swollen or inflated; plump or swollen as a result of internal water pressure

turgidity—the state of being rigid or swollen as a result of internal water pressure

tylosis (pl. tyloses)—a balloon-like extrusion of parenchyma cells into the lumina of contiguous vessels, partially or completely blocking them

ultrastructure—the submicroscopic structure of a macromolecule, cell, or tissue

unicellular—one celled (*see* multicellular)

uniflagellate—having one flagellum

uninucleate—having one nucleus per cell (*see* binucleate; multinucleate)

urediniospore, **urediospore**, **uredospore**—the asexual, dikaryotic, often rust-colored spore of a rust fungus, produced in a uredinium; the repeating stage of a heteroecious rust fungus, in which it is capable of infecting the host plant on which it was produced

uredinium (pl. uredinia), uredium (pl. uredia)—the fruiting body (sorus) in which urediniospores of a rust fungus are produced

vacuole—a generally spherical organelle within a plant cell, bound by a membrane and containing dissolved materials, such as metabolic precursors, storage materials, and waste products

variegation—a pattern of two or more colors in a plant part, as in a green and white leaf

variety (adj. varietal)—a plant type within a species, resulting from deliberate genetic manipulation and having recognizable characteristics, such as color; shapes of flowers, fruit, and seeds; height; and form (syn. cultivar)

vascular—pertaining to fluid-conducting tissues (xylem and phloem) in plants

vascular bundle—a strand of conductive tissue; usually composed of xylem and phloem (in leaves, small bundles are called *veins*)

vascular cylinder—the cylinder of vascular tissue in stems and roots (syn. stele)

vascular wilt disease—a xylem disease that disrupts the normal uptake of water and minerals, resulting in wilting and yellowing of foliage

vector—a living organism (e.g., insect, mite, bird, higher animal, nematode, parasitic plant, human) that is able to carry and transmit a pathogen; in genetic engineering, a cloning vehicle, or self-replicating DNA molecule, such as a plasmid or virus, used to introduce a fragment of foreign DNA into a host cell

vegetative—pertaining to the somatic or asexual parts of a plant, which are not involved in sexual reproduction

vegetative propagation—asexual reproduction; in plants, the use of cuttings, bulbs, tubers, or other vegetative parts to grow new plants

vein—a small vascular bundle in a leaf

vein banding—a symptom of virus disease in which the regions along veins are darker green than the tissue between veins

vein clearing—disappearance of green color in or around leaf veins

vermiform—worm shaped

vertical resistance—resistance thought to be conferred by a single gene or a few genes and completely protecting a host but only against specific races or strains (genetic variants) of a pathogen

vesicle—the thin sac in which zoospores are differentiated and from which they are released; the bulbous head terminating the conidiophores of *Aspergillus* spp.; a structure formed by an endomycorrhizal fungus within living cells of the root

vessel—the water-conducting structure of xylem tissue, with pit openings in end walls

viable (n. viability)— alive; capable of germination (e.g., of seeds, fungus spores, sclerotia, etc.); capable of growth

virescence—a state or condition in which normally white or colored tissues (e.g., flower petals) become green

virion—a complete virus particle

viroid—any of various small, unencapsidated (naked), circular, single-stranded RNA molecules capable of causing disease in plants

viroplasm—an inclusion in a virus-infected cell, where viral components are synthesized and virus particles are assembled

virulence—the degree or measure of pathogenicity; the relative capacity to cause disease

virulent—pathogenic; having the capacity to cause disease (*see* avirulent)

viruliferous—virus laden, usually with reference to insects or nematodes as vectors

virus—any of numerous submicroscopic, intracellular, obligate parasites consisting of a core of infectious nucleic acid (either RNA or DNA) usually surrounded by a protein coat

volunteer—a self-set plant; seeded by chance

water soaking—a disease symptom in which plant tissues or lesions appear wet, dark, and usually sunken and translucent

whorl—a circular arrangement of like parts

wild type—the phenotype characteristic of most individuals of a species under natural conditions

wilt—the drooping of leaves and stems caused by a lack of water (inadequate water supply or excessive transpiration); a vascular disease in which normal water uptake is interrupted

witches'-broom—a disease symptom in which many weak shoots arise at or close to the same point, producing abnormal massed, brushlike growth

xylem—the water- and mineral-conducting, food-storing, supporting tissue of a plant

yellows—a plant disease characterized by chlorosis and stunting

zonate—pertaining to the targetlike development of a tree canker, characterized by successive perennial rings of callus; pertaining to any symptom appearing in concentric rings

zoosporangium—a sporangium (spore case) bearing zoospores

zoospore—a fungal spore with flagella; capable of locomotion in water

zygomycetes (adj. zygomycetous)—a group of fungi in the phylum Zygomycota (kingdom Fungi) that produce resistant, spherical sexual spores following fusion of hyphal gametangia

zygospore—the sexual resting spore formed from the union of gametangia of fungi in the group zygomycetes

Index

155

day-neutral cultivars, 122
DaYMV. *See Dandelion yellow mosaic virus*
(DaYMV)
Delia platura, 107
Dermaptera, 115
Diabrotica
balteata, 108
undecimpunctata undecimpunctata, 108
dieback. *See* lettuce dieback
Diglyphus, 107
Diplotaxis tenuifolia, 20
Diptera, 102, 106–107
Agromyzidae, 102, 106–107
Anthomyiidae, 107
disease pyramid, 16, 18
disease resistance
applications of biotechnology and genomics
to, 9–13
genome editing, 11–12, 13
metagenomics, 12, 13, 30
molecular markers and genome
sequencing, 9–10, 13
opportunities from model and other
species, 12
status of molecular markers for resistance
to specific diseases, 10–11
tissue culture, 9, 12
transgenic approaches, 11
breeding and, 6, 7, 8
disease management and, 19
dodder, 17, 18
downy mildew, 32–35
causal agents of, 10, 16, 32–33
foodborne pathogens and, 23
gray mold and, 137
resistance to, 10–11
cultivars with, 6, 13, 34, 91, 92
genes for, 7, 8, 10–11, 12, 34
drop. *See* lettuce drop
dung beetles, 23
dwarf mistletoe, 17

E-4 (cultivar), 92
earwigs, 101, 102, 115
eggplant, 52, 81, 95, 98
Egyptian broomrape, 98
Elateridae, 109–110
elegant zinnia, 71
Empire (cultivar), 6
Empoasca
fabae, 105
mexara, 105
solana, 105
endive
anthracnose on, 25, 26
Bidens mottle in, 71
bottom rot on, 27
ENMV in, 93
escarole yellows on, 80
LMV in, 82
marginal leaf blight on, 61
Rhizorhapis suberifaciens on, 59
in spring and mesclun mixes, 3
TSV in, 88, 89
TuMV in, 91
varnish spot on, 62
Endive necrotic mosaic virus (ENMV), 93
endoconidia, 26
ENMV. *See Endive necrotic mosaic virus*
(ENMV)
Enterobacteriaceae, 19, 20
environmental stress, 7, 13–16
Eremophila
alpestris, 129
strigata, 130

Eruca vesicaria, 3
Eruption (cultivar), 8
Erwinia, 17, 19, 21
carotovora subsp. *carotovora,* 57, 136
Erysimum, 92
Erysiphe, 45
cichoracearum, 45
escarole
anthracnose on, 25
BiMoV in, 71
bottom rot on, 27
ENMV in, 93
LMV in, 82
MPV in, 80, 81
Pseudomonas marginalis pv. *marginalis* on,
61
TBSV in, 80
TSV in, 88, 89
TuMV in, 91
escarole yellows, 80
Escherichia coli, 19, 20, 21, 23
non-O157 Shiga toxin-producing, 130
O157:H7, 23–24
Estigmene acrea, 110, 113
Estival (cultivar), 123
ethylene, 137
Eurasian collared doves, 129
European earwig, 115
European flower thrips, 76, 90

faba bean, 72, 98
faba bean phyllody phytoplasma, 63, 64
Fabaceae, 72, 98
Fabavirus, 66, 72
falcons, 130
false chinch bug, 105–106
false root-knot nematode, 94, 96
false wireworms, 110
far-red light, 14, 15
fava bean. *See* faba bean
Feltia subterranea, 110, 112
fennel, 98
fertilizers
application of, 5, 58
excessive use of, 90, 128
improper use of, 18
nitrogen, 5, 48, 60, 119, 128
organic, 5, 21
potassium, 119
sulfur, 120
tipburn and, 121
fiddleneck, 69
field crickets, 102, 114–115
field mustard, 3
field testing, 4, 8, 9. *See also* breeding
filth flies, 23
Flavobacterium, 19
flax, 46, 98
flea beetles, 107–108
Florida flower thrips, 90
Foeniculum vulgare, 98
food safety, 22–24
Forficula, 115
auricularia, 115
Forficulidae, 115
foxglove aphid, 103
Frankliniella, 114
bispinosa, 67, 90
fusca, 67, 90, 113
intonsa, 66, 67, 76, 90
occidentalis
as contaminants or pests, 101–102, 113
foodborne pathogens and, 23
viruses transmitted by, 66, 67, 76, 89, 90
schultzei, 66, 67, 90

freeze injury, 123
frost injury, 41
fungi and oomycetes. *See also specific fungi and
oomycetes*
as caterpillar pathogens, 111
diseases caused by, 12, 16–17. *See also specific
diseases*
entomopathogenic, 114
in lettuce rhizosphere, 20
morphology and multiplication of, 17
nematode injury and colonization by, 17
plant weight and diversity richness in soil,
21
transmission of, 17
viruses transmitted by, 18, 65, 67, 77
weather-related injuries and, 123
weeds as reservoirs for, 18
fungicides
ametoctradin–dimethomorph mixture,
34
anilinopyrimidine, 42
for anthracnose control, 26
azadirachtin, 34
for bacterial leaf spot control, 56
for black root rot control, 27
for bottom rot control, 29
carbendazim, 40
for Cercospora leaf spot control, 31
copper-based, 56
for damping-off control, 32
dicarboximides, 38, 42
dithiocarbamates, 56
for downy mildew control, 34
experimental applications of, 18
fenamidone, 34
fosetyl-aluminum, 34
for Fusarium wilt control, 40
for gray mold control, 42
hydroxyanilide, 42
for lettuce drop control, 38
mancozeb, 34, 56
mandipropamid, 34
maneb, 34
mefenoxam, 44
metalaxyl, 34
methyl benzimidazole carbamate, 42
for MLBVV control, 78
oxathiapiprolin, 34
phenylpyrrole, 42
for Phoma leaf spot and basal rot control,
43
phosphites, 34
phosphonates, 44
phosphorous acid compounds, 26
for Phytophthora stem and root rot control,
44
potassium phosphonate, 44
for powdery mildew control, 45
prochloraz, 40
propamocarb hydrochloride, 34
quinone outside inhibitors (QoIs), 42
resistance to, 34, 42
seed treatments, 42, 49
for southern blight control, 48
for Stemphylium leaf spot control, 49
strobilurins, 26
succinate dehydrogenase inhibitors (SDHIs),
42
sulfur-based, 45, 120
zineb, 56
Fusarium, 100, 119
oxysporum, 39
f. sp. *lactucae,* 11, 39, 40
Fusarium root rot, 38
Fusarium wilt, 11, 38–40, 50